"This is an important book for anyone who wants to ι
the complexities of reducing our material impact on
contains much knowledge and wisdom, as well as su
at the cutting edge of developing the circular economy."

Mark Miodownik, *author of* Stuff Matters *and* Liquid

"*Materials and Sustainability* contains vital clues to solve the most vexing puzzle of our age: meeting human needs with products that do not, by design, damage our health and destroy nature. It is highly readable, delightfully informative, and inspiring."

Wayne Visser, *author of* Thriving: The Breakthrough Movement to
Regenerate Nature, Society, and the Economy

"This book will help readers make connections between the complex web of our material world and systems that underpin modern life. It's a catalyst for meaningful engagement with sustainability that unpacks confusing issues in a clear, insightful, and actionable way."

Sioban Imms, *CMF writer and strategist*

"Despite my 26 years in packaging, this book reinforces that there is so much more to learn! Kudos to the authors for sharing their wisdom to help readers understand the history of materials, which is key to developing sustainable packaging options."

Cory Connors, *Director of Sustainable Packaging,
Orora Packaging Solution*

"*Materials and Sustainability* lays out clearly, in terms that do not require detailed scientific knowledge, the abundance of materials that are available to manufacture 'everyday' products. This book helps designers, producers, consumers, and policymakers through that complex web of choices and points them toward greater sustainability."

David Newman, *Chairman, European Bioeconomy Bureau*

Materials and Sustainability

This book examines sustainable manufacturing, from the extraction of materials to processing, use, and disposal, and argues that significant changes in all of the above are needed for the world to progress toward a more circular economy.

Materials and processing methods are usually chosen with performance as the key metric. Why has our society embraced plastics? Because they work. In most cases, they are lighter, easier to manufacture, and less expensive than the metal, wood, glass, or stone they have replaced. Why do industrial manufacturers use toxic chemicals? Because they are effective, but the unintended consequences may be severe. By learning how various materials are made and what happens when they are recycled, readers will better understand the value of materials and the challenges that manufacturers face when trying to make their facilities and products less toxic and less wasteful. The three chapters in Part I provide essential background about materials in the circular economy, chemicals, and waste. Part II delves into specific materials. It includes chapters on plastics, metals, wood and paper products, glass, and novel materials. Part III covers recycling and manufacturing processes, and Part IV delves into practical considerations, including the effect of regulations, concluding with a chapter that helps readers translate the information presented into action. Interviews with industry experts round out the chapters and offer valuable insights.

Materials and Sustainability is a must-read for business professionals who are serious about making their companies as environmentally responsible as possible and for business and engineering students who want to begin their careers with practical knowledge about materials and their impacts.

Julia L Freer Goldstein is the founder of JLFG Communications, a member of 1% for the Planet. Her company works with manufacturers to help them connect business goals, environmental action, and effective communication strategies. She has a background in engineering, journalism, content writing, and teaching. She holds a PhD in Materials Science from UC Berkeley. Julia has over 25 years of experience working in and writing about the semiconductor manufacturing industry. She writes a Sustainability 101 column for 3D InCites, an online publication and membership community serving that industry. Julia's book *Material Value* is a B.R.A.G. Medallion Honoree, finalist in the 2019 San Francisco Writers Contest, and semifinalist for the 2020 Nonfiction BookLife Prize. She is also the author of two other books and many articles in trade and business publications.

Paul Foulkes-Arellano is the founder of circular economy consulting business Circuthon® Consulting, where he advises global brands and bioeconomy start-ups. His areas of expertise are raw materials, packaging, apparel, and footwear. His particular focus is NextGen fibers, biomaterials, and novel material development. Paul sits on the advisory boards of alternative fiber producer, ReStalk, and textile upcyclers, Must Had. He is a non-executive director at cellulosic pigments specialist Sparxell. Paul runs two non-profit initiatives: The Circular Footwear Initiative and The Circular Fashion Initiative.

Materials and Sustainability

Building a Circular Future

**Julia L Freer Goldstein and
Paul Foulkes-Arellano**

LONDON AND NEW YORK

from Routledge

Designed cover image: Getty images

First published 2024
by Routledge
4 Park Square, Milton Park, Abingdon, Oxon OX14 4RN

and by Routledge
605 Third Avenue, New York, NY 10158

Routledge is an imprint of the Taylor & Francis Group, an informa business

British Library Cataloguing-in-Publication Data
A catalogue record for this book is available from the British Library

ISBN: 978-1-032-52931-8 (hbk)
ISBN: 978-1-032-52932-5 (pbk)
ISBN: 978-1-003-40926-7 (ebk)

DOI: 10.4324/9781003409267

Typeset in Times New Roman
by codeMantra

Contents

Figures

Tables

Acknowledgments

First, we (Julia and Paul) are thankful to each other. Writing a book is a rewarding and often lonely experience. It has been fantastic to have a coauthor to share the workload, give feedback on our ideas, and be an encouraging collaborator throughout the process. Even though we live thousands of miles apart and will not meet in person until after this book is published, we have gotten to know each other through our regular Zoom calls over many months. Paul thanks his wife, Conchita, for her unwavering support and huge patience while he has been locked in his office, working on the book for the past couple of years.

We are grateful to our editorial associates, Eleanor Ronabio and Tomáš Slaný, for their work chasing down citations, researching data to support our thesis, formatting chapters, and helping us keep track of all the details. Thanks to Sirajum Munir Galib for your creative diagrams and charts and to Tomáš for making sure Sirajum had all the information he needed to create the figures. Thanks also to our assistant researcher, Jasmin Lopez.

Our beta readers read an early, flawed version of the manuscript and kindly pointed out inconsistencies, errors, and places where our explanations could be clearer. Thanks to you, we reorganized paragraphs, moved content between chapters, and even moved entire chapters. Our sincere thanks to Christina Philpott, David Newman, Drew Pronovost, Lelia Hawkins, Meta Cunder Balzanti, Michael Ross, Patrick Bryson, Sioban Imms, and Tom Hallam for helping us make the book more valuable to readers.

We also thank our commissioning editor at Routledge, Annabelle Harris, for championing this project and answering our many questions along the way. We appreciate the advice of our peer reviewers and their suggestions to diversify our initial list of interviewees. The people we interviewed for this book hail from nine countries and four continents.

This book wouldn't be what it is without the interviews. Thanks to Alexis Eyre, Andrew Winston, Aston Fuller, Brion Hurley, Chelo Escrig, Dan Schwartz, Elisa Cones, Francois Minec, Jan Dell, Jen Keane, Jonatan Kleimark, Joost de Kluijver, Karen Brown, Marcia Frieze, Neva Murtha, Oliver Harry, Pat Teoh, Paul Randle, Ramon Arratia, Reinhardt Smit, Sherri Monroe, Smokey Peck, and Theo Rondozai. You took the time to speak with us, reviewed your interview sections, and gave us permission to share your stories and expertise. To those who chose to remain anonymous, we appreciate your contributions.

Thanks in advance to our readers. This book is for you and people like you. If you learn something worthwhile from it, we invite you to post a review and let your friends, neighbors, and colleagues know about the book.

Preface: Why This Book, Why Now

In the spring of 2020, as Paul Foulkes-Arellano was on the verge of launching his circularity consultancy firm Circuthon, he bought a book that changed his way of thinking. The book was *Material Value: More Sustainable, Less Wasteful Manufacturing of Everything from Cell Phones to Cleaning Products*. Paul reached out to the author (Julia) on LinkedIn, and, to his amazement, she agreed to a video call. Thus began the connection that makes this new book possible.

"More than anything, *Material Value 2*—the 2020s—is much needed," Paul wrote to Julia a year later. "So much is changing—the fundamentals are the same, but we're reaching a new level of complexity with biomaterials and biosynthetics."

Julia thought about writing an updated edition but was immersed in expanding her ten-year-old content writing business to offer workshops and corporate training about materials and sustainability. She was also working on a new book proposing that the way you communicate sustainability—first within your company; and then with consumers, investors, and other stakeholders—is the essential foundation of any successful green initiative. She couldn't devote the time needed to create another book, even one where most of the content was already written.

Still, Paul's suggestion kept nagging at Julia. She was proud of *Material Value*, and book sales were stronger than ever as more people searched for resources to make manufacturing more sustainable. Given the growing awareness of the importance of materials to environmental sustainability and advances in commercially viable materials, it made sense to review the whole book for opportunities to make it more valuable for readers.

Julia thought back to Paul and everything he had been working on at Circuthon around circular fashion, footwear, and beverages. Their knowledge and expertise complemented each other. Paul also had resources and connections to influential entrepreneurs, academics, and business leaders.

It was time to put their heads together, so in early 2022, Julia sent Paul a message. "I have an idea. How would you like to be a collaborator on the second edition of *Material Value*?"

Julia's journey

My journey started long before I began writing *Material Value.* I first became fascinated by materials science—a field of engineering focused on materials selection, materials processing, and development of new materials—in college. I entered Harvey Mudd College in 1984 as a physics major. In the second semester of my sophomore year, I took a class called "Modern Physics" and realized that I didn't want to be a physics major. I wanted to study something more practical than quantum mechanics. I just wasn't driven to understand the world at that fundamental level.

In my junior year, after switching my major to engineering, I took my first materials science course. Something about the idea of tailoring a material's physical properties by adding minute quantities of other materials or changing processing conditions fascinated me. That fascination led me to graduate school in materials science and later to the semiconductor manufacturing industry.

Back when I was in college, I didn't think much about the ethical implications of materials selection and designing new materials. This now strikes me as peculiar, given the mission of Harvey Mudd College, which hasn't changed over the decades. As stated on its website,

> Harvey Mudd College seeks to educate engineers, scientists, and mathematicians well versed in all of these areas and in the humanities and the social sciences so that they may assume leadership in their fields with a clear understanding of the impact of their work on society.

I did, however, attend college in the 1980s, a decade not known for emphasizing environmentalism or social responsibility. That was for the hippies. My generation graduated with engineering degrees and pursued available job opportunities, many of which involved military contracts and required security clearances. The ethical and moral implications of their work just weren't at the forefront of most of my peers' minds as they pursued their careers.

I took a course named "Ethical Issues in Engineering" when I was working on my MS in materials science at Stanford that got me thinking about product liability, but the environmental sustainability piece hadn't occurred to me. Over the years, my perspective has shifted. I now believe that sustainable materials management is crucial. It needs to be addressed throughout the supply chain, from raw materials extraction through the entire life cycle of a manufactured product.

My voyage into materials toxicity began with my PhD research at UC Berkeley. A chance comment from another student in my research group changed the course of my research and my career. She mentioned that the US Congress was considering a ban on tin-lead solders in electronics, with the goal of eliminating lead, a toxic element. I decided almost on the spot that I needed to research lead-free solders. Would these alloys exhibit the same microscopic changes that tin-lead solders experienced when deformed at high temperature? I was curious.

The title of my PhD thesis, published in 1993, was "Microstructural Development and Mechanical Behavior of Eutectic Bismuth-Tin and Eutectic Indium-Tin in Response to High Temperature Deformation." In some ways, I was ahead of my time—it would take more than a decade before the Restriction of Hazardous Substances Directive, known as RoHS, was adopted in the European Union (EU). RoHS restricts the use of six hazardous materials in electronics, including lead.

My involvement in the early days of RoHS shaped my perspective. As an engineer, and later a journalist, in the semiconductor packaging sector, I became acutely aware of the struggles to find a replacement that worked as well as tin-lead solder. I also became aware of the absurdity of the whole effort when put in a wider context. The amount of lead in solder joints is minuscule compared to the quantity of lead in lead-acid batteries, for example.

Throughout my career, I have been especially drawn to stories about new materials or better ways to use existing materials. In my content writing business, I liked to highlight ways in which my clients were reducing waste, saving energy, and creating less toxic, more sustainable manufacturing processes. When I decided in 2017 that I wanted to write a book, I knew I needed to write about materials and sustainability.

First-time authors often sell the first 50 or 100 copies of their book to people they know. My friends weren't necessarily the primary audience for *Material Value*. Most of them didn't work in manufacturing industries. They especially appreciated the practical advice in the recycling chapter. That feedback prompted my second book, *Rethink the Bins: Your Guide to Smart Recycling and Less Household Waste*.

I have enjoyed the opportunity to give presentations to libraries and community groups about recycling and composting. But I can make a greater difference by reaching people who work at manufacturing companies or aspire to do so. Hence, my consulting work and the book you are reading now.

Paul's journey

After I graduated in 1986, one of my close friends went to study Industrial Design Engineering at the Royal College of Art, and this was my first encounter with industrial design. When I decided to enter publishing in 1988, my friend encouraged me to work at *DesignWeek* magazine. Within one year, I took on a marketing role at an industrial design and branding agency, Packaging Innovation, in London. Packaging Innovation was a global pioneer in industrial packaging design, and was renowned for stretching the boundaries of machinery capabilities.

Before I was allowed to interact with clients, the agency sent me on a three-month learning tour of packaging factories across Europe. I visited injection molders, label printers, and much more. I was truly hooked on packaging, and thus began three decades working in packaging design (with a slight detour into footwear manufacture in the 1990s).

For the past decade, I have been mentoring start-up businesses and global conglomerates. Many of those businesses are in the fashion and footwear sector, and I found that the materials knowledge I built up over decades in packaging is applicable to garments and shoes.

I am a frequent speaker on sustainable design and new materials. In recent years, I have been a vocal advocate of the circular economy, lecturing at universities and talking at industry events.

I have been a guest lecturer on the Design Management Masters course at University of Southampton, England. I contributed to an executive education program on circularity for the Centre for Business, Climate Change, and Sustainability at the University of Edinburgh, Scotland.

All of this would not have happened without my early factory-based education, and subsequent decades project-managing complex packaging design programs.

The new book

Awareness about the need for environmental action has grown since *Material Value* was published in 2019. We seem to be entering a new era. More and more, consumers want to know which chemicals and additives are in the products they buy and use, persuading various industries to become increasingly transparent about their products and their manufacturing methods.

Manufacturing companies are taking a closer look at their operations and rethinking how environmental and social responsibility is connected to their purpose. All types of businesses are considering more carefully where to buy the products they need, from coffee cups to furniture. Businesses large and small are analyzing their materials usage, waste streams, and carbon footprints. However, some changes may be "feel-good" measures that do not make much of a difference.

This book, *Materials and Sustainability,* answers more of the questions that manufacturers want to know about how to make choices that are less harmful to people and the environment. It includes content from *Material Value* about metals, plastics, and the challenges manufacturers face.

Engineered materials—those made by humans rather than occurring in nature—include far more than metals and plastics. Therefore, we added chapters on glass, wood-based products, and novel biomaterials. We now cover nearly all materials that are used in both product packaging and durable goods.

Although this is a derivative work, it is not a re-issuing of a previously published book. We have revised every chapter, removing outdated content, reorganizing the concepts, and adding new information. We include over two dozen interviews with materials experts, business leaders, and industry commentators from around the world. While some people's stories also appeared in *Material Value,* we reinterviewed them for this book.

We believe this is the perfect time to publish a new book looking at environmental sustainability and circularity through a lens of materials extraction, processing, use, and disposal. We see it as a valuable resource for business professionals who are serious about making their companies as environmentally responsible as possible and for business and engineering students who want to begin their careers with practical knowledge about materials and their impacts.

A note about the interviews

The interviews are interspersed throughout the chapters in Q&A format. We edited the transcriptions from our Zoom meetings for length and clarity, but otherwise, these are the words of our interviewees. Some of what they say is fact, and other statements are their opinions. In some cases, the opinion of one interviewee conflicts with that of another. We present both so that readers can understand that many issues around materials and sustainability are not clear-cut. Our life experiences affect how we interpret things, and new knowledge can bring new insights. We hope that this book will offer you both knowledge and insight.

Part I

Setting the Stage, Posing the Problem

1 Introduction

Materials and the Circular Economy

This book's subtitle, *Building a Circular Future*, sprang to life after we reviewed feedback from readers of the initial manuscript. We firmly believe that there will be a circular future and that thoughtful materials choices are necessary to achieve it. First, we need to explain what we mean by the circular economy and circularity and clear up common misconceptions about these terms.

Defining the circular economy

Wild spaces that are untouched by human activity are circular by nature. Energy comes from an infinitely renewable source, the sun. The balance of plants and animals in a habitat supports life, ensuring resources for all species to survive for generations. However, human habitats are far from circular.

The circular economy stands in contrast to our current, mostly linear economy. A lot of literature has already been published on the circular economy, with much more to be published over the coming years, as it's a hugely important business topic. It's central to the survival of the majority of businesses, but not something that is automatically on their risk radar. Although corporate boards, C-suite executives, and leadership teams discuss circularity, we are losing ground.

According to The Circularity Gap Report 2023,[1] the global economy is getting less circular. Rising material extraction has shrunk global circularity from 9.1 percent in 2018 to 7.2 percent in 2023. This leaves a huge Circularity Gap: production almost exclusively relies on new (virgin) materials.

We need to reverse that and make fast progress in the opposite direction towards absolute circularity. Absolute circularity means that for every kilogram (kg) of material input, one kg of that material goes into circulation and stays there. Even though absolute circularity is not feasible for most product applications (the laws of physics tell us that zero loss is impossible in many cases), the concept is useful to direct governmental and corporate policies.

In the linear economy, we extract resources from the earth, use them to create products or energy, and discard them into the atmosphere or a landfill when they have served their purpose. In a completely circular economy, those resources

DOI: 10.4324/9781003409267-2

would stay in circulation indefinitely. The ideal concept is a circular loop that continues without end.

In practice, progress toward circularity occurs by implementing various circularity strategies, also known as R-strategies. The R-strategies, ordered by their preferability regarding environmental impacts and resource conservation, are refuse, reduce, reuse, repair, refurbish, remanufacture, repurpose, recycle, and recover energy. Considering these strategies in order requires rethinking much of how businesses operate.

A circular economy is an economic system that aims to reduce waste and pollution by keeping products, materials, and resources in use for as long as possible. Circularity is a focal point of this book, and circular economy concepts run through every chapter.

The role of materials in circularity

To understand the elements that are required for a circular economy, we must understand the fundamental role of materials within it. This means first understanding the environmental impacts of each material, and then how more circular systems will reduce these impacts.

Environmental impacts occur at each stage of the material value chain, spanning from the raw material acquisition to end-of-life treatment. Circular strategies are especially instrumental in mitigating adverse effects associated with raw materials extraction, material processing, product manufacturing, and end-of-life treatment of materials and products.

Common concerns include:

- Air pollution,
- Water pollution (seas, rivers, groundwater),
- Soil pollution,
- Damage to ecosystems and loss of biodiversity.

Air pollution is associated with ozone depletion, human health hazards, and climate change. Changes in materials extraction and processing methods can mitigate these effects. Moving away from incineration (burning waste) to reuse will lessen air pollution. In addition, reuse and retention of the material value in a circular economy reduces the demand for virgin material production, hence mitigating the associated impacts.

Water pollution occurs when toxic byproducts of materials production enter seas, rivers, oceans, and groundwater. Moving to nontoxic or less toxic process chemicals and packaging materials will alleviate potential disruption to the aquatic ecosystem.

Soil is polluted by heavy metals and synthetic polymers, as well as by a multitude of industrial chemicals. Closed-loop production methods, as well as reuse systems, reduce this source of contamination.

Ideally, a circular system will prevent damage to ecosystems and support biodiversity. If we include strategies that regenerate the ecosystem, then we have a win-win solution. This type of system can help to protect biodiversity by reducing the need for land clearing, water pollution, and other activities that can harm ecosystems. For example, ecological mangrove restoration at abandoned aquaculture ponds rebuilds carbon stocks, but a truly circular system would produce food and materials as well as just rebuilding the carbon.

This establishment of a more circular economy can improve raw materials usage in several ways. More circularity:

Reduces the need for virgin materials. When we reuse, repair, and recycle materials, we reduce the need to extract new materials from the earth. This can help to conserve natural resources and protect the environment.

Increases the value of waste materials. In a circular economy, excess or discarded materials are seen as resources that can be reused or recycled. This can create new business opportunities and help to reduce the cost of raw materials.

Improves the efficiency and reliability of the supply chain. A circular economy can help to improve the efficiency of the supply chain by reducing the need for transportation and storage. In addition, retaining materials in closed loops within local regions minimizes the supply risk associated with virgin materials, the production of which is distributed across the globe unevenly. This advantage is especially important for critical raw materials. This can save businesses money and reduce their environmental impact.

Creates jobs. The transition to a circular economy will create new jobs in the areas of recycling, repair, and remanufacturing. This can help to boost the local economy and create a more sustainable future.

Here are some specific examples of how a circular economy can improve raw materials decisions.

In the automotive industry, companies are starting to use recycled plastics and metals in their cars. This helps to reduce the need for virgin materials and can also save businesses money. We are also seeing second-generation feedstock such as hemp and linen agro-waste being used. For example, the linings on the Alpine A110 E-ternité's hood, roof, rear window, seat shells, and rear skirt are linen.

In the fashion industry, companies are starting to offer clothing rental services. This allows people to access new clothes without having to buy them, which can help to reduce the amount of textile waste. There remain some questions about the reduction in emissions, but business models that rely on renting rather than owning generally reduce material and energy consumption.

In the construction industry, companies are starting to use recycled materials in their buildings. This helps to reduce the environmental impact of construction and can also save businesses money. The lowest emission construction is refurbishment. When choosing materials for refurbishment, it is important to select those that have a low carbon footprint. This includes materials that are made from recycled content or that are grown or harvested in a sustainable way, such as hempcrete (hemp mixed with concrete). It is important to minimize the amount of waste that is generated during a refurbishment project. This can be done by using prefabricated materials or by reusing existing materials whenever possible.

In circular economy thinking, optimizing the energy efficiency of a building is key in refurbishment. In this way, energy can be seen as a resource to be kept in use for as long as possible. The energy efficiency of a building can be improved by making changes to the insulation, windows, and heating and cooling systems. This can help to reduce the amount of energy that is used, which will also reduce emissions over the life cycle of the building.

Material compatibility with circularity

When striving for absolute circularity, it is also important to take into account the main factors determining the compatibility of a given material for a circular economy. Several pre-conditions should be fulfilled for a material to be truly circular.

Either the material needs to biodegrade entirely within a reasonable time period and without toxic co-products, or suitable end-of-life infrastructure needs to exist. Such infrastructure will include treatment processes that allow the recovery of the material without quality degradation.

The ability of the material to retain its desired properties or performance over a long time period makes a difference. This quality is important for the prolongation of the material service life. Aluminum and glass are examples of materials that can keep their performance for a long time without performance deterioration. On the other hand, some steel alloys have a limited lifetime when exposed to outdoor conditions as they are prone to corrosion.

Consider the non-toxicity of the material and its use. A truly circular material must be benign toward human health and the environment. In addition, it should not be emitted into the environment during its use, preventing overall material loss. This is a particular problem for plastics, which are known to emit microplastic particles and also toxic additives, such as phthalates, into the environment.

In addition to material choice, product design is another important factor that determines the resulting circularity. Here, it is imperative that the product is designed with circularity in mind:

- Modular design allowing easy repair and disassembly at the end of life,
- Use of standardized components allowing easier remanufacturing,
- Use of materials with high recycled content,
- Product life extension by design.

Ideally, circularity should transcend the product level and be embedded into entire business models of companies. For instance, in the product-as-a-service business model, a product is rented to the customer and returned to the manufacturer once the customer does not want it anymore. This allows the product to be reused and maximizes the value obtained from the materials.

Historic exploitation of materials

Every physical object or substance on the planet is formed from some combination of elements in the periodic table. Natural materials like rocks and minerals, created deep in the earth millions of years ago, predate human history. People have been using materials in creative ways since prehistoric times, but civilization has come a long way since our ancient ancestors used wood and stone to create tools.

Since this is a book about mostly human-made materials, we want to share some historical context about how long people have been exploiting different types of materials. This information may surprise you or perhaps be no surprise whatsoever. Even for those of us who work with and educate on materials every day, it's not something we always bear in mind.

Material innovation has gone from a slow amble to hyper speed.

For most of human existence, there were limited materials from which to choose. Humans survived with just wooden tools until metals began to be used six millennia ago. Wood breaks down in a matter of years or decades, while metals, the first engineered materials, last "forever." Table 1.1 illustrates how new petroplastics are. No one would have predicted their dominance as a material choice until toward the end of the last century.

We arranged our coverage of the materials in this table (see Part II) roughly in the order in which humans started using them. (A word on terminology: we use the terms CE for Common Era and BCE for Before Common Era rather than the more familiar but Christian-centric terms AD and BC.)

The challenge of materials selection

Materials and processing methods are usually chosen with performance as the key metric. Why has our society embraced plastics? Because they work. In most cases, they are lighter, easier to manufacture, and less expensive than the metal, wood, glass, or stone they have replaced. Why do industrial manufacturers use toxic chemicals? Because they are effective. They efficiently clean surfaces or help create durable coatings. But the unintended consequences may be severe.

Table 1.1 Historical material exploitation by humans

Material	First Exploitation	Location
Wood	500,000 BCE	Global
Timber	10,000 BCE	Global
Bronze	4500 BCE	Iran
Glass	3500 BCE	Mesopotamia/Syrian Coast
Iron	3500 BCE	Hittite Empire (Anatolia)
Papyrus	2560 BCE	Egypt
Paper	25 CE	China
Bioplastics	1855 CE	UK
Petropolymers	1907 CE	USA

In the twenty-first century, an additional metric has come into the conversation—sustainability. This has spurred a whole new conversation about material choice.

By learning how materials are made and what happens when they are recycled, readers will better understand the value of materials and the challenges that manufacturers face when trying to make their facilities and products less toxic and less wasteful. This is a huge subject, and we cannot possibly convey the whole story. Entire books have been written about the topics in each of the chapters.

We have chosen instead to provide enough background so that even readers who have forgotten everything they learned in high school chemistry can understand the concepts. Stories from our experience and that of the inspiring individuals we interviewed bring a personal touch to the narrative. We hope to awaken in our readers a new sense of the importance of materials selection, development, and processing.

As companies struggle to find replacements for materials, either to reduce real or suspected toxicants or to reduce the amount of material wasted to manufacture a product, it can be hard to keep a proper perspective. Which efforts really matter, and which ones are a waste of time and effort? Which should be prioritized? We don't have all the answers but want to shed light on the problem and guide you, our readers, toward solutions that make a positive difference.

How do we make choices, given the bewildering away of general information available—from the suppliers of the materials themselves through to peer-reviewed academic reports, which often differ wildly in their conclusions and recommendations? Getting to the truth is no easy matter—there are so many factors to consider.

The energy cost of materials

One critical factor is the energy cost of producing a ton of material, as the value determines the material's environmental sustainability. The energy varies by many orders of magnitude depending on the material in question. This energy is measured in units of gigajoules (GJ), or billions of joules, and includes all the heat needed to produce the material, starting from harvesting or extracting it from the earth through processing it into a material that can be used to build a product.

Energy costs range from as low as 1.5 GJ per metric ton for lumber to 53,000 GJ per metric ton of gold.[2] This, by the way, is the reason gold is so expensive. Gold is present in such minute quantities in mineral deposits that many tons of rock need to be mined and broken up to yield an ounce of gold.

Figure 1.1 shows how much more energy it takes to produce metals and plastics compared to natural materials that require much less processing before use. Because the vertical axis of the graph is a logarithmic scale, the differences are greater than they appear at first glance. Gold takes 1,000 times more energy to produce per metric ton than the average plastic. Silver is much less costly to mine than gold but is still energy-intensive, at 2,900 GJ/metric ton.

Improving production methods can help reduce energy consumption. The key example of success in this area is steel. In 1970, it required around 60 GJ to produce

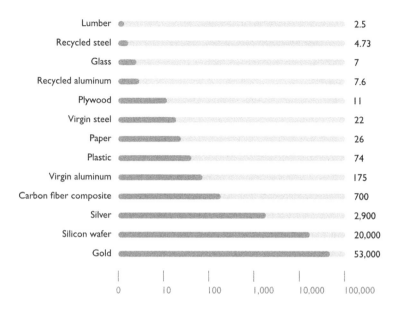

Figure 1.1 The energy cost to produce various materials, gigajoules per metric ton (logarithmic scale).

a metric ton of steel from iron ore.[3] This value is now down to 20 GJ, achieved by developing more efficient methods of producing steel (more on that in Chapter 4).

Producing metal from recycled scrap instead of mined ore reduces energy consumption dramatically, especially for aluminum. The effect is not as great for steel, but making steel from scrap steel is still substantially more energy-efficient than making it from iron ore.

Gold mining is incredibly inefficient, but because gold is seen as desirable, it can fetch an open market price that makes it economically worth the effort to extract it from ore. What if there were a source of gold that required crushing much less material to produce every ounce? There is. An object that people around the world use every day can provide an impressively efficient source of gold.

According to American Bullion, the average smartphone contains approximately 0.034 grams of gold.[4] This is worth US$2.14 or €2.00 based on 2023 gold prices.

An ounce is about 28 grams. This means that it is technically possible to recover an ounce of gold from fewer than 1,000 phones. Assuming each phone weighs 200 grams (the weight of Julia's 2021 phone), this translates to extracting an ounce of gold from less than 0.2 metric tons of phones. The weight of the printed circuit boards inside the phones that contain the gold is even lower.

For perspective, data from Barrick Gold showed that, in the first quarter of 2023, the company mined between 7 and 83 metric tons of ore to produce each ounce of gold.[5] Mines in different countries have different recovery rates, as illustrated in Figure 1.2.

US (Nevada)   17.9
Dominican Republic   15.5
Argentina   82.6
Mali   7
DRC   13.75

Figure 1.2 Metric tons of ore mined to recover an ounce of gold from sites in five countries.[6]

Conventional e-waste recycling processes do not extract all the gold from phones, so the actual recovery rate is lower than an ounce per 1,000 phones. According to Closing the Loop (see our interview with Reinhardt Smit in Chapter 10), phones do not contain the claimed €2 worth of gold. The value is at most half that, probably a lot less. Even so, the concentration of gold in cell phones is clearly much greater than that in mines.

This is merely one example of rethinking where raw materials come from. A circular economy will incorporate innovations that involve all types of human-made materials.

A lens for reading through the chapters

We do not expect you will read the entire book from cover to cover in order (although you are welcome to do so). You may focus on specific chapters that relate to your work or a university course you are taking. We intend to make each chapter stand-alone while also referring you to related content in other chapters.

As you are reading, pay particular attention to:

- The source of the information being shared,
- Whether something is stated as a fact or an opinion,
- Any discrepancies between different sources or between interviewees,
- How knowledge and understanding might change over time,
- The remarkable speed of technology and how quickly processes become redundant,
- How difficult it is to predict the future—is the right answer in 2025 going to be valid in 2030 or 2045?

How this book is organized

This book is divided into four main parts, each broken into several chapters. Part I, "Setting the Stage," serves as an introduction to the parts that follow. The remaining chapters fill in the details: Part II covers materials, Part III focuses on manufacturing, and Part IV discusses the role of regulations and certifications and suggests strategies for readers wanting to incorporate a greater focus on sustainability in their lives.

Part I: Setting the stage, posing the problem

Part I begins with the chapter you are reading now and continues with chapters on chemicals and waste.

Chapter 2 puts the concepts of chemicals and chemistry into perspective. It is both extremely challenging and vitally important to get rid of environmental toxicants. These are chemicals and compounds that endanger human health and threaten ecosystems. Not all toxicants are created equal, and sometimes the consequences of removing a toxic material are counterintuitive or unexpected. Removing a dangerous material is not helpful if you only introduce a bigger problem in its place.

The fewer natural resources manufacturing consumes, the less chance there is for excess waste, toxic or not, to pollute the earth. At the bare minimum, we should aim not to make existing environmental problems worse. That's the premise behind Chapter 3, which also addresses how lean manufacturing practices relate to more sustainable approaches to materials management.

Part II: The materials we use

All the items we use in our daily lives are made from materials. Some are created from natural materials, changed very little from how they appear in nature. However, most of the objects that humans interact with are made from engineered materials. These materials have been transformed through manufacturing processes, in many cases designed to serve specific purposes. Plastics are an obvious example of a highly processed material that looks and feels nothing like its original source. But glass and metal, while created from naturally occurring minerals, undergo extensive manufacturing processes before they become raw materials for creating useful objects.

Metals, glass, and plastics are the primary building blocks for many everyday objects. For example, a smartphone contains dozens of different metals, in quantities ranging from substantial to minuscule, and several plastics. Automobiles are made of many metal, glass, and plastic parts. Manufacturing of all sorts of products involves equipment made from these classes of materials. Wood is common in the built environment, and paper products surround us even in the digital age.

The circular potential of these materials varies.

Metals (Chapter 4): For certain metals like aluminum, there are well-established processes for high-quality recovery through recycling. However, economically viable recovery of numerous critical metals, such as rare earth elements, is hampered by a lack of infrastructure and treatment processes.

Paper (Chapter 5): When recycled, paper tends to undergo some loss in quality. However, it remains a commonly recycled material.

Glass (Chapter 6): Glass is known for its high-quality recycling, and it can be recycled repeatedly without a significant loss in quality.

Plastics (Chapter 7): Most plastics experience a loss in quality during recycling due to insufficient recycling processes. Additionally, some types of plastics are not recyclable at all.

Composite materials (Chapter 8): Recycling composite materials presents challenges as it is difficult to separate and recover their individual constituents. Consequently, recycling composite materials is more complicated compared to other materials.

The chapters in Part II cover all of the materials above plus novel materials that aim to replace these historic materials with more environmentally friendly options, including biodegradable materials. Chapter 8 focuses primarily on bioplastics with some discussion of composites.

All of the categories of materials we cover in this book are used for packaging various products. It is these disposable applications that create many of the problems that these materials, especially plastics, cause to society. Plastics are also used in durable, long-lasting applications, where their properties can be most valuable.

There are certainly other types of materials that are important in our society. The construction industry, for example, couldn't have developed as it has without concrete. Ceramics are used in applications ranging from cookware to packaging for computer chips. Computer chips rely on semiconductors like silicon for their computing power. This book touches on these materials briefly, but they are not our primary focus.

Part III: Rethinking the product life cycle

The environmental impact of the products we use lies not only in their ingredients but in how the products are manufactured and how they are handled at the end of their useful life. No discussion of efficient manufacturing would be complete without addressing the entire life cycle of materials.

Part III opens with two chapters on recycling, looking at both why and how. Chapter 9 puts recycling into perspective and dives into the details of the recycling process. It includes extensive discussion on the challenges involved in recycling various materials. As we explain, plastics are especially troublesome to recycle for several reasons.

Chapter 9 explains why recycling should not be the first approach to improve sustainability. End-of-life (EOL) considerations are a major component when considering responsible manufacturing. Bear in mind that technological solutions are only valid if they are available in the markets in which you are operating. Options vary market by market, often down to a city level. What might be standard practice in the capital city may not exist just 100 miles (or 30 km) from the capital.

The topic of electronic waste (e-waste) is deeply entwined in both reducing waste and handling hazardous materials and deserves a separate chapter. While e-waste is a huge global problem, there are solutions on the horizon, which is encouraging. Chapter 10 highlights the problems with existing e-waste infrastructure and points to ways in which it can be improved.

Chapter 11 focuses on industrial manufacturing and examines ways to reduce waste. Many conventional manufacturing processes are subtractive. The process starts with a block or sheet of material that is etched or machined away to leave the desired shape or pattern. These processes necessarily produce waste in the form of excess material that does not form part of the finished product. Much of this waste, however, can often be recycled in-house and reused, creating the most efficient form of recycling.

Additive manufacturing, a term that includes 3D printing, has the potential to be much more environmentally friendly. Materials are deposited layer by layer, making the process naturally less wasteful than subtractive manufacturing. Various additive processes are likely to play an increasingly important role in manufacturing from here on out and come with both expected and perhaps surprising sustainability benefits.

Part IV: Practical considerations to motivate change

Many companies have taken steps to make manufacturing less wasteful, but there is still plenty of room for improvement and opportunity to effect greater change. Change can come about through internal or external motivation. External motivation arrives in the form of laws and regulations designed to restrict undesirable practices or certifications and incentives designed to encourage desirable practices. While a segment of the business community will be internally motivated to "do the right thing" as part of company culture, external motivators are needed to effect widespread change.

Chapter 12 discusses various industry and government efforts to regulate and certify businesses. Are certifications and reporting standards achieving their desired goals, or are they creating unnecessary paperwork and falling short? This chapter examines B Corp certification as one path toward more responsible business practices.

Chapter 13 discusses the importance of transparency and disclosure. More and more companies have jumped on the "sustainability" bandwagon. They make claims that may or may not resemble reality. Sometimes their efforts reflect an honest desire to reduce the environmental impact of their operations, but in other cases, they greatly exaggerate progress and cover up what they don't want people to see.

There are certainly examples where corporations appear to be acting with profit as the only goal despite harm to workers, the local communities, and the environment. In other cases, manufacturers may be negligent but not willfully so and need guidance to better consider the consequences of their production methods or supply chain.

Chapter 14 overlays a societal lens on the information from earlier chapters. In our roles as citizens, employers, employees, and consumers, we have the power to encourage positive change. Business professionals can consider how they want to incorporate choices in materials, manufacturing, and suppliers into their company's practices. Consumers can influence supply and demand through what they choose to buy or avoid and can educate themselves to better understand how their purchases can make a difference. Everyone has a role to play in moving toward a vision of more environmentally responsible manufacturing.

The book concludes with a reminder of the importance of materials to the circular economy, a glimpse into innovative efforts in development in the 2020s, and our hopes for a circular future that will support human society for generations to come.

Notes

1 Circle Economy and Deloitte, "The Circularity Gap Report 2023" (Amsterdam, the Netherlands: Circle Economy, 2023), https://www.circularity-gap.world/2023.

2 A metric ton, also known as a tonne outside the US, equals 1000 kilograms. This is not the same as a ton, also called a short ton, which equals 2000 pounds. Measurements in this book appear in metric tons. When we write "ton" alone, we use it in a general sense to mean a large weight of materials and not a specific quantity.

3 Alberto N. Conejo, Jean-Pierre Birat, and Abhishek Dutta, "A Review of the Current Environmental Challenges of the Steel Industry and Its Value Chain," *Journal of Environmental Management* 259 (April 1, 2020): 109782, https://doi.org/10.1016/j.jenvman.2019.109782.

4 American Bullion, Inc., "How Much Gold Is in a Cell Phone?" *American Bullion*, May 25, 2023, https://www.americanbullion.com/how-much-gold-is-in-a-cell-phone.

5 Barrick Gold, "Results for Q1 2023," 2023, https://s25.q4cdn.com/322814910/files/doc_presentations/2023/Barrick_Q1_2023_Results_Presentation.pdf.

6 Source: Barrick Gold. 2023. "Results for Q1 2023" https://s25.q4cdn.com/322814910/files/doc_presentations/2023/Barrick_Q1_2023_Results_Presentation.pdf.

2 Chemicals

The Challenge of Removing Toxicants

Even when the EPA has lots of toxicity data, it's incredibly difficult to ban a chemical.
—Marcia Frieze, Case Medical

Helpful and harmful chemicals

Everything on earth is made from chemicals. Some chemical compounds, like water, sustain life. The human body is made of chemicals. The problem arises when we ingest or absorb the wrong types of chemicals or in the wrong quantities. Some elements in the periodic table are metals that the body needs. Others, such as lead and arsenic, can kill.

When thinking about how materials production fits into the circular economy, we have to consider toxicity. A circular loop that incorporates toxic chemicals is not a healthy one. At the same time, it is impossible to produce engineered materials without using any hazardous substances.

The real problem with chemicals comes when people are exposed to specific elements or chemical compounds, either through accidental contamination or purpose-driven use. The level and intensity of exposure matters. Humans are exposed to many harmful substances regardless of where we live or what we do. Still, greater knowledge can help us better understand the hazards and risks and what various industries can do to limit exposure.

Certain chemicals, often labeled "substances of concern," are toxic to humans and other living creatures even in extremely minute quantities. Substances of Very High Concern (SVHCs) are substances that have hazards with serious consequences. For example, they have been proven to cause cancer, they have other extremely hazardous properties, or they remain in the environment for a long time and accumulate in animals (including humans) with repeated exposure.

Some naturally occurring compounds are toxic, but for the most part, dangerous chemicals are those that have been developed in laboratories and were never intended to exist in nature. We refer to those synthetic chemicals as toxicants, in contrast to naturally occurring toxins.

The companies making industrial chemicals don't often sufficiently weigh the toxicity of the compounds they are producing. Corporate negligence is more

DOI: 10.4324/9781003409267-3

common than many of us want to believe. Companies continue to disregard evidence they don't want to see. In some cases, they deliberately hide evidence that their products cause harm. This happened with tetraethyl lead early in the twentieth century. We have more to say about that later in this chapter.

Something in the water

Unfortunately, deceptive business practices around toxic compounds are not a relic of the past. For example, the cancer-causing perfluorochemicals (jointly called PFAS chemicals) used to make nonstick coatings and hundreds of other products are present in water sources around the world. PFAS chemicals have also been detected in fast food cartons and other consumer goods.

The PFAS story first made headlines with a 2016 story in the New York Times.[1] It told the saga of Wilbur Tennant, a farmer in West Virginia whose cattle mysteriously began falling ill and dying. Tennant knew there had to be a reasonable explanation for the problems on his farm. He suspected that a landfill near his property, owned by DuPont, was responsible.

Tennant found that no local politicians, doctors, or veterinarians would listen to his concerns. He contacted lawyer Rob Bilott and showed him graphic footage of what was happening to the cattle. Bilott took the case.

DuPont's response to Bilott's lawsuit was to commission a study, hiring its own veterinarians. They concluded, not surprisingly, that Tennant was delinquent in the care of his cattle, despite Tennant's evidence showing that the cattle had been healthy for decades. The problems started shortly after Tennant's brother sold land to DuPont and DuPont built a landfill near Tennant's property.

Finally, compelled by court order, DuPont gave Bilott access to huge stacks of archived documents showing that the company knew for decades that it was discharging toxic chemicals into the landfill but had hidden all evidence.

The culprit was PFOA—perfluorooctanoic acid—which DuPont bought from 3M and used to produce Teflon and other products. DuPont's records specify that PFOA is to be disposed of in chemical waste facilities and never discharged into any bodies of water, but DuPont blatantly ignored its own guidelines.

PFOA, and a related compound, PFOS (perfluorooctane sulfonate), have been identified as biotoxins, poisons that accumulate in humans and animals and cause health problems. Medical studies on rats showed that PFOA is extremely damaging to internal organs. DuPont knew that PFOA was present in the local water supply, based on its own testing, but failed to disclose this detail.

Bilott filed a class action lawsuit against DuPont, which resulted in a $16.5 million settlement with the US Environmental Protection Agency (EPA), but this hardly put a dent in DuPont's profits. Large companies can afford to pay millions of dollars to avoid further court battles and then go back to doing business as usual.

The PFOA problem extends well beyond a single farm in West Virginia. A nonprofit organization conducted a survey and found that water supplies in 27 states exceed safe PFOA limits, as defined by researchers at Harvard and the University of Massachusetts. The survey results are from 2015.

PFAS pollution is not limited to North America. In Europe, Belgium is home to the highest pollution levels. PFAS was found in groundwater at concentrations of more than 73,000 nanograms per liter (ng/l) around 3M's PFAS manufacturing site in Zwijndrecht, Flanders. Measurements of over 100 ng/l in drinking water trigger remedial action.[2]

People living within 15 km of the site were told not to eat any homegrown vegetables or eggs laid in their gardens. Meanwhile, 70,000 people living within a 5 km radius of the plant were offered a blood test to look for the presence of PFAS. In 2023, 3M agreed to remediate the site and signed an agreement with the Flemish region with an investment amount of €571 million ($615 million). It also announced plans to stop manufacturing PFAS and phase out PFAS from all products by the end of 2025.

In the Netherlands, an accident involving PFAS in firefighting foam contaminated land around Schiphol Airport in Amsterdam, resulting in soils containing extremely high levels of PFOS. Some airports and military sites in Germany have been found to have similar problems.

PFAS and manufacturing

Regarding DuPont and its handling of PFOA, finding replacements for toxic compounds is not a simple matter. In 2000, 3M announced that it would stop manufacturing PFOS. As recently as 2014, however, 3M customer Dow (at one point, part of DuPont) was still working on finding alternative materials for some of its photoresists and antireflective coatings, materials that are used to produce patterned layers on the silicon chips that form the brains of electronic devices. The company had been gradually phasing out products that contained PFOA and PFOS but found it a daunting process.

Product information on Dow photoresists and coatings containing PFOA, published in 2014, warned about the solvents in these products. These liquid solvents, which evaporate when the photoresists and coatings are used in manufacturing, are "slightly to moderately toxic to aquatic organisms," according to Dow's product data sheets. The exposure risk occurs for workers handling the materials during the manufacture of the chemicals and industrial use of them, though the risk can be minimized by following proper safety procedures. Communities surrounding manufacturing facilities become exposed to toxicants if there is a leak or spill, or improper disposal, which is what happened in the DuPont case.

DuPont no longer produces these PFOA-containing materials that came from Dow, but it is important to understand that it took 15 years of research and development (R&D) to remove PFOA from the ingredient list. Without legal action from the EPA, the company wouldn't have had an incentive to invest the time and money necessary to invent new versions of chemicals that were free of the offending compounds.

This is merely one example of one particular PFAS chemical. The PFAS family contains tens of thousands of chemicals, all of which probably pose similar health risks. These chemicals are used throughout semiconductor chip manufacturing.

They also appear in firefighting foams, waterproof fabric coatings, and hundreds of other products. Regulations banning the use of all PFAS chemicals, while well-intentioned, will shut down multiple industries unless regulators allow time for manufacturers to develop replacements.

DuPont stands as an example of both the ways in which companies try to shirk responsibility and the challenges they face in replacing toxic materials with less toxic ones.

Detecting toxicants

Some elements and compounds have been proven toxic, and it is in everyone's best interest to limit exposure and dispose of waste in a properly controlled manner. Other compounds are suspected toxicants, but the level of danger is not as well understood. Not everyone agrees on which compounds should be considered safe and what level of potentially dangerous ingredients or contaminants should be considered acceptable.

Advances in sensing are changing the landscape. Sensors too small to see with the naked eye measure temperature, pressure, motion, and the presence of minute quantities of chemical substances. These sensors can detect the presence of solid, liquid, or gas molecules.

More sensitive measurements mean that toxicants can be detected when contamination is low enough to measure in parts per billion or even parts per trillion. This creates a moving target for safe limits. Advances in measurement sensitivity make it harder for a company to argue that it didn't know that its product contained a certain toxicant. Chemical analysis is readily available and at a cost that can hardly be considered a barrier to knowledge.

Increased tracking makes it easier to evaluate a complete supply chain to determine where in a process a contaminant or substance of concern is finding its way in. This makes transparency less of a choice and more of a requirement. Despite the improved technology, however, supply chains are still very complicated. Multiple companies enter the picture from the point where materials are extracted from the earth to the point where an end customer receives a product. Problems can still hide and remain undetected, especially if those causing the problems want them to remain hidden.

Toward safer chemicals and ingredients

The EPA began its Safer Choice program in 2008. As part of the program, the EPA maintains a list of Safer Chemical Ingredients. The government evaluates chemicals to screen for those known to cause cancer, genetic mutations, asthma, or damage to internal organs. To be given the green light, chemicals must not accumulate in the body under repeated exposure or cause endocrine disruption.

Products that meet the Safer Choice guidelines must be thoroughly tested for safety and efficacy. If a product doesn't work to achieve its desired goal—cleaning clothing, or removing stains from carpet, for example—it doesn't matter how safe the product is because no one is going to buy it more than once. A bad experience can sour consumers not only on a particular product but also on greener products as an entire category.

Having a list of certified chemicals should, in theory, keep the public safe from toxic chemicals, but that isn't necessarily the case. Not all companies go to the trouble of having their products tested. And the screening itself remains imperfect—new formulations and chemicals are being developed all the time, and the government doesn't have the time to evaluate all of them.

One industry where the best use of chemicals can be confusing is in healthcare. Medical professionals want to keep patient safety the top priority, but some products that are supposed to enhance safety come with unintended consequences. Opinions about single-use disposable items versus reusable ones that require sterilization vary depending on who you talk to. We spoke with Marcia Frieze, founder of a US-based medical device company that has been named Safer Choice Partner of the Year five times, to get her perspective.

Interview

Marcia Frieze, Case Medical

Tell me about your professional journey.
I've always been interested in helping others solve problems. I have a master's degree in social work from Columbia University and worked as a clinical social worker for more than decade, during which time I developed a strong commitment to addressing problems and finding solutions. I started my professional journey as an entrepreneur and business owner when my husband, Allan, recruited me to help manage the operations of our first company, providing shared medical services to a network of hospitals. It wasn't until 1992 that I first became directly involved in manufacturing medical devices and formulating environmentally preferred instrument chemistries.

How did you become interested in reducing the use of toxic chemicals?
As chief executive officer (CEO) of Case Medical, I was alarmed when I saw how caustic instrument chemistries and toxic cleaners routinely used in healthcare settings were destroying the surfaces of our reusable sterilization containers as well as the medical instrumentation they were designed to clean and decontaminate. I learned that the same cleaners that were discoloring and pitting surgical instruments could render them potentially harmful to patients during routine medical procedures, and when the wash water was dispensed into the wastewater stream, it introduced toxic chemicals to our water supply. What we developed was a solution including eco-friendly, fast-acting enzymatic catalysts for extra efficacy and quicker turnarounds in hospital environments. Enzymes used to get rid

of troublesome stains could also be added to medical cleaners to remove organic contaminants, bacteria, and other infectious agents.

My initial goal was to make our manufacturing facility sustainable, environmentally preferred, and as safe as possible for our workers and for the neighboring community. We selected materials that were recyclable and chemicals that were the least harmful to people and to the environment.

Case Medical's manufacturing plant is located in a suburban neighborhood surrounded by family homes and residences. As a result, we take responsibility for maintaining a safe workplace for our workers and for our neighbors. We eliminate toxic chemicals wherever possible and treat any chemicals for passivating our metal components such that the solids can be collected and removed from our premises, and the wastewater treated so that it can be released directly into the sewer system.

Our entire factory has a whole-building water filtration system and four reverse osmosis water treatment systems, as well as several filtered air handling systems that are balanced and vented to eliminate toxic fumes. Our company was recently certified as a Green Building by the State of New Jersey. We participate annually in the Chemical Footprint Project, and have participated in the EPA Safer Choice Program since 2015.

I've always been interested in safety, sustainability, and standardization. I became aware that many chemicals in industry and in health care facilities are not only toxic, but used excessively when safer alternatives exist. I've found over my 30-plus years in the industry that most health care facilities use way too many chemicals for cleaning and for decontaminating medical devices. Many of the cleaning agents are caustic (highly alkaline), and the recommended dilution range for use is unnecessarily broad. Further, many cleaning chemistries are not necessarily free rinsing, and subsequent rinse steps are frequently eliminated in automated washers to save time. Thus, I became committed to not only reducing the chemical footprint but also developing instrument chemistries that are formulated using only the safest ingredients in their class and to use only what is needed and validated for infection prevention.

The intention of these chemicals is to promote sterilization?
Yes, the intention for formulating our nontoxic, sustainable chemistry line was to promote subsequent sterilization, while reducing the amount of chemicals needed for proper processing of devices beforehand. At Case Medical, we are best known for manufacturing reusable medical devices, specifically sterilization containers and procedure trays, that are durable, universally compatible, and made from anodized aluminum and passivated stainless steel.

In 1992, we acquired a sheet metal company, only to find out later that the health care industry was going primarily to plastic materials for most of their sterilization trays, not because of efficacy, but for display and cosmetic reasons. It didn't take us long to realize that plastic was a terrible packaging material for the intended purpose of terminal sterilization of reusable devices. One, it's not biodegradable;

it may never break down in a landfill. Plastic isn't thermally conductive. Furthermore, it retains moisture. For surgical procedures, instrumentation must be decontaminated, cleaned, and dried for subsequent sterilization or disinfection. Our intention was to develop a reusable sterilization containment device that can be repeatedly cleaned using highly effective nontoxic detergents.

Frankly, I feel that there are too many toxic chemicals in use in homes, in factories, and in health care facilities. Chemicals are required for cleaning, disinfection, and for device functionality. We saw what toxic chemicals were doing to our sterilization containers and trays and how pitted or corroded medical devices could potentially affect patient care. But what are these chemicals doing to our environment and our planet? We did our homework and, using only the safest ingredients available, developed a line of enzymatic and non-enzymatic detergents that are nontoxic and pH neutral. These were composed of only validated, environmentally preferred ingredients, along with active enzymes that serve as catalysts, designed to target specific contaminants found on used medical devices. We utilized Green-Blue's CleanGredients and the EPA list of environmentally preferred components to formulate our cleaning chemistries.

While many in the industry, especially in the European community, still feel that only the most caustic cleaners and toxic disinfectants are necessary to remove resistant contaminants from surfaces of used surgical devices, we found that our enzymatic and nonenzymatic detergents, at the right dilution, using high-quality water for rinsing, cleaned better than the toxic cleaners currently available and importantly preserved the useful life of the devices after repeated usage and hundreds of sterilization cycles.

There are several other cleaning products that are misrepresented as safe. These are labeled as "aluminum safe" or "aluminum friendly" cleaners that are highly caustic with a pH above 12, far from compatible with aluminum or for that matter any metal. Many health care facilities use single-use germicidal wipes for cleaning medical devices, although they are designed for environmental disinfection. These disposable wipes are saturated with toxic, high-pH chemicals that are corrosive to metals. Worse is that these same wipes are being used to not only disinfect but also clean surgical devices and then never rinsed off once applied. There are also single-use disposable wipes used for personal care that have no clear labeling. People flush them down the toilet where they collect as "fatbergs" and clog the sewerage system.

In 2011, our company entered a partnership with the EPA under their Design for the Environment Program (DfE) to advance the use of safer chemical usage. Then in 2015, when the Safer Choice program started, Case Medical became one of the first companies to be recognized as a EPA Safer Choice Partner of the Year for our instrument cleaners and lubricants. In 2022, we got an award from the EPA Safer Choice Program for a skin cleanser. I thought, if we can make a product that's safe, environmentally preferred, and so effective in removing all types of organic contaminants and bacteria from medical devices, we can also apply the same science and similar knowledge to people's skin. Why are people using soap? It's very caustic.

My goal in business was never to just to make profit, but to do the right thing for people and for the community. That's evolved from a commitment into more of a passion, maybe an obsession at this point. We're manufacturers, so we do have a lot of chemicals in our facility to maintain our equipment and to chemically treat our metal parts and products. We also learned that water quality is very important. The municipal water that comes into facilities and homes includes contaminants that have chronic effects. These can include disinfection byproducts, solvents and pesticides, as well as chemicals to treat the water such as chlorides, chloramine, or chlorine dioxide.Recently, we tested our tap water and found that Pseudomonas bacteria was present. It was time to change the membranes. We use reverse osmosis to treat the water used for most of our manufacturing processes, especially for manufacturing our instrument chemistries. We found that even though the ingredients in our instrument chemical solutions are the safest in their class, that's not a guarantee that water quality is consistently safe. That is why we monitor the water quality daily and validate that each cleaner we manufacture is safe before filling and packaging.

Let's talk more about safest in class. How you use the Safer Choice program to incorporate that?
Chemicals are necessary, and while none are 100 percent safe, especially in high concentrations, we refer to the Safer Choice Ingredients List (SCIL) when we choose the various components in our formulations. We have also been very involved with GreenBlue, which is another sustainability advocacy group. Options are available out there, if anybody cares to look. Our goal wherever possible is to promote the use of Safer Choice ingredients and Safer Choice labeled products. We have a great concern for infection prevention and further for skin health and respiratory safety wherever any product touches a healthcare worker, patient, or member of the community.

Are there situations where you feel like what you want isn't available, or you can't get it at scale?
There is a continuing supply chain crisis, and all that is required may not be readily available. Some chemicals, like enzymes, are very costly and are sensitive to high temperatures. We usually stock up before the summer months to protect the concentrated enzymes from denaturing and losing activity. At times, ingredients that were listed on the EPA SCIL list are removed and a new ingredient must replace that one. This is not always easy to do, and the newly formulated product now must be validated and approved by EPA all over again. Nevertheless, keeping watch on the CleanGredients and SCIL list can also be an advantage. We are now able to apply to Safer Choice for certification of an existing product by replacing one ingredient that isn't Safer Choice labeled with a new ingredient that was recently added to the list.

We have one or two cleaners that are not Safer Choice certified, but they're the best that we could possibly find for the intended purpose. When it comes to descaling automated washers, we would hope that people would use our Safer Choice certified cleaners, and then they won't have to descale as much. We've been able to help hospitals do much less reconditioning and much less descaling by using our non-enzymatic cleaners, which have high levels of chelating agents to remove hard water ions and scale. They're noncorrosive.

And more than that, they're also free rinsing. And that's a very important attribute. Not only do they rinse down the drain safely but they also remove organic and inorganic contaminants very well.

My husband was complaining to me the other day that dish soap, whether it's Palmolive or Dawn or any other commercial brand, doesn't rinse off easily. The point that I'm making is in hospitals, even though they sometimes say they have sustainability initiatives, they really don't. It is too easy to use a less effective, more expensive, toxic cleaner that the equipment manufacturer supplies, than one that is safer, validated, and cost effective. Facilities claim to support sustainability, but when it comes to really acting on it, that's another story.

What is your take on working with the EPA?
I am very proud to be a part of the EPA Safer Choice community that advocates for safer chemical usage. The ability to display the Safer Choice label on our cleaners gives us several advantages in the marketplace, for example in hospitals that have sustainability initiatives. As a Safer Choice Partner, I have much more exposure to the EPA than other companies might.

That being said, while I respect and participate in their mission, I've found it very difficult to get an innovative solution through that differs from what EPA and their pesticides or antimicrobial division have accepted. Both EPA and U.S. Food and Drug Administration (FDA) operate by substantial equivalence. This means that any new product has to be the same or equivalent to something they've already cleared before.

There are laws on the books, such as TSCA [the Toxic Substances Control Act], that only require chemical manufacturers to submit information about the production, use, exposure, and environmental fate of new chemicals and to control any of the substances that were determined to cause unreasonable risk to public health or the environment. Whatever was once cleared remains.

However, the EPA now routinely requires manufacturers to provide more information about new products, even those not likely to present an unreasonable risk. This has increased both the review time and the cost to manufacturers, and it has increased the number of restrictions on new chemicals that enter commerce. This lag delays innovation.

Small differences to an existing product are easier to introduce, but to present something substantially different is a challenge. Unfortunately, even when the EPA has lots of toxicity data, it's been found to be incredibly difficult to ban a chemical, and even harder to introduce a new innovative solution that does not fit the mold.

The air we breathe

Airborne pollutants are a serious public health problem. Studies completed between 2019 and 2021 report between 6.7 and 8.8 million deaths globally per year from indoor and outdoor air pollution.[3] For perspective, about the same number of people died from COVID-19 from the start of the pandemic through mid-2023.[4] These numbers are orders of magnitude greater than annual deaths from homicide or car accidents.

The most dangerous pollutants come in the form of tiny particulate matter—particles that are less than 2.5 microns in diameter and impossible to see without a microscope. Some particles, like dust from deserts or pollen from plants, occur naturally. Many more result from human activity, including burning wood or fossil fuels to produce heat and electricity.

In his book *The Unnatural World*, author David Biello emphasizes that humans have been changing the natural world for tens of thousands of years, beginning with the establishment of agriculture.[5] He recognizes, however, that these changes have been accelerating since the second half of the twentieth century. "Our need for fire has left a consistent black smudge that covers the globe," writes Biello. That smudge is the result of soot, particles of carbon created from combustion. Anyone who has ever stood around a campfire has seen soot and probably gotten it on their fingers or clothing.

In the summer and fall of 2017, the western US suffered from unprecedented fires. The fires destroyed acres of forest and thousands of homes and made the air dangerous to breathe for days on end. The air in Seattle and Portland looked like Los Angeles in the 1970s. Unfortunately, summer smoke may be the new norm, and not just on the West Coast of the US. The 2023 fire season affected large swaths of Canada. The smoke from Canadian fires brought orange skies and polluted air to the entire Northeast, as far south as New York.

Even without fires, air pollution from smog can cause health problems. The word "smog" is a portmanteau of "smoke" and "fog." Smog occurs when sunlight interacts with nitrogen oxides (NOx) from vehicles and factories plus volatile organic compounds (VOCs). Common sources of VOCs include gasoline, industrial solvents, and paint.

When I (Julia) was growing up in Southern California, the Los Angeles basin was nearly always smog-ridden. A brown haze hung over the horizon, especially in the inland regions far from the breezes of the Pacific Ocean.

I attended college in Claremont, which is as far east as you can travel while remaining in Los Angeles County. The smog there at the time was so bad that many days we could not even see the San Gabriel Mountains, a mere 11 miles north of campus. When the occasional rains came and cleaned up the smog momentarily, the mountains reappeared as though by magic. It amazed me how close they were. Today's Claremont College students and Inland Valley residents enjoy far cleaner air most of the time.

Overall improvements in air quality in California in the past few decades have occurred thanks to reduced NOx and sulfur dioxide (SO_2) emissions. In the US, such emissions were halved between 1970 and 2000.[6] It is not a coincidence that a process called flue gas desulfurization became commonplace in the US in the 1970s. This process removed sulfur from the gases emitted from coal-fired power plants. More stringent regulations on emissions from vehicle exhaust, which led to the development of modern catalytic converters, contributed to a drop in NOx emissions.

In China and India, however, SO_2 emissions continued to rise rapidly well into the twenty-first century as these countries brought electricity and cars to more and more of their citizens. As a result, large Chinese cities were notoriously known for their poor air quality, at levels that make even 1970s and 1980s Los Angeles air seem clean. The flue gas desulfurization process was finally added to Chinese power plants in 2004.[7] The efforts for cleaner air continued with the implementation of the coal-to-gas program, which contributed to major improvements in Chinese air quality.[8]

Cities such as London have taken drastic action. Each year air pollution causes thousands of Londoners to die prematurely and develop life-changing illnesses like cancer, lung disease, dementia, and asthma. The city introduced the Ultra Low Emission Zone (ULEZ) across greater London in August 2023, having trialed it initially just in the center of London starting in April 2019. This regulation requires all cars to meet minimum emissions standards [Gasoline: Euro 4 (NOx), Diesel: Euro 6 (NOx and PM)] when traveling within the ULEZ or pay a daily charge of $16, which would total around $500 per month. Almost all car owners switched to vehicles meeting the standards.[9]

In the central London trial, there was an almost 50 percent reduction in toxic NO_2 pollution, which equates to thousands of hospital admissions being averted. According to the World Health Organization guidance, every outer London borough not in the ULEZ exceeded the safe limit for toxic air particles.

The decrease in sulfur emissions through flue gas desulfurization led coal proponents to talk about "clean coal." Coal, however, is certainly not a clean source of energy, considering its adverse effect on the air quality and carbon footprint. Nor is it efficient—the amount of energy that can be generated by burning a ton of coal is less than half that from a ton of natural gas. Coal is finally becoming a poor choice from an economic standpoint, which is good news for public health. The sooner our society can transition to cleaner energy sources, the better. Fortunately, the cost of renewable energy sources like solar and wind power is dropping, and adoption is growing.

Shifting away from coal toward other sources of fuel is merely one example of a drive toward reducing the amount of toxicants in the air, water, and soil. Many more environmental toxicants pose a risk to people all over the world. It sounds like the obvious answer for better public health is to remove them. That goal, however, is not easy to achieve.

Removing toxicants

Getting rid of environmental pollution is hard, harder than you might think. There are multiple technical reasons for this: the extensive presence of certain toxicants, difficulty removing toxicants from polluted soil and water, uncertainty regarding toxicity of certain materials, and the challenge of finding safer replacements. There are also practical roadblocks: a lack of regulation combined with lax enforcement of existing regulations, and resistance from industries that benefit financially from materials that happen to be toxic.

The extensive presence of toxicants

Certain toxic materials have infiltrated cities around the world. Removing the offending chemicals requires a huge expense of time and money. Who is going to pay for it? The polluters themselves will likely do so only if regulations compel them to act. Government funding for cleanup and replacement of infrastructure can be hard to come by. Private companies aren't going to be motivated to tackle the problem if there isn't any money to be made in doing so.

Nongovernmental organizations (NGOs) dedicated to improving public health and the environment have an interest in creating solutions. Sufficiently large NGOs may be able to make a dent, but even well-funded organizations face funding limits and a lack of qualified staff. Partnering with universities provides a source of funding, but university research is notoriously slow.

The prevalence of lead in water systems is a prime example of a toxic material that has become ubiquitous. The pipes themselves have not been made from lead in a very long time. Modern plumbing in many parts of the world uses plastic or copper piping. Even plumbing solder for copper pipes has been lead-free in the US since 1986 as result of the Safe Drinking Water Act Amendments. Despite these changes, many miles of legacy water pipes contain lead. Replacing this infrastructure is an overwhelming and expensive task, but one that is necessary for public health. The story of Flint, Michigan (see Chapter 4) is an example of what can go wrong if old pipes aren't replaced.

Removing toxicants

The life cycle of toxic materials follows many possible paths. In some cases, companies have dumped toxic waste into their communities for decades, either accidentally or on purpose, ignoring the associated risk. In these cases, the contaminants often leach into soil and groundwater and dissipate to such an extent that they are hard to find, let alone isolate and remove. Areas with large enough concentrations are easier to clean up, but trace quantities often remain in sufficient concentration to be harmful.

Some products are only obviously toxic or hazardous during manufacturing. Once the product is in the customer's hands, it is perfectly safe. Dangerous solvents have evaporated or been cleaned off. Reactive chemicals have completed the reaction process, leaving nontoxic substances in their place. If the only issue with a specific chemical is worker exposure, it is easier to put in safeguards for workers than to change the product. Such safeguards include properly venting work areas or having employees wear protective gear. Another "solution," which doesn't actually solve the problem but merely moves it, is to manufacture products in countries where worker protection regulations are nonexistent or poorly enforced. Unfortunately, this approach has been all too common.

Some products that contain toxic compounds are stable and safe during use, only to reveal their toxic nature when the product is discarded into a landfill or burned. For example, QLED televisions made with cadmium selenide quantum dots contain very small quantities of cadmium, but the toxic element is embedded deep inside the product, so users aren't at risk for exposure. The risk of cadmium exposure during e-waste processing of televisions is also small compared to the other hazards present at many e-waste facilities (see Chapter 10), but it is still worth considering.

In other cases, even compounds commonly believed to be safe and stable aren't so harmless. One example is the various additives present in plastics, including the plasticizers that give plastics their desirable properties. Unfortunately, recycling concentrates toxicants while not adding value to the recycled plastic. We have more to say on this topic in future chapters.

Burning trash for energy can be considered a better alternative than extracting and burning coal and oil from the standpoint of greenhouse gas emissions, but it comes with risks. Fumes emitted from burning often contain dioxins and other carcinogens, so it's important to capture and filter the smoke to minimize exposure. In countries with poor waste management infrastructure, waste is sometimes burned in modern incinerators with excellent filtration systems, but NGOs have also documented regular burning of paper and plastic waste on open land right next to housing.

Where are the replacements?

Toxic materials aren't chosen for their toxicity (except in the case of pesticides and the like), but for their beneficial properties or lower cost. Manufacturers are resistant to replacing something that works well, especially in the absence of a strong case that end users are exposed to any toxicants. Fortunately, there are many examples of nontoxic products that are as effective, or sometimes more effective, than the conventional products they are replacing. Case Medical (see the interview with Marcia Frieze earlier in this chapter) is far from the only company dedicated to replacing toxic chemicals. Environmentally friendly products have improved significantly, and consumers have more reasons than ever before to give them a chance. Later chapters discuss specific examples.

Minimizing exposure during manufacturing is helpful. Avoiding the use of toxic chemicals in the first place is better. Sometimes, however, drop-in replacements aren't available. If no commercial material exists to replace a toxic one, a company generally assumes it can either continue using the offending material or stop production while waiting for someone to develop a replacement. In most cases, companies decide that the second option doesn't make sense financially. If they lack the expertise in-house to develop new materials and don't have the clout to convince their suppliers to do so, companies are stuck with a functional but problematic material. They can implement the best safety practices available until a better solution becomes available. They can also be more proactive, either ramping up internal R&D or supporting startups that are developing alternatives.

A note on drop-in replacements: as with the case of PFAS chemicals, sometimes the replacement is so similar to the chemical it is replacing that it presents the same hazards. Part of the challenge in regulating these chemicals is that banning a specific compound doesn't rule out companies switching to a similar but equally bad alternative. Hence, some of the laws passed between 2021 and 2023 that aim to ban all perfluoroalkyl and polyfluoroalkyl substances.

Cause and effect

Cause and effect can be hard to prove, and correlation does not necessarily imply causation. Studies that suggest a lack of evidence of toxicity are not necessarily impartial. Companies have a vested interest in demonstrating that their products are safe and often fund studies that are designed to show that no danger to consumers exists. In situations where a substance is undeniably toxic, and studies consistently show this, industries lobby to suppress or refute results.

Companies producing tetraethyl lead as a gasoline additive knew that the chemical was toxic before it became a commercial product. They decided to go ahead with commercializing it. The companies assumed that they could control exposure to lead in their manufacturing plants through proper safety procedures. They further assumed that the amount of lead in the final product was so small as to not be a public health hazard.

Both assumptions proved false. In 1924, several workers at a tetraethyl lead production facility died as a result of exposure.[10] The company involved managed to avoid publicity, and production continued. Later, the public health hazard became clear. Even in the face of data linking elevated levels of lead in the blood of US citizens to exposure to leaded gasoline, tetraethyl lead production continued. Finally, the US Clean Air Act of 1970 forced the gradual phasing out of lead in gasoline.

Uncertainties and the lack of knowledge

Companies developing safer alternatives to existing products sometimes exaggerate the dangers inherent in conventional materials. The warnings feed on consumers' fears and can raise red flags where they aren't warranted. In some cases, the new materials come with dangers of their own.

The chemical industry produces tens of thousands of different compounds, and it is nearly impossible to track them all. Product manufacturers, whether in construction, transportation, or electronics, have developed their own lists of chemicals that are not allowed. These so-called red lists specify chemicals that are forbidden because of their established level of toxicity.

Companies that buy chemicals will ideally consider all the toxicants that are known and develop a definitive list that will guide their purchasing decisions. But suppliers are constantly developing new formulations.

Attempts to create industry-wide red lists have often failed. As an example, Green Wizard created a database of more than 100,000 green building products, aimed at an audience of architects and developers. The funding that Green Wizard would have needed to leverage industry experience and create a meaningful list wasn't forthcoming, however, and the company went out of business in 2015.

The primary players in chemical regulation have developed vastly different versions of red lists. Some of the most obviously toxic materials appear on all lists, but beyond those, there is very little overlap. If organizations that have been studying chemical safety for years can't agree on a list of hazardous chemicals, how can a manufacturer trying to evaluate its supply chain know what choices to make? They need to make the best decisions they feel will address employee and customer safety while meeting product performance and cost goals. There will necessarily be trade-offs.

The SIN List from ChemSec (see our interview with Jonatan Kleimark later in this chapter) is a great step toward having a comprehensive list that applies to manufacturers in all industries. SIN stands for Substitute It Now, the concept that companies using any chemicals on the list should phase them out as soon as possible.

Resistance from industry

The technical hurdles of inventing new materials and removing toxicants are substantial, but the policy hurdles look even harder to overcome. Many years of R&D have gone into creating existing products and manufacturing processes. Industries tend to become entrenched and fight aggressively against policies that will force them to redesign their product lines. Even if safer materials exist, the path is not straightforward.

Changing materials is relatively easy if the new material is a drop-in replacement, meaning that the production process remains unchanged or only needs minor adjustments. For example, companies wanting to switch to a safer chemical in a metal electroplating bath can generally do so without sacrificing quality. All they need to do is adjust the plating time while keeping everything else the same. Other changes, such as implementing a different type of plating method to properly coat parts with new materials, require a huge capital expense to buy new equipment and months or years to develop and refine new processing methods. Some changes, like replacing fossil fuels, threaten the existence of entire industries and the economies of entire nations. If our society stops generating energy from coal, the companies whose only product is coal will go out of business unless they can pivot rapidly to another source of income. Other sources of heat and electricity also need to be readily available for the transition to occur without widespread societal disruption.

Despite the above challenges, pressure exists to create healthier, less toxic products in safer manufacturing environments. Businesses that have traditionally been tagged as the evildoers who create products that endanger public health—the chemical and energy industries come to mind—are shifting gears. They are not doing so as fast as we wish to see, but we appreciate signs of progress. The list of companies that are making great strides in removing toxic chemicals and reducing the emission of hazardous substances is growing longer every year. The following chapters include stories from many such companies and also of industry-wide collaborations that benefit not only the companies involved but their customers and the communities in which they operate.

Calling out hazards and risks

Manufacturers of industrially produced materials are required to create a Safety Data Sheet (SDS) for each product. These documents, which used to be called Materials Safety Data Sheets, spell out the hazards and precautions associated with specific chemicals. The SDS lists the chemical compounds present in the material and explains hazards associated with using it, such as fire risk or adverse health effects from inhaling vapors or dust generated from mechanical grinding. The document must specify safe handling procedures for any foreseen use of the product.

Ideally, manufacturers can't hide anything in an SDS. If a material produces toxic fumes during use, the SDS calls that out. If a product contains a suspected carcinogen, the SDS must say so.

In practice, SDSs from different manufacturers of the same chemical can vary widely. I (Julia) learned this after I gave a talk at the Surface Preparation and Cleaning Conference in 2022. In my presentation, I mentioned issues with a common industrial cleaning chemical, dimethyl sulfoxide (DMSO). Afterward, some attendees questioned my assertions.

The SDS I referred to said that DMSO is highly flammable, not biodegradable, and causes mutagenic and adverse reproductive effects. I did some more research, pulling up SDSs from multiple manufacturers. I found that flammability ratings range from two (moderate) to four (high). Some manufacturers say DMSO is readily biodegradable, and others say it isn't. At least part of the variability is because the various SDSs aren't all considering the same concentration of DMSO. The one I quoted reported on 100 percent DMSO, whereas others evaluated a much more dilute solution with a concentration more representative of real-world applications.

The SDS provides useful information, but it is important to read the fine print to understand the real risks for each particular application. Also, despite the existence of SDSs, it can be difficult to find out what is really in products sold to consumers and whether something advertised as nontoxic or "safe" lives up to that promise.

Microplastics and repiratory illness

In 2022, the World Health Organization published a report, "Dietary and Inhalation Exposure to Nano- and Microplastic Particles and Potential Implications for Human Health." The report expressed clear concerns, but all reports contain caveats. This report expressed one that turned out to make a difference. They wrote, "The weight of the scientific evidence provided by current data on adverse effects of nano- and microplastic particles (NMP) on human health is low, because of substantial limitations of the available information."

This caveat was seized upon by the plastics industry and brand owners to claim that there wasn't enough evidence to suggest any harm to human health, despite a 154-page report suggesting the opposite.

There are other indications that plastics are not benign. Workers exposed to nylon, polypropylene, polyethylene, and rayon flocking debris can develop a condition called flock worker's lung. Exposure to higher concentrations of respirable flock particles is associated with more severe disease.[11]

There are parallels for workers making other types of materials. Byssinosis is a crippling occupational lung disease caused by cotton dust. It is a well-known occupational respiratory disease among cotton mill workers.

Looking at progress

Removing toxicants requires a major investment of time and money. In the long run, however, such investment will pay off. Public health risks will decrease. In many cases, the businesses involved will be able to continue their operations. Ideally, they can keep the best aspects of their businesses and replace what needs fixing to create products that are safer and healthier.

Fortunately, progress has been made in our (the authors') lifetimes. For example:

- Gasoline no longer contains lead.
- Levels of sulfur dioxide in the atmosphere are lower due to improved controls on vehicle emissions and reduced usage of coal for heating, greatly improving air quality in the US.
- Water treatment in cities has improved.
- Raw materials are produced more efficiently, using less energy per unit of material produced.
- Recycling of paper, metal, and plastic has become commonplace in many cities.

These steps are encouraging, but efforts need to go further. Part of the problem is that unless the threat is dire, many businesses and governments are not going to invest the time and money required to do something about it. They sometimes take tiny steps and pat themselves on the back. A business that uses recycled paper in its North American or European offices but still emits plumes of toxic smoke from its factories or subjects its workers in far-flung countries to inhumane, unsafe conditions is hardly doing the right thing.

Businesses need to look at the big picture and delve into how the materials and the manufacturing processes that they, or their suppliers, use affect people and the planet. Chemical pollution needs to be addressed in a more comprehensive way. A 2022 article in *Environmental Science & Technology* further explains the challenge.[12]

Some government-supported organizations are doing something about the problem. ChemSec, the International Chemical Secretariat, is a Swedish organization dedicated to reducing the use of hazardous chemicals. Its funding comes about half from the Swedish government and half from NGOs from Europe and the US.

We spoke with ChemSec Chemicals and Business Advisor Jonatan Kleimark to learn about what the organization is planning.

Interview

Jonatan Kleimark, ChemSec

What are the ambitions of ChemSec for the next five to ten years?
The main ambition is to try to ensure that the targets stated in the chemical strategy for sustainability that the European Commission presented in 2020 are reached. That's what we want to achieve in the coming years.

ChemSec is also working with different businesses and organizations in the transition away from harmful chemicals. We want to highlight positive examples from the different businesses. That is something very powerful when we talk to policymakers. We will keep on developing new tools for companies to use and host discussions regarding chemicals management.

We also assist investors in their path toward understanding the chemical industry and financial risks and opportunities within that industry because that has been, I would say, very underworked. Through our tool ChemScore, investors can get insights on chemicals producers. We need to show the investors why they should invest in some companies and why they should engage with these companies and discuss their production of hazardous chemicals. We see this as very, very powerful.

What are the most pressing challenges for ChemSec, and what suggestions do you have to address these challenges?
The most pressing challenge is that we're facing a lot of pressure from the chemical industry. We try to bring positive examples from the business world to policymakers. It's sometimes very hard for us because even though the chemical industry can be a place for innovation, and we see a lot of that happening, for the major part, there is a lack of that. That's a big problem because that means business as usual will keep on, and that's not something we can have if we want to reduce the use of hazardous chemicals.

Currently, 74 percent of the chemicals used in Europe are hazardous in some way, and that's something we need to move on from. The chemical industry is, in many cases, very hesitant to help. That's something that we really are working on every day.

You mentioned the European figure. What's the global figure for the use in terms of hazardous chemicals?
I think that it's higher. In Europe, we have the data. We don't have that global figure, and I think that's a big problem within the chemical industry. There's a lack of

transparency in what they produce, there's a lack of transparency in the volumes, so there are many things that we don't know.

Where we know, we know that 74 percent is hazardous. Asia is the biggest producer of chemicals in the world. We have no idea what's happening there. One of the big challenges is to get hold of the data. What's happening? What's produced, what's in it? What will end up in our products?

You have this challenge of companies not wanting to be transparent, wanting to keep on business as usual. What are the solutions?
It's legislation that will move a business, which will move the laggards. So, we need legislation. And if we see that there are a few companies that want to have sustainable solutions, and want to advance the circular economy, that's something we can use when we talk to policymakers to show them examples of businesses being sustainable but still very profitable and successful. That way we can promote stricter legislation that's more progressive and that will force the other companies improve their work on chemicals.

Could you name two to three successes that exemplify the work you're doing and how it's moved things forward?
The most famous tool that the ChemSec has developed is the SIN List, the "Substitute It Now" list, which is our list of chemicals that fulfill the criteria for inclusion in the REACH candidate list and should therefore be banned.

A lot of NGOs and companies are using the SIN List. I think that in many cases, they don't know that ChemSec is behind the list. If you want to do a substitution, if you want to phase out chemicals, it's a great guideline for companies to understand where to start.

Today the SIN List is around 1,000 chemicals and that's a bit too many just to have as a list. It's better to understand which are relevant for your business, which are relevant for your industry, and then you can use that to create a Restricted Substances List.

In addition, we have established ChemSec Marketplace, which is a global online platform for safer alternatives to hazardous chemicals, as well as the Investor Initiative for Hazardous Chemicals, IIHC. The IIHC helps investors better understand the chemical industry and supports them in moving the industry towards more sustainable solutions.

Does it tell you what to substitute that with?
From the SIN list, you can find if we have a safe alternative. You can click the link, and you will end up on that alternative on Marketplace. With the SIN List, we want to show what you should not use. With Marketplace, we want to show this is what you should use.

Of course, the business of substituting a chemical is a much bigger project than finding an alternative because you need to understand if it is viable for your process. Can you use it, and should you use it? Maybe it's a liquid, and the company was using a powder. We know what people are searching for and filtering for on Marketplace, which gives as an indication of the most important areas. Leather and textiles is every month one of the things that ranks highest on that list.

Which manufacturing sectors require the most work?
Naming a few sectors is hard, because I think most of the sectors have a problem with chemicals. We've had a lot of discussions with the electronics sector lately, especially around PFAS. I think that there has been a shift in awareness in that sector, when they have been forced to understand more about the chemical content in products and processes, and I hope this will be a positive change that can drive other sectors.

If we're looking at awareness on chemicals issues, some sectors like the textile industry have been a bit more aware. In automotive, electronics, construction, there has been a lot less awareness. But there are a lot of companies that are front runners and want progressive chemicals management.

Where to go from here

Our interviewees point out some significant challenges in making substitutions for hazardous chemicals. One question to think about is what is a regrettable substitution, and how can it be prevented? The information and stories in the coming chapters will shed some more light on this question.

Notes

1 Rich, Nathaniel. 2016. "The Lawyer Who Became DuPont's Worst Nightmare," *The New York Times*, January 6, 2016. https://www.nytimes.com/2016/01/10/magazine/the-lawyer-who-became-duponts-worst-nightmare.html.

2 Salvidge, Rachel, and Leana Hosea. 2023. "Revealed: Scale of 'Forever Chemical' Pollution across UK and Europe," *The Guardian*, February 23, 2023, sec. Environment. https://www.theguardian.com/environment/2023/feb/23/revealed-scale-of-forever-chemical-pollution-across-uk-and-europe.

3 Roser, Max. 2021. "Data Review: How Many People Die from Air Pollution?" *Our World in Data*, November 25, 2021, https://ourworldindata.org/data-review-air-pollution-deaths.

4 World Health Organization. 2023. "WHO Coronavirus Disease (COVID-19) Dashboard," https://covid19.who.int/table.

5 Biello, David. 2017. *The Unnatural World: The Race to Remake Civilization in Earth's Newest Age.* New York: Scribner.

6 US EPA, "Air Pollutant Emissions Trends Data | US EPA," US EPA, May 31, 2019, https://www.epa.gov/air-emissions-inventories/air-pollutant-emissions-trends-data.

7 Wiatros-Motyka, Malgorzata. 2016. "An Overview of HELE Technology Deployment in the Coal Power Plant Fleets of China, EU, Japan and USA," United States Energy Association (IEA Clean Coal Centre, December 2016), https://usea.org/sites/default/files/

An%20Overview%20of%20HELE%20technology%20deployment%20in%20the%20
coal%20power%20plant%20fleets%20of%20China.

8 Leng, Xuan, Xuemei Zhao, and Houjian Li. 2022. "Assessing the Effect of the Coal-to-Gas
Program on Air Pollution: Evidence from China," *Environmental Science and Pollution
Research* 30, no. 9: 24027–42. https://doi.org/10.1007/s11356-022-23739-6.

9 Greater London Authority, "The Ultra Low Emission Zone (ULEZ) for Lon-
don | London City Hall," www.london.gov.uk, 2023, https://www.london.gov.uk/
programmes-strategies/environment-and-climate-change/pollution-and-air-quality/
ultra-low-emission-zone-ulez-london.

10 Hamilton, Alice, Paul Reznikoff, and Grace M. Burnham. 1925. "Tetra-Ethyl Lead,"
Journal of the American Medical Association 84, no. 20 (May 16, 1925): 1481–86,
https://doi.org/10.1001/jama.1925.02660460017008.

11 Turcotte, Scott E. et al. 2013. "Flock Worker's Lung Disease," *Chest* 143, no. 6:
1642–48. https://doi.org/10.1378/chest.12-0920.

12 Blumenthal, Jonathan D., Miriam Diamond, Matthew J. Hoffmann, and Zhanyun
Wang. 2022. "Time to Break the 'Lock-In' Impediments to Chemicals Management,"
Environmental Science & Technology 56, no. 7: 3863–70. https://doi.org/10.1021/acs.
est.1c06615.

3 Reining in Excess Waste

It's cheaper than it should be to throw things away.

—Brion Hurley, Lean Consultant

Considering material consumption

Manufacturing requires a huge quantity of raw materials. The drive for greater wealth throughout the world has led to greater consumption of material goods. Common wisdom says that to remain healthy, an economy has to grow at a certain percentage a year, and that requires producing more and more things to sell to a growing population.

We wish more economists would heed author Kate Raworth's advice and reconsider these assumptions about economic growth. The principles that Raworth outlines in *Doughnut Economics* make so much sense. Constant growth is not sustainable. It benefits the wealthy in the short term and is likely a path to ruin in the long term. This chapter offers context around material consumption, including the challenges of controlling it and the reasons it is vitally important to do so.

The measure of wealth in a country is, in large part, related to how much stuff the average person owns. The book *Material World: A Global Family Portrait* by Peter Menzel and Charles Mann shows the stark contrast in wealth around the world through photographs of the "average" family in 30 countries, surrounded by all their possessions. Families literally emptied out their houses to create the photographs.

This book was published in 1995, before Western-style material consumption had spread to more rural nations and before consumer electronics had become ubiquitous. The American family in the book owned several cars and lots of furniture but only one computer. It would be interesting to see what a similar book would look like today.

Per capita materials usage in the US grew more than sixfold during the twentieth century. These calculations of material consumption don't even account for the materials in imported goods. Much of this increase is a result of the growth in the size of homes in the US, from an average of 1,000 square feet in 1,900–an average of 2,500 square feet in 2005.

DOI: 10.4324/9781003409267-4

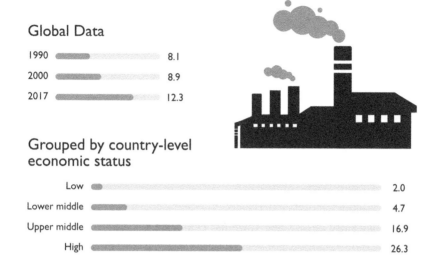

Global Data

1990		8.1
2000		8.9
2017		12.3

Grouped by country-level economic status

Low		2.0
Lower middle		4.7
Upper middle		16.9
High		26.3

Figure 3.1 Metric tons of engineered materials extracted per capita: Worldwide data from 1990, 2000, and 2017; Data grouped by country-level economic status from 2017.[1]

Europe has done a better job than the US in constraining excess consumption and reducing waste. This is in large part thanks to greater overall population density and more efficient transportation systems in European cities. Cars and homes are generally smaller in Europe, and per capita materials usage has declined in some European countries in the past decade. Rising materials usage in parts of Asia, Latin America, and Africa, however, more than makes up for it. The global trend remains one of increased production of materials and goods, as illustrated in Figure 3.1. Most of the resources are used to make engineered materials—metals from mineral ores, plastics from fossil fuels, and construction materials such as concrete, brick, and tile—as well as providing the fuels needed for transportation, heating, and electricity.

Reducing these quantities remains a good idea, but perhaps not for the reasons that some people think. The real problem of resource extraction is not that the world is going to run out of resources. Extraction causes pollution and damage to the land around a mine, as well as emitting greenhouse gases that contribute to climate change. Without delving into the science behind climate change here, suffice it to say that climate change is a real problem, and materials usage can play a role in shrinking that impact.

Are we really running out?

People sometimes promote recycling as a solution to the risk of running out of natural resources. This concern pertains not only to water but also to the production of both plastics, which today rely on fossil fuels, and metals, which rely on ores. As you will read about in Chapter 9, recycling is a helpful partial solution for materials like metals and glass, and less so for paper. Recycling is ineffective and even harmful for some types of plastics.

In the case of water, local scarcity is a real problem, exacerbated by droughts and floods that are more severe than ever. For Cape Town, South Africa, 2017–2018 marked the third straight season of severe drought. When combined with a growing population, the drought presented a huge problem. In the spring of 2018, the city of four million was on the verge of running out of water before the rainy season started in June or July. In January, city officials estimated that reservoirs held only 90 days' worth of water. The city barely avoided "day zero," defined as the day when municipal water taps are shut off, which was originally forecast to occur in April. Doing so required extreme conservation measures. Residents lined up for hours to fill containers from natural springs and rationed those containers carefully.

In the years since 2018, Cape Town has continued water conservation efforts. The city developed a new water strategy plan in 2020 to ensure access to clean water for all its residents.[2]

Water is a critical resource not just for cities but for many manufacturing industries. However, when comparing water usage between different sectors of materials production, we need to define "water usage" and understand the source. Is it rainfall, is it irrigated water, is it desalinated? The metrics for every region and every country are different. Many times, we have seen one materials industry attack another over water usage; we see NGOs and governments doing the same. But more often than not, this demonstrates a misunderstanding of how twenty-first-century manufacturers process and filter water before returning it to the municipal water system.

Industrial wastewater treatment is little understood by those not working in manufacturing plants. In many cases, effluent water from one process is reused in another process after suitable filtration and purification. This can reduce costs in several ways. Manufacturers benefit from lower water consumption bills, less need to pay for effluent disposal because of reduced wastewater volume, and lower energy costs due to the recovery of heat from recycled wastewater.

A good case in point is the pulp and paper industry (see Chapter 5) where water can be returned to the municipality after industrial use and sophisticated water treatment. There is a minor loss from evaporation, but the loss is only a tiny percentage of the water used. Calculations of the amount of water needed to produce paper products do not always account for water recycling.

Managing oil and mineral reserves

Fossil fuels and mineral ores do not present the same level of resource scarcity risk as water supplies. Predictions of "peak oil," when oil and gas reserves were going to start a downward trend early in the twenty-first century, have not come to pass.

When supplies of certain ores have reached diminishing returns, new mining locations have been found.

Part of the challenge is in distinguishing between the existence of potential new sources of resources on earth and the expense—in both money and harm to the environment—of extracting them. If the expense to extract the wealth within specific sources of fuel or materials is prohibitive, then the source might as well not exist as far as commercial extraction is concerned. The environmental impact of newer technologies such as hydraulic fracturing of rocks to extract the resources inside them—better known as fracking—is another concern.

It is also important to distinguish between reserves and resources. The supply of any specific resource—the total mass of material located within the earth's crust—is unknown. The estimate is a moving target that changes every time exploration reveals a new possible source. Even if we knew the total quantity of a resource, it would not be feasible to extract it all. Minerals that exist deep underground or in extremely small concentrations at a specific location cannot be extracted at a cost that makes it worth the expense of extracting them.

Reserves stand as the more important measurement. The quantity of material in reserve represents the share of a resource that can be extracted using existing techniques and at an acceptable cost. The value changes over time but is well-defined.

By comparing annual production needs to the amount of a mineral in reserve, it is possible to calculate the number of years the supply will last. Some alarmists use these calculations to suggest that the earth is at risk of running out of some mineral or another. The reality is that the mining industry is continually finding new sources and developing more efficient techniques for extracting the minerals within them.

As an example, the ratio of reserves to annual production of copper was 42.8 years in 2011.[3] This does not mean that the earth will run out of copper by the time today's teens are middle-aged. The ratio was about the same in 1980.[4] According to the author Vaclav Smil, who has studied historical data in excruciating detail, there is no risk that society will run out of any common metals in the next 60 or 80 years.[5]

Smil was not considering the specialty metals used in minute quantities in cell phones. Still, these are probably not in danger of disappearing from the earth either. Plenty of ores containing these metals exist in the earth's crust. The problem lies in the feasibility of extracting enough of them within timelines that device manufacturers demand, and at a price they are willing to pay. When considered from this viewpoint, there exists a real risk of supply shortages. There are also geopolitical concerns because of where some ores are located. These concerns are driving efforts to discover more diverse sources of a variety of minerals.

Extraction strategies need to consider the time horizon between discovering a new location where a mine could be constructed and mining the minerals within it. It takes between 10 and 15 years from initial exploration to productive mining. This is quite a long time compared to the production cycles of consumer electronics.

When a potential mine is located in a country with an unstable government, this adds to the risk and complicates the challenge of extracting and distributing the minerals.

Resource availability and critical materials

The European Commission's list of critical raw materials—those that are critical to the EU economy and important for the transition to cleaner energy—has grown since the commission published its first list in 2011. The 2020 list includes 30 entries.[6] Most are metals or minerals.

There are uncertainties surrounding the availability of resources. A 2017 article in *Nature* warned about challenges in maintaining sufficient mineral supplies to satisfy society's increasing demand for technology.[7] The challenge becomes more pressing as demand extends to regions of the world that are relatively unconnected today and the number of devices in circulation worldwide skyrockets. Author Saleem Ali pointed out the demand for large quantities of many different minerals and suggested that recycling will not be sufficient to ensure availability.

Ali's concerns may or may not come to pass depending on how reuse and e-waste recycling efforts develop (see Chapter 10). Regardless, Ali's point about the importance of managing the global mineral supply seems valid. He proposes coming up with international agreements to ensure stable prices for minerals needed for technology-related applications. These minerals are sold through individual dealers rather than a global commodities market, which tends to make prices fluctuate widely.

The challenge of reducing materials usage

Reducing the global extraction of raw materials is a noble goal and an extremely difficult one. Historically, as manufacturing efficiency improves, similar products can be made with lower consumption of energy or materials and therefore at a lower cost. As a direct result, the total number of products produced tends to increase. Mass ownership promotes greater consumption.

The cell phone provides a perfect example. It is possible to look at the cell phone as replacing many objects that used to be commonplace in everyday use: a traditional corded phone, alarm clock, camera, map, and address book. The weight of all these products is several kilograms (several thousand grams), compared to 100–200 grams for a smartphone.[8]

But the vast quantity of cell phones being produced more than makes up for any supposed savings. Approximately 11 million cell phones were produced in 1990, with an average weight of 300 grams.[9] Around 1.5 billion cell phones are now produced and sold every year.[10]

But is that volume necessary? In 2021, Apple started telling its customers that they could fix their own iPhones with the company's new online Self Service Repair Store. This is a notable advance for a company whose products have been historically among the least repairable.

Apple is anticipating much-heralded future legislation. This EU legislation, proposed in March 2023, will ensure that more products are repaired under warranty or legal guarantee. Consumers will also have easier and cheaper options to repair electronic products that are technically repairable (such as vacuum cleaners, tablets, and smartphones) when the legal guarantee has expired or when the item is not functional anymore as a result of wear and tear.

There are cell phones that are designed to be disassembled and repaired: The Fairphone and HMD's Nokia G22 are two examples. But their sales are minuscule compared to global market leaders Samsung and Apple.

Other commentators—Nokia CEO Pekka Lundmark, for example—believe that with the advent of 6G in 2030, people will stop purchasing cell phones, and will "use wearable electronic products and even implant chips in their bodies."[11] That is a fascinating and somewhat worrisome prospect to contemplate.

If reducing the total amount of global resource consumption is not realistic, what then? One avenue involves reaching an easier goal of reducing the waste generated per product. This approach is a good starting point, although reducing absolute resource consumption should be the ideal.

The four system conditions

The focus of this book is on how decisions regarding materials selection and manufacturing processes contribute to environmental sustainability. We argue that environmental sustainability is all about engineered materials—materials developed by humans. We must account for the full impact of extracting and processing fossil fuels, minerals, and wood when considering climate action. Unless we do that, any decisions will ignore critical information.

The concept of "four system conditions" embraces a comprehensive but practical approach, recognizing the need to avoid increasing certain undesirable practices. Eliminating such practices entirely is a laudable but probably unachievable goal. The Natural Step, a multinational nonprofit with a mission to "accelerate the transition to a sustainable society," has reworded the four system conditions in terms of four principles:

1 Eliminate systematic increases in the amount of material extracted from the earth.
2 Eliminate systematic increases in production of toxic substances of concern.
3 Avoid systematic increases in destruction of natural resources.
4 Avoid practices that contribute to undermining people's ability to meet their basic needs or create unsafe working conditions.

Three of the four conditions mention avoiding or eliminating systematic increases. The assumption is that materials will still need to be extracted from the earth in the foreseeable future. The chemical industry is not disappearing. The four system conditions focus on shrinking the rate of increase by considering where materials come from and how they are being extracted and processed.

Given the climate crisis and pledges to achieve net zero carbon emissions, a goal to drastically decrease production would be more appropriate. That is much more challenging. Though technically possible, it would require such large-scale behavior change that it is hard to imagine it happening in our lifetime. Having said that, the EU Circular Economy Action Plan (CEAP) requires an absolute reduction in resource exploitation to meet the plan's mandate. We discuss the CEAP further in Chapter 12.

Resource reduction is not straightforward

Sometimes moves that seem to obviously reduce material consumption do not have as great an effect as we might think. As one example, the trend toward electronic rather than paper copies of documents certainly reduces the number of trees that need to be cut down to produce paper. What is often left out of the story, though, are the resources required to produce the computing power that enables electronic document generation and transfer.

The internet is not resource-neutral, and cloud computing happens on earth, not in the sky. Banks of servers, built with raw materials, are required to manage all that global data flow. Huge quantities of energy and water are needed to run the data centers and cool the buildings to keep servers from overheating. Big data requires big resources.

Companies that make servers and the components inside them are well aware of this issue. Waterless immersive liquid cooling of the chips inside data centers drastically improves efficiency and performance. A non-corrosive liquid runs in a closed loop to control the operating temperature. This technology allows for smaller or more densely packed servers without the risk of overheating. In 2021, Microsoft announced a plan to reduce water use in its data centers by 95 percent by eliminating the need for evaporative cooling in all but the hottest climates.[12]

Manufacturers in various industries are developing ways to make more effective use of materials and reduce waste. Replacing steel and glass with aluminum and plastics is one way to create lighter, more efficient computers, vehicles, and airplanes. As we noted in Chapter 1, these lighter materials require much more energy to produce per ton of product. This doesn't mean that such substitutions are a bad idea, however. The products require fewer pounds or kilograms of materials, so the energy of materials production may balance out. Without doing the calculations, however, it isn't clear that replacing materials has the level of positive effect that designers intended. Weight is not the only aspect that needs to be considered.

Moving toward zero waste

Reducing global materials consumption by a significant amount requires a shift in mindset away from the buy-consume-discard approach. Efforts need to go beyond nominal increases in rates of recycling. Businesses and their customers need to consider each product as part of the bigger picture. What materials are used to make the product, and how were they produced? How long can the product itself be used? Is there a resale market for the product? What happens to the product once it has outlived its usefulness as originally intended?

The idea of shifting from a linear economy to a circular one is not new. William McDonough and Michael Braungart published *Cradle to Cradle* back in 2002. Instead of products moving from cradle to grave, they find continual use. Biobased or organic materials—anything that can decompose or biodegrade—return to the earth in a continuous cycle. They enrich the soil, much like wastes from plants and animals have done for millennia. Inorganic materials become part of a technical cycle. They are ground up and melted to produce materials for the next generation of engineered products.

The idealized version where nothing becomes waste and the circles continue forever sounds great. Unfortunately, reality doesn't quite add up. The technical cycle cannot be as efficient as many people want to believe. Products that are made of many different engineered materials cannot be easily separated into individual materials and recycled back into circulation. Chapters 9 and 10 delve further into this challenge.

Still, we believe that we need to strive toward a more circular economy. Businesses—especially large businesses producing millions or billions of products every year—have the clout to insist that such a shift take place. On the flip side, companies also have the ability to put the brakes on attempts to change and continue the status quo while appearing to take positive action.

What level of responsibility is the business community willing to take on? The level appears to be growing as more businesses publicly announce commitments to addressing their roles in polluting the environment and creating mountains of waste. While this is a promising trend, we advise looking deeper into the actions behind the words.

Merely an intent to save resources is, of course, not enough. The trick is to accurately measure resource usage and track progress toward concrete goals. Saving resources often leads to saving money. Without tracking exactly how much they are spending on electricity, water, or waste disposal, a company won't know the best places to look for cost savings.

It isn't possible for a business to produce zero waste, but it can create zero waste to landfill. The methods for achieving this goal matter. Ideally, zero-waste-to-landfill programs reduce the total quantity of materials needed to make products and reuse more resources on-site while considering the overall environmental impact of any changes.

The alternative, burning excess waste to avoid sending it to a landfill, increases energy use and releases toxic fumes and greenhouse gases into the environment. There are exceptions where a closed-loop waste-to-energy system inside a manufacturing facility can be part of a zero-waste-to-landfill strategy. Even so, reduction needs to be the top priority.

Brewer Science, based in Rolla, Missouri, has a robust zero-waste-to-landfill program. The company produces chemicals and materials used to make computer chips. This is a resource-intensive industry, and one that requires many hazardous chemicals. Brewer achieved its goal of zero waste to landfill in 2015 and has maintained the certification every year since. For more about Brewer Science, see our interview about its B Corp certification in Chapter 12.

Most people understand that zero-waste-to-landfill programs are not just good for the environment; they are good for the bottom line. As mentioned earlier in this chapter, some manufacturing facilities filter wastewater at their production plant and recycle it back into the system. The water bill goes down, and the facility doesn't have to pay for permits to release wastewater. Machine shops collect metal scraps and remelt them to make more products. Making more products with the same quantity of incoming metal is more efficient and saves money. The manufacturing process also creates less solid waste, reducing waste disposal costs.

Lean and sustainability

Reducing toxicants and working toward zero-waste-to-landfill goals tie very nicely into the concept of lean manufacturing. Companies typically adopt lean to make manufacturing more efficient. When executives at these companies think about waste, they might first consider eliminating wasted time and money. But reducing waste of raw materials is related. For example, better control of inventory means buying and storing less material. By keeping a tight lid on the quantity of raw materials being ordered, it is possible to manage multiple sources of waste.

I (Julia) met Brion Hurley at the GoGreen Portland conference in October 2017 and interviewed him for *Material Value*.

Brion came from the world of lean and Six Sigma, focused on ways to improve quality and efficiency of business practices, and hadn't thought much about environmental sustainability early in his career. He started his consulting practice in 2017 with the goal of either teaching sustainability professionals about lean or teaching lean or Six Sigma professionals about environmental sustainability. I spoke to Brion in 2022 to get an update.

Interview

Brion Hurley, Founder of Business Performance Improvement

What have you been working on for the past few years?
Some recent projects have been pretty promising. One organization was struggling with wood waste. They are home builders, and they had piles of wood scrap. So what they did was organize that scrap wood, and cut the pieces into standardized sizes.

That seems like such a simple solution. When they came to you, what was the problem that the company was trying to solve?
They were looking at the wood waste and saying, "That's a lot of expensive wood. And now we're buying it at much higher rates, and actually running short on supplies."

They realized they need to figure out how to take advantage of what's already here. You might think that would be something they would have jumped on earlier.

Once they identify and focus on it, it's not that complicated, but they need to decide this is a problem. When it becomes urgent, that is when they put the effort in.

It is useful to connect the lean concepts to sustainability. It would seem like an obvious connection. Are there still disconnects between those concepts?
What I'm finding is that it's still not top of the list of priorities. The groups that are working on those issues aren't always tied in with the business folks. If your environmental health and safety (EH&S) people are working on physical waste reduction, are they tied in with the process improvement groups? Let's say they're doing a process improvement in one department. Is EH&S pulled into those events, or are they brought in at the last second, when they can't really influence decisions?

A lot of it is getting the right people at the right time, connecting them a little more closely, or aligning them to the existing activities that are happening. People can ask, what happens to the waste after it leaves your area? What do we have to do on the back end to process all the paperwork, all the documentation?

Another challenge is that sometimes the costs aren't allocated correctly. And so they don't see it in their budget. Maybe they're charged per square foot of the space they use, but not by what's happening in that space. Are they being held responsible for the full impact that they're creating? How much water are they consuming? How much trash are they generating? How much electricity are they consuming? I don't think it always matches up cleanly.

What do you think we, as consultants, can do to help bring those groups together so that they can better solve these problems?
One thing is to look at existing activities and bring in these other experts or groups into that discussion. If you're doing a project, and you have paint being consumed and thrown away, maybe you should bring in someone from your local county or your state Department of Ecology.

What if we could bring everyone together do a dumpster dive or we could do some kind of action where we see the whole process? Focus not on the business performance of the flow or the cycle time or the quality but focus on the waste stream. What I find is that those projects will highlight a lot of process inefficiencies as well. We call it the hidden factory, the things you don't see.

Do you mean the materials that don't actually end up in your products?
Yes, or you don't see it in your budget, or you don't see it in the visual processes, or you don't see the inefficiency taking place. But it's there. It's always there. It's just not visible. But sometimes when we focus on the waste stream, or the green part of this, it exposes some of those opportunities that they're not seeing today.

It's been really eye-opening for people when they know what the company spends on wastewater management, electricity, hazardous waste treatment and processing, and transportation. Maybe those things are in their budget somehow, but it doesn't hit their radar. Or it's not at the top of the list of priorities. Sometimes these green opportunities get overlooked or overshadowed by other business processes. The big one I think is just seeing what happens after something leaves their department, their area, and how that impacts the business. Each individual process doesn't seem like that big of a cost. But when I roll this up across the whole site, or the whole facility, we see a huge opportunity. Electricity is a good one because it's usually a high-cost item. Hazardous waste, I think that's definitely going to get some attention because of the hauling and the processing and permitting costs associated with that.

I've heard there has been a pushback against lean or just-in-time manufacturing because of some of the serious supply chain problems that we've had, especially between 2020 and 2022. There's this fear that we can't have just enough because our supplies can be cut off and we can't make products for several months. What are some good ideas to deal with that?
People were looking at it differently from what lean would recommend. Lean is about developing long-term partnerships with your suppliers and reducing transportation by having them located nearby. Then you can be flexible and agile to respond to the changes in the market and changes in what's happening in your business.

Some companies have suppliers deliver multiple times a day to have the right amount at the right time. If you order weeks or months' worth of material, you have to store it somewhere, which means you need a bigger warehouse. Now you have all this money tied up in inventory, hoping that you're going to use it. And then all of a sudden demand changes and shifts, and you may be left with inventory that you can't get rid of.

During the pandemic, it would make sense to have a large supply of whatever item ran low. But how would you know what item was going to run low? When you order huge amounts of inventory, you're robbing everybody else of that. And that's what happened as people started hoarding.

What do you think we can do to get businesses to understand and embrace that message?
It goes back to lean. What I like about lean is it's not based on making great predictions. It's about responding quickly to the changes and what actually happens. It's looking at total process time, which includes shipments and deliveries. If you see that it takes a month to get supplies from somewhere, you find a way to get that quicker. Otherwise, you have to order earlier, you have to forecast earlier, and you're going to carry more inventory.

From your perspective, what approaches work to achieve the goal of reducing waste?
One of the sites where I used to work at Rockwell wanted to expand a building because they were running out of room. Management didn't think they leveraged the space they had fully, so they pushed back. I'm glad they did. They said, reevaluate everything you're doing on the site. Look at your purchasing and your inventory and how you're storing parts, and challenge what you're doing now. Part of that is organizing and getting rid of stuff that you no longer need. There's a method called 5S, which is an organization method for decluttering, basically, but it's a formal business approach to do that. It's something that we teach in the lean methodology.

Tell me a little bit more about 5S.

It's a five-step process: Sort, Set in order, Shine, Standardize, Sustain. The first step, Sort, is to take everything and lay it out and look at what is still needed. Get rid of and remove anything that's no longer necessary. Maybe you keep it but you put it somewhere else. It doesn't need to be in the main area where we're doing the day–to-day activities. Let's keep this core space that we need to do our work with only the essentials.

Once you actually see what is absolutely needed, then you arrange it in a logical sequence so that it's easy to find quickly. And then there's a cleaning and a sweeping process called Sweep or Shine.

In Standardize, we get consistent about how we're marking and labeling everything. Last is the sustainment piece. How are we going to keep it going and not have to come back and do this all again next month or next year?

What happened at Rockwell?

They looked at every part of their facility. What they found was that they had capacity at other sites. They decided to move a product out into those other sites that actually need the work and have the space. So long story short, they realized they didn't need to expand the building. They saved money on the construction and all the material that goes into a new building and the time that that would have taken up.

Other facilities needed the work and had the space already. So it was looking across it at a system level and choosing the best place to optimize what they already had without just throwing money at a new building or expanding the building. They had the space. They just weren't using it as efficiently as they should have been. And part of it was how they manage the inventory. But other part of it was what work they actually had been doing there.

You have a contract with Impact Washington. Tell me about that work.

We ran a wastewater reduction project for a client in 2021. By looking at the way that parts were being cleaned, they figured out that there's a smarter way of setting up their tanks that would reduce the amount of wastewater being dumped and create a more consistent manufacturing process.

They were considering adding a new line of tanks to meet their growing demand. And they realized that this project helped reduce the time it took parts to go through their process. That allowed them to increase their capacity without having to set up this new line. The other cool part was they were able to cut down the number of times that they had to dump the baths. It was safer in those areas because they were using fewer gallons of chemicals in the process.

These are metal parts going through a tank. They apply a coating and go through a cleaning process. The residue from that has to be treated before it goes down the drain, so they're paying for that cost. They save money on the disposal fees because there is less sludge, and less water that needs treatment. It was a matter of connecting the client with an expert who really understood tanks and sustainability and had done this many times.

Materials-specific approaches

To determine the best way to approach resource management, we need to understand how various materials are made and how they can be made in more efficient ways. There are both economic and environmental benefits to reducing materials extraction and consumption. In Part II, we talk about these benefits as they apply to specific classes of materials.

Notes

1 Source: United Nations Statistics Division. 2019. "SDG Indicators." Un.org. 2019. https://unstats.un.org/sdgs/report/2019/goal-12/.

2 City of Cape Town, "Our Shared Water Future: Cape Town's Water Strategy," resource. capetown.gov.za, n.d., https://resource.capetown.gov.za/documentcentre/Documents/ City%20strategies.

3 USGS, "Material Flows," USGS (National Minerals Information Center | U.S. Geological Survey, 2013), http://minerals.usgs.gov/minerals/mflow/.

4 Doggett, M. D. and R. A. Leveille, "Assessing the Returns to Copper Exploration, 1989-2008," *Exploration and Mining Geology* 19, no. 1–2 (January 1, 2010): 23–33, https://doi.org/10.2113/gsemg.19.1-2.23.

5 Smil, Vaclav. 2014. *Making the Modern World: Materials and Dematerialization.* Chichester: Wiley.

6 European Commission. 2023. "Critical Raw Materials." Single-Market-Economy. ec.europa.eu. 2023. https://single-market-economy.ec.europa.eu/sectors/raw-materials/ areas-specific-interest/critical-raw-materials_en.

7 Ali, Saleem H. et al., "Mineral Supply for Sustainable Development Requires Resource Governance," *Nature* 543, no. 7645 (March 1, 2017): 367–72, https://doi.org/10.1038/ nature21359.

8 Julia's 2021 Samsung Galaxy 20 weighs 200 grams.

9 Sullivan, Daniel E. "Recycled Cell Phones—A Treasure Trove of Valuable Metals," U.S. Geological Survey (Denver, CO, USA: U.S. Geological Survey, 2006), https:// pubs.usgs.gov/fs/2006/3097/fs2006-3097.pdf.

10 Statista, "Cell Phone Sales Worldwide 2007-2017 | Statista," Statista (Statista, March 31, 2021), https://www.statista.com/statistics/263437/global-smartphone-sales-to-end-users-since-2007/.

11 World Economic Forum, "Strategic Outlook on the Digital Economy," World Economic Forum, May 24, 2023, https://www.weforum.org/events/world-economic-forum-annual-meeting-2022/sessions/strategic-outlook-on-the-digital-economy.

12 Walsh, Noelle. "Supporting Our Customers on the Path to Net Zero: The Microsoft Cloud and Decarbonization," The Official Microsoft Blog, October 27, 2021, https:// blogs.microsoft.com/blog/2021/10/27/supporting-our-customers-on-the-path-to-net-zero-the-microsoft-cloud-and-decarbonization/.

Part II

The Materials We Use

4   Metals and Mining

Routes to Responsible Practices

Metals can be kept in the economy forever.

—Ramón Arratia, Ball Corporation

Where do metals come from?

Metals come from the earth, but extracting the minerals they reside in is a messy, expensive, dangerous, and destructive process. Improvements in mineral extraction and processing methods, as well as more efficient transportation and distribution, can go a long way toward reducing the amount of energy needed to create metals. But there is a limit to how effective such changes can be. Metal production remains energy-intensive. Therefore, metal recycling is a key component of the circular economy.

Mining usually involves exploration to find a mineral resource, digging an underground passage to the location, and then drilling and blasting to remove the rock and convey it to the surface. The next step is to crush the ore into small particles before sending it to refineries to extract the individual metals. That process involves heating to extremely high temperatures.

I (Julia) ought to know something about mining. After all, I defended my PhD dissertation in the Hearst Memorial Mining Building at UC Berkeley. That building was the headquarters for the Materials Science and Engineering Department. It is a beautiful historic building, completed in 1907, that was retrofitted in 2002 to meet earthquake-related building codes. Given that a UC Berkeley press release lists the location of the building as "800 feet west of the Hayward fault," the retrofit was a wise move.

In 1907, 20 percent of male students at UC Berkeley majored in mining (presumably there weren't any female students in the department). Those students crushed rocks and created metals in that very building. By the time I was in college, though, mining engineers were a bit of an anachronism. Civil engineers and geologists are now the ones involved in mining, attempting to make it safer and more efficient.

The early twentieth century may have been the heyday of mining, but its origins are much, much older. The invention of smelting—the process of heating mineral ores to extract the metals inside—is what brought civilization from the Stone Age to the Bronze Age. Ancient people discovered that when they crushed ores and heated them, the oxygen burned off and metal remained. Multiple cycles

DOI: 10.4324/9781003409267-6

of heating produced ever-purer metals as contaminants with lower melting points burned off.

Copper, smelted from copper sulfide ores, was the first metal to be widely mined. Combining soft copper with tin created bronze, the first alloy. The aptly titled Bronze Age began around 4,500 BCE.

See the table of historic exploitation of materials by humans in Chapter 1 (Table 1.1) to place this into context with other materials.

Iron and steel

The discovery of magnetite, an ore rich in iron, brought about the Iron Age. Iron smelted in charcoal furnaces ended up with a small percentage of carbon incorporated between the iron atoms, creating the first steel. Forging—beating on the steel while it was hot—distributed the carbon atoms more uniformly.

During the 1700s, steel became increasingly popular for forging nails, horseshoes, swords, and tools. Over the next century, improvements in smelting made steel production a much less energy-intensive process.

It's remarkable to think that windmills were built with only interlocking wood joints until nails could be made industrially. Until the 1800s, each individual nail was the work of a blacksmith.

Steel is not just one single material. Varying the type and quantity of alloying elements—carbon plus various metals added to the steel—produces steels with specific compositions and properties tailored to the end use. Stainless steel, for example, contains up to 20 percent chromium, which makes it resistant to corrosion.

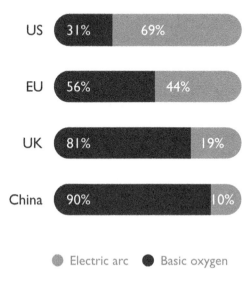

Figure 4.1 Types of furnaces used to produce steel in the US, the EU, the UK, and China in 2022.[2]

Other alloying elements improve the strength of the steel or make it easier to form into thin sheets.

Today, basic oxygen furnaces, using a combination of virgin iron and scrap steel, are used to produce much of the steel in the world. In the US, electric arc furnaces are more common. These furnaces use solely scrap metal and, therefore, require much less energy input per ton of steel produced. In 2022, 70 percent of US steel was produced using electric arc furnaces, but only 10 percent of steel production in China took advantage of this type of equipment (see Figure 4.1). The balance of China's steel was processed in basic oxygen furnaces.[1] Since China is the largest steel producer in the world, that country's impact matters.

Processing methods can be chosen with energy savings in mind. Continuous casting of hot metal, as opposed to casting individual ingots and then reheating them to roll into the final desired shape, creates less scrap metal and saves up to 75 percent of the energy needed for casting and forming.

Plant Tour: Nucor Steel

I (Julia) enjoyed the opportunity to tour Nucor Steel in Seattle and see firsthand how they turn scrap steel into the reinforcing bars (rebar) that strengthen concrete. We were a small group: the environmental engineer leading the tour, a newly hired engineer who wanted to gain insight into the production process, and the three women besides myself who had signed up for the tour. After grabbing foam ear-plugs and donning hard hats, goggles, and bright orange jackets, we were ready to walk through the facility.

The Seattle facility is a mini mill, a designation that refers not to the size of the facility nor its production volume but to the energy efficiency of its steel-producing operations. Nucor opened its first mini mill in 1969 to provide steel for its division that produced steel joists for the construction industry. As of 2023, the company produces about 25 percent of raw steel in the US and operates hundreds of facilities that make finished steel products.

Nucor's micro mills, built in 2002 or later, provide the ultimate in energy efficiency. At those plants, molten steel gets turned into thin steel sheets in a single step (see Figure 4.2). No energy is wasted by cooling the steel and then re-heating it to shape it into its final form. In Seattle, steel goes through a less efficient but equally fascinating process.

Steel production starts with scrap steel that arrives in Seattle by truck, rail, or barge from the western US and Canada. Each plant minimizes the need to add alloying elements to the steel by taking in scrap from sources that provide steel with a composition as close as possible to that of the final product. Some of the scrap shipped to Seattle comes from car junkyards, where old cars get dismantled and the chassis shredded into piles of debris.

During the tour, we walked by the mountains of scrap and got to see electromagnets several feet in diameter pick up loads of shredded steel and dump it into a charge bucket. Once the charge buckets are fully loaded with 100,000 pounds

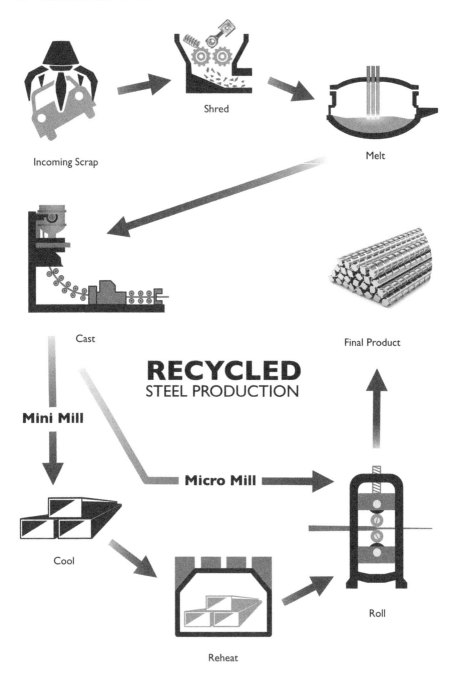

Figure 4.2 The manufacturing process for recycled steel production. The more efficient micro mill saves two process steps.

(45,000 kg) of steel, they move on overhead tracks into a warehouse-like building that houses the electric arc furnace. The furnace holds three buckets' worth of steel.

We walked upstairs to a glass-enclosed room where an employee sat in front of an array of computer monitors. He pointed out the screens displaying views from the multiple cameras located throughout the building and a chart showing the temperature of the steel inside the furnace. The man seemed glad to have company and a short break from his work. I imagine the job must be monotonous until one of the displays shows a problem and he needs to spring into action.

A charge bucket slid into view and its clamshell bottom opened up, dumping the contents into a huge container called a ladle. As the electric arc furnace cranked up, the graphite electrodes that melted the steel scrap glowed a blinding white. The heat was intense enough to feel, even from behind insulated glass walls. The temperature gauge climbed to 3,100 degrees Fahrenheit (1,700 Celsius). Our tour guide explained that the temperature probes have two functions, monitoring the temperature of the molten steel and extracting samples for chemical analysis. The on-site lab measures the chemical composition to ensure consistency.

The ladle containing the molten steel is itself made from steel, lined with brick to keep the ladle from melting. The ladle moves into a different part of the building to cast the steel into long beams called billets. Molten steel pours out of the bottom of the ladle from four openings into hollow copper molds with a six-inch-square cross-section. The molds are lined with chrome on the inside and water-cooled from the outside to maintain exactly the right temperature and ensure that the copper doesn't melt. After following a curved path, the resulting steel billets need to be straightened. This step occurs when the steel is in the soft-boiled-egg stage—solid on the outside and still liquid in the middle.

If the outer casing isn't properly cooled, molten steel can break through. That sounds scary, but safety procedures ensure that workers maintain a sufficient distance. By the time the steel bars emerge from the molds and make their way onto outdoor cooling racks, they are completely solid. They are still hot, around 1,100°F or 600°C. The presence of dozens of hot bars of steel warms the surrounding air considerably. The warmth wasn't unwelcome on the cool fall day when I visited, but I'm sure it would feel sweltering in the heat of summer.

The steel bars make their way to the rolling room with the help of a conveyor belt, propelled by cables that look like thick, dirty bicycle chains. Debris accumulates on the chains and eventually sheds off onto the ground below. At this steel mill where recycling is embedded in production, even the debris is valuable. It gets swept up and sold to concrete manufacturers, who mix it into their concrete to achieve the optimal iron content.

Steel manufacturing uses a lot of water, and this too is recycled. The water that flows along copper casings to cool the steel billets is reused as many times as possible. As the water evaporates, the steam passes through filters and exits out the top of the building. Chimneys that look like smokestacks aren't spewing smoke—they emit only pure water vapor.

Nucor Steel buys water from the city and also collects rainwater on-site. The plant uses as much rainwater as possible, but heavy storms can fill up the storage tanks. When rainfall exceeds the on-site storage capacity, the excess water gets filtered and sent into Elliot Bay, the body of water just west of Seattle. This is a very similar water recovery system to the paper factory that Paul visited in Northern England. There is a misbelief that factories somehow squander water, but as it's a cost, the opposite is true.

As a bar mill, Nucor's Seattle facility is in the business of producing rebar, the cylindrical steel bars used to reinforce concrete buildings. Each billet passes through a rolling machine that reheats the billet to glowing hot and squeezes the steel into a long cylindrical bar. The hot bar shoots rapidly out the rolling machine horizontally, where a cutting blade chops it into individual pieces that fall into a waiting bin. These pieces are ready to be bundled up and sold to fabricators who will then sell them to the construction industry.

The Seattle-area building boom provides Nucor with a ready-made local market. Expansions to the region's light rail system, a decades-long project that began with the approval of a 2008 ballot measure, are a key example. The aboveground tracks are built with dozens of concrete pillars, all of which are reinforced with 100 percent recycled steel rebar from Nucor.

Aluminum production

Aluminum is a relative latecomer to the collection of commercially produced metals, having not been discovered until the nineteenth century. Aluminum production is not nearly as efficient as iron production. Whereas magnetite contains 72 percent iron, it takes more than four tons of the source mineral bauxite to produce a ton of aluminum.

In addition to being one of the most energy-intensive metals to produce, aluminum production is quite toxic. Residues from bauxite processing contain heavy metals that are present as contaminants, caustic byproducts (sodium hydroxide is added during processing to extract the aluminum metal), and radioactive waste.

The "red mud" dumped into pits near bauxite mines has a consistency that could make it attractive as a source of materials for building bricks. Unfortunately, the red mud contains significant levels of radioactive isotopes of radium and thorium. Red mud, therefore, can't be safely used in the construction industry, which is something that people had considered to reuse this mining residue.

Despite concerns about the consequences of aluminum mining, existing processes are relatively cost-effective, making aluminum inexpensive. Aluminum is desirable as a construction material because it is light, with a good ratio of strength to weight, and easily formed into complex shapes. Reducing weight is critical for aircraft and also a good idea for motor vehicles. The lighter the car or truck, the easier it is to make it fuel efficient.

Like other metals, aluminum is easily recycled. The drawbacks of producing aluminum from mining bauxite have made aluminum recycling, covered more extensively in Chapter 9, commonplace for decades. More recently, as businesses aim for Net Zero GHG emissions, they appreciate the lower carbon footprint of recycled aluminum.

As major aluminum producer, Novelis, explains on its website, "Our extensive use of recycled aluminum—currently 61 percent of our inputs—is at the core of our innovative, circular business model."

The largest manufacturer of aluminum packaging in the world, Ball Corporation, based in Colorado, US, is on a mission to have as close to 100 percent recycled aluminum in their products as possible based on supply. We spoke with Ramón Arratia to get his perspective on this goal.

Interview

Ramón Arratia, Ball Corporation

What sparked your interest in joining the Ball Corporation?
First of all, the product. Aluminum is a material with wonderful circularity properties, and society wasn't doing it justice. Second, my role combines sustainability and public affairs. That's the only way. Sustainability on its own never happens. That's why public affairs are critical.
Tell us more about your role.
My role is to help the company realize the sustainability opportunities of aluminum. A lot of systemic changes need to happen for the circular transition and the low-carbon transition.

What do you find most rewarding about your work at Ball?
Making changes at the systemic level. What we're doing is changing legislation, changing how people think about packaging. I think it's pretty disruptive what we're trying to do. It's not just about selling more products, it's making systemic change.

What is the most pressing challenge for sustainability and circularity educators?
The main challenge is to be able to speak in a way that other people understand. It's different to talk to a 16-year-old or an engineer or a marketer. It's different to talk to an investor. It's different to talk to a company that sells materials versus a company that sells services. I think sometimes people in sustainability focus too narrowly and not in the context of how other people see the different issues.

Why are metals key to circularity?
Metals recycle by melting, so it's so easy. You have maybe a little bit of oxidation and that's it, so the metals can be kept in the economy forever. Our metals have been in the economy since Neolithic times when they were first used. No other materials have this ability to preserve value over multiple cycles.

In terms of sustainability, are there any fundamental differences between aluminum and other metals?
Aluminum melts at a much lower temperature than steel. Also, aluminum is much more malleable, it is much lighter, and you use less metal in general. Aluminum use

has been growing and growing because of those combinations of light weight, low melting temperature, and then society keeps coming up with new alloys with better properties. It's a key metal for the energy transition, it's a key metal for packaging, it's a key metal for construction, and that's why people love it.

Are there any other consumer goods sectors Ball is considering within the next five to ten years?
I think we're going to see opportunities in the refill sector in terms of cosmetics. If you put a pump on an aerosol can, you have refillable packaging. You take an impact extruded bottle, which is thicker than a can, and then you have a refillable solution for water, as we're doing for Boomerang. [See more about Boomerang Water later in this chapter.] We can also make miniature aluminum bottles for vitamins and medicines.

Outside the area of consumer goods, what are other opportunities for metals, not just aluminum? Do you think metals can go where unrecyclable materials are currently being used?
Transportation and construction are obvious ones. I think if you look at other industries that need properties such as conductivity and malleability, metals can be pretty good too. As circularity comes in, packaging will come first because you have shorter design cycles. But other industries are also feeling the pressure. With more interest in circularity, people will realize that maybe it's better to spend a bit more money in the first place and have a metal we use and reuse over multiple cycles.

How important is legislation in comparison to pledges and sector initiatives and encouraging recycling?
It's the only way in my view. It sets a minimum common standard. It sends strong signals to innovation, rather than "yes, maybe" pledges. I haven't seen a pledge that has really worked in the last ten years. I think we're going to move toward regulation. Before, people loved pledges because a lot of bad regulations had come, but I think regulators are getting much smarter. A lot of people with deep experience in circularity are also now working for the regulators. I think that with smarter regulation, people are going to see the value in that.

Also, the more circular a society becomes, the more power the recyclers have. Those recyclers have a bigger voice, which also influences politics. It used to be only a "take the waste" sort of business model, and now we're shifting gradually. It's building toward that thinking of, "the more you get in there, the faster people adapt."

What is the most effective way to increase aluminum recycling in North America?
If you look at packaging, it's mostly through extended producer responsibility (EPR) and deposit return schemes (DRS). Having EPR and DRS working together gives a strong signal to packaging manufacturers to redesign products so that they are easy to recycle. Of course, cans are there already, but some of the aluminum that is mixed with other materials could be better designed in order to facilitate recycling.

The same thing could be done for automobiles. America has a huge opportunity, both in automotive and construction, to have end-of-life legislation. In construction, you have non-legislative drivers such as LEED certification for buildings, where recycled content counts toward certification, and gives an incentive for recycling. But legislation is absolutely key.

Where are your R&D efforts being focused? What do you want to achieve from a sustainability standpoint?
We keep lightweighting and downgauging our packaging. We keep increasing the recycled content with the aim to reach 85 percent by 2030. We look at our plants and how we can reduce carbon emissions through innovations such as changing the way we consume energy and electrifying the equipment.

We focus on opportunities such as impact extrusion. It's an interesting concept that today has been applied mostly to aerosols, but could also be applied to reusable water bottles and packaging for cosmetics, shampoos, and soaps.

Platinum mining

Platinum has long been used in jewelry and as a catalyst in automobile engines. More recently, it is appearing in hydrogen fuel cells. We spoke with several people working in the platinum mining industry in Zimbabwe who asked to remain anonymous. Here is what we learned about platinum mining and recent trends in the industry.

Platinum does not occur naturally in isolation. Mining companies refer to platinum group metals, ores that contain roughly 50 percent platinum along with palladium, gold, nickel, copper, and ruthenium. Once mined from underground, the metals are concentrated using a process called flotation. Mines that have smelters on site export matte, a mixture of the different platinum group metals, to refineries for further processing.

The Bushveld Complex in South Africa is the source of 80 percent of the world's platinum. Mining in that region began in the early twentieth century with the ores that were easiest to extract. With those reserves depleted, the industry has moved to other zones within the complex, but those ores are trickier and more expensive to process.

Mines are emphasizing waste reduction with initiatives like zero waste to landfill goals. Much of the focus is on local reuse. Powdered reagents come in 1,000-kg bags. The empty bags, made from tightly woven plastic, get reused for packaging other materials. Wooden pallets get used multiple times. Excess pallets can go to people outside the mining industry to make furniture or other wooden items.

Some mines own and maintain landfills, so that anything that cannot be reused or recycled does not have to travel far, and the mine has an incentive to keep landfill use to a minimum. In some places, there is an on-site biodigester to process biodegradable waste. That turns into biogas that fuels kitchen stoves for employees who stay in camps near the mine.

The people we talked to believe that their companies do more good than harm and provide a critical resource. A plant manager expressed optimism. "I would say the treatment of people is now positive," he told us. "They are looked at as very important assets of the business. Also, every year we have to budget a specific percentage kept aside for the rehabilitation of the mine site after it closes. If you destroy trees, you have to make sure that you plant near the same number."

Companies that purchase metals can choose a mine that aims to be industry-leading in this regard. The advice is to trust, and then verify. As one person explained,

> It's about doing your due diligence. Don't take it for granted. If someone says this is how we're operating, touch base with the auditors to get the evidence, the proof to say that things are actually being done the way they have been described.

The conflict mineral problem

Mining has a second dark side, beyond the damage to the earth. Many of the minerals that society relies on are found in war-torn regions, where working conditions are extremely unsafe and child labor is prevalent. As a result, slavery is still happening today in Africa. People are being forced at gunpoint to dig up minerals out of the ground.

Minerals mined under these extremely unsafe working conditions are known as conflict minerals. They are mined in Angola, Rwanda, and the Democratic Republic of the Congo (DRC). The list of conflict minerals, collectively known as 3TG, includes tantalum, tungsten, tin, and gold. These elements all appear in electronics—tantalum in capacitors and resistors, tungsten in filaments, tin in solder, and gold in circuit board connections.

As of 2023, cobalt isn't on the official conflict mineral list, but that doesn't mean that cobalt mining is problem-free. Dan Schwartz, whose interview about batteries appears in Chapter 10, has more to say about cobalt.

Just because a product contains 3TG metals doesn't mean that by buying it you are funding the conflict mineral industry. There are many mines in the world where industry-leading safety practices are common and where worker abuses are not part of the problem.

The website of Barrick Gold Corporation states, "Our vision is the generation of wealth through responsible mining." Surely that is better than conducting irresponsible mining to make a profit regardless of the company's impact on workers and the surrounding communities, but Barrick's vision is necessarily myopic. Mining companies need to continue mining if they want to stay in business.

The global supply chain is complex, meaning that many different companies are involved in the path from extracting a metal ore from the earth to selling an electronic device. Electronics manufacturers often do not know the sources of the metals in their devices. So long as manufacturers can get the materials they need, at a cost they can afford, they don't necessarily dig deeper. Fortunately, the tide is turning toward greater transparency.

Toward more responsible mining

Platinum is far from the only sector of the mining industry focused on improvements in human rights and environmental impact. One-third of the companies in the global metals and mining industry are members of the International Council on Mining and Metals (ICMM). ICMM is dedicated to supporting the industry in becoming as safe and sustainable as possible. The overarching goal, as ICMM Manager Bryony Clear Hill explained at the GreenBiz Circularity 2023 Conference in Seattle, is to "bring transparency into what has been an opaque industry."

ICMM defines best practices for mining in terms of 39 performance expectations covering multiple social and environmental concerns. Member companies commit to working with each other, governments, and local communities to lead the industry in best practices. Members include Alcoa, Anglo American, Barrick, Newmont, Rio Tinto, and many less familiar mining companies, as well as NGOs and metals trade associations.

ICMM was founded in 2002, but as of 2023 was little known outside the mining industry. Representatives like Hill are working to change that by speaking at conferences and engaging with companies that buy metals.

Global standards also govern mining practices. The Global Industry Standard on Tailings Management (GISTM) covers six topic areas:

1 Human rights, including those of indigenous and tribal peoples,
2 Knowledge about the social, environmental, and local economic impact of proposed and existing facilities,
3 Design, construction, and operation of facilities to minimize the risk of failure,
4 Responsible ongoing management and governance with independent reviews of systems and processes,
5 Emergency preparedness in case of facility failure,
6 Public disclosure and transparency about the facility.

Leading mining companies consider GISTM standards as the bare minimum and often develop internal standards that are much stricter. New approaches to mining, which are often required when specific reserves are depleted, bring new challenges.

One metallurgist from a platinum mine told us,

We are anticipating that we're going to go to an open-cast setup. Right now, the mine is underground. This is going to be open pits where we can extract the ore. And that brings about a change in mineralogy. We're going to move from a sulfide ore to an oxide ore, and that is going to change the chemicals that we need to use to process that ore. We need to ask, will the chemicals be more dangerous, and will they require special handling compared to what we're used to?

She went on to discuss the importance of engaging with local communities.

> We need a social license to operate. The community has to accept us. If they
> don't, then we can't operate. We ask, how else can we make the communities
> better? Because it's not just about working in peace and harmony. How can
> there be a lasting positive impact that the mine will have even after closure?
> What's the generational impact, the legacy to say these things were developed
> for the community by the mining company?

What makes a metal heavy?

Concerns about contaminated water supplies often center around the presence of
heavy metals, among other contaminants. Heavy metals contain more protons in
each atom than lighter metals. Elements on the periodic table are arranged in order
of increasing atomic number, defined by the number of protons in each atom. A
quick glance at the periodic table reveals that metals range considerably in atomic
number. Lithium is the lightest metal, with atomic number 3. Lead, one of the elements that come to mind when thinking about heavy metals, has an atomic number
of 82. Gold is nearby, with an atomic number of 79.

Heavy metals are not necessarily toxic—gold being an obvious example—but
many of them are. Permits for solid waste disposal in the state of Washington
require companies to comply with a vast array of requirements, including reporting
on the metal content in their waste stream. They must include data on concentrations of the following metal contaminants: arsenic, barium, cadmium, chromium,
copper, lead, mercury, molybdenum, nickel, selenium, and zinc. Not all these metals present the same degree of concern, and not all of them are heavy metals.

On a federal level in the US, the presence of any of eight specific elements
above certain threshold concentrations renders waste "hazardous" because of its
toxicity. Hazardous waste cannot be discarded into landfills.

Many of the heaviest naturally occurring metallic elements—including radium,
uranium, and polonium—are radioactive. Radioactive materials are health hazards,
but they can also be used to improve health. For example, nuclear medicine for
cancer treatment involves injecting a patient with radioactive tracers to identify
the precise location of a tumor. In this case, the benefit of destroying the tumor
outweighs the risks of exposure to the radioactive tracer.

Thankfully, however, knowledge of the dangers of radioactive elements has
progressed sufficiently in the past century that safeguards are in place to limit the
risk when these elements are used for beneficial purposes. The dangerous working conditions that occurred at the Radium Dial Corporation (see the story in
Chapter 13) are unlikely to recur.

The focus here, however, is not addressing the proper use of radioactive elements or policies related to the handling of radioactive waste. We have plenty
to discuss regarding the safety of lead, cadmium, and other nonradioactive toxic
metals.

Getting the lead out

Lead (Pb) is one of the heavy metals known to be toxic to humans, even in very small doses. It has been conclusively linked to mental retardation in those continually exposed to lead as children, through the paint on the walls of their homes and the water flowing through their pipes. Though children are the most susceptible because of their small size and growing brains and bodies, people of all ages can suffer ill effects from ingesting lead.

We, as a society, have not always been informed about the toxic nature of lead or been sufficiently concerned about it. The 1958 Encyclopedia Britannica, which I (Julia) inherited from my grandparents, barely mentions toxicity in its lengthy entry on lead. It calls lead "one of the more important industrial metals." But the Ethyl Corporation knew that lead was toxic at least as early as the 1930s. Like other companies before and after it, the Ethyl Corporation suppressed the data implicating tetraethyl lead because it didn't like results that conflicted with its business plans.

It is somewhat ironic that ancient alchemists tried to turn lead into gold. All radioactive elements eventually decay to lead, so just waiting long enough will theoretically turn any radioactive substance into lead. Depending on the half-life—the time it takes for half of the atoms in a sample to decay—this process could take centuries or even millions of years. Turning lead into something else is even harder. Many barriers exist when attempting to replace lead in applications where its properties have proved useful for decades if not centuries.

The ancient Romans made extensive use of lead. The chemical symbol Pb comes from the Latin word for lead, "plumbum," which is also the origin of the word "plumbing." This is no coincidence. Romans used lead alloys to construct their water pipes. Today, newly constructed water pipes are made from copper or plastic, but our water systems are unfortunately far from lead-free (more on that later in this chapter).

Not only were the Romans unaware of the dangers of lead, but they also willingly consumed it. The lead acetate that used to be a common additive in twentieth-century paints was also known as lead sugar, because of a sweetening property that Romans took advantage of: they stored wine in lead vessels to make it taste better. These vessels probably contained lead in quantities sufficient to cause lead poisoning. We won't go into the controversies about whether lead poisoning brought about the fall of the Roman Empire. However, the concept of ingesting lead on purpose is strangely reminiscent of the late nineteenth and early twentieth centuries when people thought that radium, the "wonder element," was healthy.

What is lead good for?

Lead has many desirable properties. It is a relatively soft metal, although not quite as soft as the lanthanides (a subset of the rare earth elements, discussed later in this chapter), which can easily be cut with a table knife. Compared to structural metals like aluminum, lead is much easier to deform into complex shapes, even without heating above room temperature. Lead's softness is part of what made it so desirable for water pipes. Its low melting point also makes it easy to melt and pour into molds to create cast metal objects. Lead is present in high concentrations in several naturally occurring ores, making it inexpensive to extract and therefore much less costly than other commercial metals.

Because of its high atomic number, lead blocks radiation. This is why people wear lead aprons when getting medical X-rays so that parts of the body not being examined will not be exposed to damaging radiation. The lead is sealed inside the aprons and does not present a hazard in this application.

Lead has been phased out of certain products, notably gasoline and paint, because of concerns about toxicity. Tetraethyl lead used to be a standard additive in gasoline. It provided a valuable benefit of improving engine performance and reducing knocking. Data on dangerous lead exposure linked to gasoline eventually resulted in a push to remove the additive.

When I (Julia) was growing up, gas stations offered regular, premium, and unleaded gasoline. My parents' 1967 Volvo took premium, a leaded type of gasoline, but our newer cars used unleaded. Although unleaded gasoline became available in the 1970s, the US did not ban tetraethyl lead until 1995. Japan was the first country to enact a ban, in 1986. Leaded gasoline didn't disappear from European and Chinese markets until 2000.

The largest use of lead today is in batteries, primarily for lead-acid batteries for vehicles. A typical 12-volt car battery contains 10 kg (22 lb) of lead, while larger truck batteries require 13 kg (29 lb). This translates to more than 11 million metric tons of lead per year, just for vehicle batteries. The large batteries that power electric vehicles are lithium-ion batteries, which do not contain lead.

Solder: leaded or unleaded?

Many solders that connect dissimilar metals also include lead as a critical component. Although the total volume of lead in solders is much lower than that in batteries, the existence of lead poses similar health concerns. Solder joints may be relatively large, as in those used in plumbing, or so small that they aren't visible without a microscope, as in those used to connect computer chips to printed circuit boards. Lead is desirable in solders because it forms low-melting compounds that easily adhere to metal surfaces.

Eutectic tin-lead solder, comprised of 63 percent tin and 37 percent lead, was the standard solder for electronics for decades. The term "eutectic" refers to the composition that produces the lowest possible melting point for an alloy made from two or more metals. Just like a single metal, a eutectic has a fixed melting point, one that is lower than those of both the metals from which it is made. Tin melts at 232 °C, and lead at 327, but eutectic tin-lead melts at 183, which happens to be just right for soldering chips onto circuit boards. After decades of working with the alloy, engineers figured out the best temperature profile needed to create long-lasting solder joints.

In the 1990s, the European Union threw a wrench into the works when it proposed regulations aimed at eliminating six toxic materials from electronics manufacturing. Over the following decade, the industry had to figure out a way to eliminate lead, mercury, cadmium, hexavalent chromium, and several flame-retardant materials. The Restriction of Hazardous Substances directive, known as RoHS, originally became law in 2002 and has since undergone multiple revisions.

Since 2006, manufacturers wanting to sell electrical and electronic equipment in the EU have had to comply with RoHS. One aspect of compliance meant getting rid of tin-lead solder. Although nonconformists like entrepreneur Joe Fjelstad propose removing solder entirely, the commonly accepted approach is to use lead-free solders. These solders are made primarily from tin (Sn), with additions of silver (Ag) and copper (Cu) and are known as SAC alloys.

Simply put, SAC alloys don't work as well as eutectic tin-lead when it comes to soldering computer chips onto circuit boards. They melt at a higher temperature, typically 217–220°C. If the solder doesn't fully melt, it is impossible to create a reliable solder joint. Consequently, the ovens used to melt the solder joints on circuit boards need to be set to higher temperatures. Ironically, ovens operating at a higher temperature consume more energy, which may have a greater negative environmental impact than continuing to use tin-lead solder. However, the semiconductor industry didn't have a choice, and after 15 years, manufacturers have learned how to work with SAC alloys and produce sufficiently reliable solder joints.

I (Julia) interviewed Joe Fjelstad for *Material Value*. Joe is convinced that his quest to remove solder from electronics is something the semiconductor industry should embrace. He has long claimed that the way around restrictions on lead in solder is not to remove the lead from solder, but to remove the solder from the printed circuit board. His take on the effort to switch to lead-free solders is that the semiconductor industry has spent a billion dollars to solve a non-problem. But, despite Joe's 20-year crusade, today's electronic devices are loaded with lead-free solder joints.

Regardless of whether banning lead in solder made sense from a safety or environmental viewpoint, that's what happened. People from the Tin Research Institute, who had a vested interest in removing lead because the likely substitute alloys were more than 90 percent tin, convinced government officials in Europe to ban lead. The scientific data suggested waiting for a more thorough analysis, but the parliament went ahead. And what happened? For one thing, tin prices escalated.

People were understandably worried about the dangers of lead, but what about the unintended consequences of the metals used in lead-free solders? Silver may seem benign, but it has antimicrobial properties. Self-cleaning fabrics are infiltrated with silver-containing compounds. The antimicrobial nature of silver, however, means that it kills microbes indiscriminately. It doesn't only attack undesirable microorganisms but may also destroy beneficial microbes in the soil. Therefore, it makes sense to ban waste contaminated with silver from landfills. And to reconsider whether self-cleaning fabrics are a good idea.

Lead in the water

Decades after we removed lead from gasoline and paint, and more than a decade since most solders became lead-free, there is still lead in the water supplies of many cities around the world. Lead pipes older than today's senior citizens, as well as copper pipes connected with tin-lead solder, still supply water to millions of people.

The Centers for Disease Control and Prevention (CDC) in the US provides guidance on its website regarding lead in water supplies. As the CDC points out, lead leaches into water supplies from solder connecting the pipes in buildings constructed before modern guidelines took effect, as well as from lead pipes in even older buildings.

In the US, the problem extends far beyond Flint, Michigan, where a change in the source of municipal water in 2015 made national headlines when an investigation revealed high levels of lead in the water coming from the new source. Water systems in all 50 states have shown excessive levels of lead. Concerned citizens can look up data on the EPA website or request a report from their local utilities and have the water in their homes tested, but these avenues may or may not yield reliable results.

The city of Redmond, Washington, where I (Julia) lived for seven years, has monitored lead levels in water annually since 1992. They test homes most likely to contain plumbing that uses tin-lead solder. Today's plumbing solders are SAC alloys, similar to those used in electronics. The 2016 Redmond report on lead states that 10 out of 429 samples over the years have exceeded 15 parts per billion (ppb), the level that triggers action to address the contaminant. In the most recent test result from 2021, none of the sampled homes exceeded the action level. This is somewhat comforting.

Unfortunately, however, a reading of zero does not guarantee the plumbing is lead-free. Water needs to sit undisturbed in pipes for lead to leach out. It is possible that faucets that are rarely used may spew out contaminated water when the valve is opened. Lead-containing solders were not banned nationwide until 1986, with the passage of amendments to the Safe Drinking Water Act. We can thank the EPA for putting in regulations limiting toxic substances in the water we drink and the air we breathe.

According to the 2021 water quality report, "There is no detectable lead in Redmond's drinking water." However, the city warns residents that older homes could have plumbing that is contaminated with lead. It began a self-reporting program in 2023 where residents can examine their pipes to determine whether they are made from copper, steel, lead, or plastic and submit a form to the city database.

One piece of advice for avoiding lead poisoning is to run cold water taps for at least 30 seconds before drinking or cooking with the water just in case. I remember being told decades ago to fill cooking pots with cold water from the tap, not hot water, even if I were going to boil the water. The reason was to minimize the chance of lead contamination as hot water accelerates any possible leaching of toxins. Since my parents' house was built in the 1960s, this was probably good advice.

Progress has been made in Flint. As of January 2017, around 600 water pipes had been replaced, which may sound good except that almost 30,000 lead pipes remain. Residents no longer get water from the contaminated Flint River, and the city added corrosion inhibitors to limit the amount of lead that leaches into the water supply.

A year after the media publicized the crisis, donations that poured in had slowed to a trickle, and the residents of Flint were still drinking bottled water and likely will need to rely on it for the foreseeable future. Extensive sales of bottled water may be good news for bottled water suppliers, but it's not a good long-term solution.

In December 2021, six years after the Flint water crisis and after several years of research, the EPA announced its plans to update the Lead and Copper Rule (LCR).[3] The existing rule specifies that governments must take action if more than 10 percent of water samples exceed the allowable level of 15 ppb lead. Possible actions include improving corrosion control or replacing lead pipes.

The EPA's 2021 announcement says the organization "intends to immediately begin to develop a proposed National Primary Drinking Water Regulation." The proposed changes to the LCR would lower the level of lead concentration requiring action, in addition to requiring all lead pipes to be replaced and prioritizing historically underserved communities when scheduling replacement.

Lead levels in Flint are below the allowed federal levels, but many residents still don't trust their water supply and continue to drink bottled water. A $600 million settlement in 2023 awarded funds to families affected by the crisis.[4] Money can't bring their children back to health, as lead poisoning is irreversible, but at least it can keep them afloat financially. Meanwhile, residents of other communities are still drinking and cooking with lead-laced tap water, in many cases without knowing whether their water supplies are safe.

Unlike some other contaminants, lead doesn't affect the look, taste, or smell of water. That is part of what makes it so insidious. If people could identify the presence of lead easily, the problem might have been taken care of long ago.

Not-so-rare earth metals

Consumer electronics such as smartphones and laptop computers contain a variety of rare earth metals. Rare earth elements are primarily those that appear at the bottom of the periodic table—the lanthanide series that is separate from the rest of the table, plus the transition metals scandium and yttrium.

Certain rare earth elements are used in extremely small quantities in consumer electronics (see Figure 4.3) but are nonetheless critical to the functioning of the components inside. They help produce colors on the screens of smartphones and computers and create the magnets inside speakers and microphones. Many of these elements are also useful in the nuclear power industry, as well as in electric vehicles and wind turbines. The future of power and communications depends on rare earth elements.

Rare Earth Elements used in electronics
(Shaded boxes)

Figure 4.3 A segment of the periodic table highlighting rare earth metals used in electronics.

Despite what the term "rare earth" implies, these elements are not rare. They exist in ores that are fairly common in the earth's crust, but they are hard to extract compared to metals like iron, copper, or even aluminum. The various rare earth elements are difficult to separate from one another chemically and are very reactive. Trade policies have exacerbated the difficulty in obtaining the rare earth elements that manufacturers need. Most of the mines where these elements can be found are in China, a country that set policies designed to artificially control the prices and maintain a monopoly.

Chinese crackdowns on illegal and dangerous mining operations, a new approach after years of minimal regulation, are changing the situation. Prices are increasing to reflect the true costs of running mining operations, including immense cleanup costs for sites contaminated with radioactive thorium. The good news is that future mining operations in China will place a greater emphasis on safety and proper waste disposal. The bad news is the risk of escalating prices and a shortage of important minerals.

Countries other than China, including Australia and Canada, are developing sources of mined rare earth elements. A more diverse global supply will reduce the risk of shortages, but increased mining is not the best answer from an environmental viewpoint.

Improved recycling of electronic waste (e-waste) presents a huge, mostly unexplored, opportunity for those looking for efficient sources of raw materials. More responsible e-waste recycling holds the promise of both reducing worker exposure to toxic metals and recovering useful metals without mining. Extracting metals from used electronic devices instead of from mines may reduce the need to discover more sources of metallic ores. Chapter 10 delves further into e-waste problems and solutions.

Metals for packaging

With anti-plastic sentiment seemingly growing across all continents, metals have been much in demand for packaging. Water, iced coffee, seltzers, and kombucha are available in aluminum cans. After two decades of development, aluminum bottles now come in many shapes and sizes after an inauspicious start when pricing was much higher than for glass bottles and aluminum cans.

By the mid-2020s, we can expect to see many major brands in aluminum bottles, both for single-use and refill. Boomerang Water, a US company founded in 2017, invented a machine to clean and refill water bottles overnight at venues and hotels, creating an in-situ closed-loop solution.

For many years, products packed in steel cans have been considered old-fashioned and not in tune with modern shopper lifestyles. The steel can is now making a comeback due to environmental concerns around plastic and the ease of recycling steel.

Packaging in steel is resource-efficient, as no refrigeration is required for food preservation. Steel cans contain a high percentage of recycled content. Steel is lighter than glass, saving transport-related emissions. It can be used not just for foods but for beverages, paint, household products, and health and beauty products.

Metals will play a key role in a circular economy, from building cities and renewable power sources to replacing less easily recyclable materials for packaging consumer goods. The challenge will be to recover metals from existing products to a much greater extent than is happening today.

Notes

1 World Steel Association AISBL, "World Steel in Figures 2023," worldsteel.org, 2023, https://worldsteel.org/steel-topics/statistics/world-steel-in-figures-2023/.

2 Source: World Steel Association, "Steel in Figures 2023."

3 US EPA, "Review of the National Primary Drinking Water Regulation: Lead and Copper Rule Revisions (LCRR)," www.epa.gov (US Environmental Protection Agency, January 3, 2023), https://www.epa.gov/ground-water-and-drinking-water/review-national-primary-drinking-water-regulation-lead-and-copper.

4 Vaughen, Kelly. "Michigan Still Dealing with Fallout from Flint Water Crisis 9 Years Later; plus New Water Worries," www.cbsnews.com, March 23, 2023, https://www.cbsnews.com/detroit/news/michigan-still-dealing-with-fallout-from-flint-water-crisis-9-years-later/.

5   Wood, Pulp, and Cellulosic Materials

Are They All Leafy Green?

Everyone working in this space needs to be aware of the full footprint of sourcing forest fiber and choose to support lower footprint circular solutions.

—Neva Murtha, CanopyPlanet

The importance of trees

The materials we talk about in this chapter, unlike other engineered materials, come from a renewable resource. But it is one that we cannot take indiscriminately without unfortunate consequences. You probably know that paper and cardboard comes from trees. But you may not know all that is involved with making paper products for writing and packaging.

This chapter answers some questions you might have about paper:

- What can paper be made from besides trees?
- Is paper more or less environmentally friendly than other packaging materials?
- What certifications exist, and how do they help protect forests?

Early paper making

Paper was first produced in China almost 2,000 years ago for the recording of drawings and writings. In the eighth century, the Chinese technique of papermaking spread to Central Asia, then via Egypt and Morocco across to Europe, with the first European paper mills being built in Spain. Papermaking reached Toledo as early as 1085 and was firmly established in Xàtiva, Spain by 1150.

Early versions of paper are unlike the paper we know today, which is made from wood pulp. Chinese paper was made from Chinese mulberry bark, hemp, and rags mixed with water, mashed into pulp, pressed out, and hung to dry in the sun. The first reported use of paper for toilet purposes comes from sixth-century China, where it was made from rice straw.

The process used in Ancient Egypt may be more familiar to you. Egyptians collected the stalk or stem of the papyrus plant. They cut its central pith into thin

DOI: 10.4324/9781003409267-7

strips, pressed them together, and dried the sheet to form a smooth thin writing surface. This paper was exported to Rome and the rest of the Roman Empire.

In the Americas, the first paper was made from the bark of the amate tree. Bark material was soaked in water to break it down into a mass of fibers. The fibers were then laid out in a frame and pressed into sheets. This paper found widespread use among Mesoamerican cultures, and archaeologists discovered samples dating back to 75 BCE.

The twentieth-century battle for paper industry dominance

In the twentieth century, timber from hardwood and softwood trees became the major, almost exclusive, feedstock for paper and pulp. Without pressure from influential individuals and corporations, however, the story could have turned out very differently.

Until 1883, 75–90 percent of all paper in the world was made from hemp fiber. The paper made out of hemp is of much greater quality than that made out of cotton, and it lasts longer. Not only did paper derived from hemp have more favorable properties, but it also produced four times the amount of paper per acre compared to trees. Despite it providing a higher yield and being more environmentally friendly, by 1933, the production of hemp fiber was almost non-existent in the US.

This seems puzzling. Paper made from hemp fibers was used for more than 2,000 years, dating back to ancient China and the Egyptians. A few hundred years ago, Bibles, maps, paper money, stocks and bonds, and newspapers were all written on hemp paper. Even the U.S. Declaration of Independence was drafted on hemp paper before being copied onto parchment. So why the change?

The responsibility lies with William Randolph Hearst, the owner of one of America's largest newspaper companies. In the 1930s, Hearst invested in thousands upon thousands of acres of woodland to provide enough pulp for the newspaper industry. Due to the size of his investment in timber, he tried to eradicate hemp as competition in the industry he sought to dominate.

Hearst formed an alliance with the DuPont Corporation, a petrochemical company that provided the means necessary to turn wood fibers into paper through a sulfur-based chemical process. After realizing the competition hemp posed to his investment, Hearst began an influential newspaper campaign to dissuade Americans from supporting the hemp industry. He portrayed hemp as an extremely dangerous and malevolent drug, weaving his agenda into the news in a way that would appeal to the fears of the time period.

His newspaper campaign had a massive domino effect. It happened to be one of the main driving forces behind the illegalization of plants belonging to the Cannabaceae family. While Hearst struck fear into the hearts of Americans to damage the hemp industry, his associates at DuPont were pressurizing the United States congress to pass a bill that would impose sanctions on those who "sell, acquire or possess" marijuana. Hemp, which looked similar, was then cast in a bad light due to the stigma around that plant family at the time. Essentially, the wood-pulp paper industry succeeded due to it being more profitable.

A resurgence for hemp

The hemp industry is fighting back in the twenty-first century with statements around yield and recyclability. Some of these are proven, while some can be viewed as spurious or exaggerated.

For example, hemp proponents claim that one acre of hemp on average will produce as much paper as four to ten acres of trees. Real harvests can vary tremendously depending on weather conditions. Claims that recycling hemp paper up to eight times is typical, while pulpwood paper can only be recycled three times, are not necessarily true. The number of cycles for recycled paper depends on the starting fiber length and intended end use.

Hemp advocates are correct when they point out that the process of making paper from trees is chemically intensive, as we note later in this chapter. More responsible practices can reduce but not eliminate harmful chemicals. As for claims that tree-based paper production is unsustainable, that depends on how we define sustainability. Truly responsible forestry practices can allow harvesting to continue indefinitely.

Some of the most convincing arguments put forward by hemp proponents around the globe are the following.

- Hemp is one of the strongest natural fibers in the world, which is one of the reasons for its longevity and durability.
- Hemp grows quickly—it takes about 2–3 months for hemp stalks to reach maturity for fiber (rapidly sequestering carbon as they reach 2–4 meters high). Trees, on the other hand, can take between 20 and 80 years to mature—typically 20 years in modern industrial forestry.
- Hemp contains a higher proportion of cellulose—the component of plants used to make paper—compared to wood. This makes hemp a more efficient source for paper production.
- Hemp pulp does not require bleaching or as many chemicals as wood pulp. Using hemp instead of trees could dramatically decrease the number of toxicants entering the water supply from paper mills in countries with poor environmental management records.

Wood for pulp making

Pulp is a very simple material made out of fibrous organic fibers from plants and wood. Although paper is a durable material (many archive collections go back hundreds of years and are still in use), it is vulnerable when exposed to poor environmental storage conditions or excessive handling.

As noted above, pulp is principally made from wood obtained from forests. The processes for both hardwood and softwood pulp are almost identical, the main differences being the structure of the wood, and some slight differences in the amounts of chemicals used during the bleaching process. Wood is typically composed of about 25 percent lignin, 45 percent cellulose, and 25 percent hemicelluloses. It could be considered one of the world's first composite materials. (You can learn more about engineered composites in Chapters 8 and 9). The lignin, a biopolymer that acts like a glue to hold the wood together, is removed in the pulp-making process. Once lignin is removed, the cellulose and hemicellulose fibers are free to bond together. This bonding creates a strong yet flexible paper that is also absorbent. The amount of hemicellulose that remains in the paper can affect its properties. For example, papers with a higher hemicellulose content are more resistant to tearing and have a smoother surface.

Common hardwood sources for pulp include birch, beech, poplar, and aspen. Eucalyptus can either be considered a hardwood, as it has hardwood characteristics, or a stand-alone wood type.

Coniferous trees like spruce, pines, and firs are among the softwoods used in paper making. Softwood is soft and strong, containing more resin than hardwood. Most softwood is grown in the Northern Hemisphere. Finland, Canada, and Sweden are major global producers of softwood pulp.

The main differences between softwood pulp and hardwood pulp are fiber characters, lignin content, and density. Softwood fiber is long, thin and with few impurities. Hardwood fiber is short, thick, and with more impurities. The most typical impurities include bark, fiber bundles or shives, knots, plastic, rubber, and sand. The main commercial difference is the paper character: Softwood pulp paper has good flexibility, high folding strength, good tensile strength, and printability. Meanwhile, hardwood pulp paper exhibits strong absorptivity, high opaqueness, high thickness, and stiffness.

Pulp manufacturing

The paper industry consumes a huge tonnage of chemicals, but processing conditions vary widely. A well-run factory in the Nordics (cited by the paper associations) may not be representative of global paper production when it comes to recycling chemicals and factory effluents.

While each manufacturing plant has a slightly different process for producing pulp from wood, all processes follow these general steps, illustrated schematically in Figure 5.1.

Debarking: Bark is removed and separated for other uses.
Chipping: Wood is broken into small pieces, called wood chips.
Cooking: The wood chips are cooked with sodium hydroxide and sulfide liquor under high pressure to remove lignin and separate the wood into cellulose fibers.

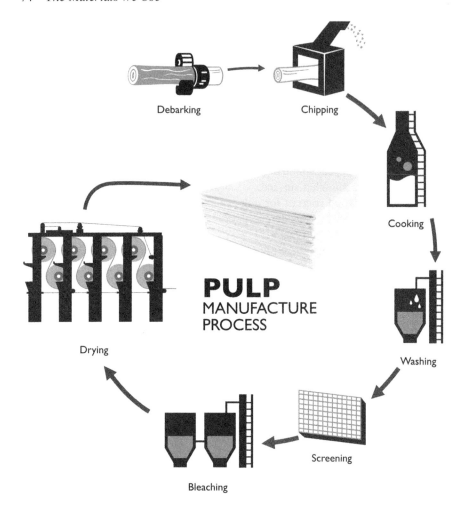

Figure 5.1 Steps in the process of making pulp from trees.

Washing: Washing involves filtration and diffusion to separate the "cooking" chemicals from the pulp. Lignin breakdown by-products and chemicals are removed as a prerequisite to the following stages.

Screening: One or more screening steps removes impurities from the pulp to improve the pulp quality.

Bleaching: This makes pulp white to improve printing properties and its ability to absorb liquids.

Drying: This is a multi-stage process using different machines and techniques to rapidly achieve evaporation of water and dry the pulp ready for transport elsewhere.

Paper making

Some paper manufacturers make their own pulp, while other paper mills buy pulp instead. Regardless of where it occurs, this is the process that turns pulp into paper (see Figure 5.2).

Initiation of process at head box: The pulp is pumped into a large paper-making machine. Starting at the first section called the head box, the pulp mass is squirted through a horizontal slit over a moving wire mesh to remove excess water.

Wire section: The fibers begin to spread out and take the form of a thin sheet, thus giving this part of the process its name, sheet formation.

Press section: The thin mats are fed into the press section, where up to 50 percent of the water content is squeezed out.

Drying: The sheets are dried at above a hundred degree Celsius over a series of cast-iron cylinders.

Coating: A film of chemicals is applied to the surface of the dried paper to improve the properties of the paper. Paper is coated with a layer of material, typically clay or calcium carbonate, to improve its surface smoothness, gloss, and ink receptivity. This coating can be applied directly to the papermaking machine or separately, and it can vary in thickness and composition depending on the desired outcome.

Winding: Paper exits from the paper machine and is automatically wound onto a jumbo reel, which can weigh tens of tons and be several meters long. The paper can be unwound subsequently and cut into smaller rolls as required.

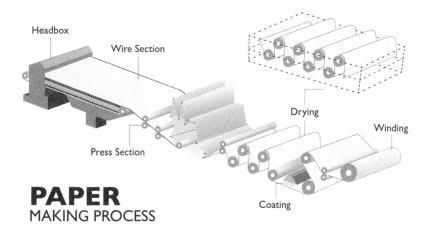

Figure 5.2 Steps in the paper making process.

Carton making

Rolls of kraft paper are transported to a corrugating, or converting, plant to make cardboard cartons. Compared to pulp and paper, the carton-making process is relatively straightforward. It can be described in one sentence: Layers of kraft paper are crimped and glued to form corrugated cardboard, which is then cut, printed, folded, and glued to make boxes, as shown in Figure 5.3.

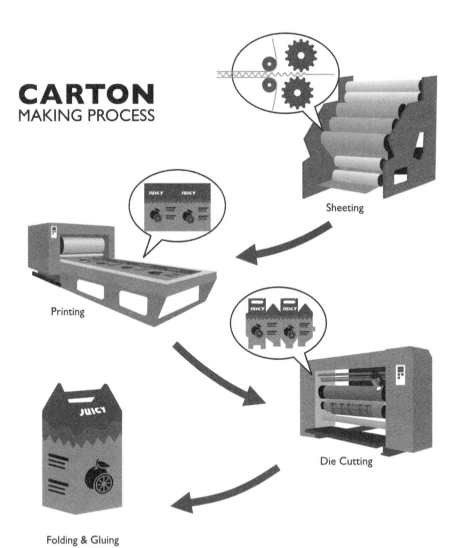

Figure 5.3 Steps to make cartons from corrugated cardboard.

There are five stages in the process:

Die-lines and sheet layout: Die-lines are the 2D flat version of what will become the final 3D folding carton.
Sheeting: Before the paperboard can be run through the press, it needs to be sheeted. As you have read in the paper-making process above, paperboard arrives from the supplier in a large roll. Sheeting is the process by which these rolls are cut into sheets of paperboard to be fed into the printing press.
Printing: During the print process, ink and coating units apply color print and varnishes.
Die-cutting: When the individual cartons have been cut out of the original sheet with the dies, the remaining stripped paper is recycled to form new paperboard.
Folding/gluing: The flat, die cut pieces are fed into a machine for folding, pre-breaking, and gluing, which is achieved in a number of passes.

Timber

Trees are much more than a source of paper. Wood has long been the material of choice for constructing buildings and furniture. The process of turning trees into timber is generally more time-intensive than chemical-intensive. Pressure-treated wood is a slightly different story regarding chemicals since it is impregnated with fire retardants and preservatives.

Wood is making a resurgence as a building material, thanks to its sustainability, versatility, and strength. In recent years, there has been a growing movement to use wood in taller and taller buildings. This is due in part to the development of new technologies that make wood stronger and more fire-resistant.

One of the most promising new technologies is cross-laminated timber (CLT). CLT is made by gluing together layers of wood in a crisscross pattern. This creates a material that is much stronger than traditional lumber, and it can be used to build buildings up to 18 stories tall.

Another new technology that is making wood more popular is glue-laminated timber (GLT). GLT is made by gluing together individual pieces of wood to create beams and columns. This process allows for the creation of large, strong elements that can be used to build buildings with large spans.

Here are the basic stages of the process for producing timber.

Felling: The first stage of preparing the timber for commercial use is called "felling"—the process of downing individual trees.
Storing/transporting: Next, the logs are stored in a clearing or in the forest until they are needed at the sawmill. This also allows some of the "free" water content to evaporate, reducing the weight of the tree/log, which further lowers the cost of transporting and handling.
The trees are usually cut into smaller lengths on-site and then picked up by a timber lorry, which transports the timber to a processing site.

Sawmilling: At the chosen site, the logs are debarked and bucked, or cut to the required length. Then they are cut into boards, using equipment such as circular saws and bandsaws. This is called "conversion."

Seasoning: Seasoning of natural wood is the process of removing excess water/moisture content. When a tree is felled, it still contains a large proportion of water/moisture—usually between 40 and 50 percent water content.

Preparing for market: After turning trees into timber through saw milling, covered in the third stage of the process—also referred to as primary processing, the market value of timber can be further increased through manufacturing sawn timber products—called secondary processing. This involves the wood being made (either by people or machines) into a more refined product, such as a door, window, or furniture, made to the specific size and dimensions.

Environmental concerns

Wood for use as timber or paper products can be harvested from controlled, managed forests or from logging uncertified forests. The first option is preferable from an environmental standpoint, as policies dictate where and how much to harvest and require replanting to maintain the health of the forest. Ideally, harvesting can be done in a way that thins specific areas to reduce the risk of wildfire.

Forest Stewardship Council (FSC) certification is often seen as the gold standard. People see an FSC label on a ream of paper or a piece of furniture and feel good that the wood came from sustainably harvested trees. FSC certification is not a perfect solution, but it is an important tool for protecting forests. FSC is also not the only certification out there. Dozens of harvesting guidelines exist.[1] Some forests, including those on government-owned lands, have their own regulations, which may be more or less restrictive than FSC regulations depending on the country.

There are many industry bodies that promote sustainable forestry and sustainable paper products on behalf of the producers. Forestry protection NGOs can work alongside these bodies, or in some cases, their aims can be very different.

Global

Forest Stewardship Council International: https://fsc.org/
Programme for the Endorsement of Forest Certification (a leading global alliance of national forest certification systems): https://www.pefc.org/
Wood Pulp Association (BWPA): https://www.bwpa.org.uk/

Asia

Japan Paper Association: https://www.jpa.gr.jp/en/
China Paper and Pulp Industry Chamber of Commerce: http://www.cpicc.org/

Europe

Confederation of European Paper Industries: https://www.cepi.org/about-cepi/organisation/

European Paper Packaging Alliance (EPPA)—https://www.eppa-eu.org/

North America

American Forest & Paper Association: https://www.afandpa.org/

China: the largest importer of forest products

There is a quandary facing importers of paper and wood products into China.

China is the world's largest importer of forest products, accounting for over 20 percent of the global market. China's imports of forest products have grown rapidly in recent years, driven by the country's economic growth and increasing demand for wood products. Many of the countries that supply China with forest products are at high risk for illegal logging and forest degradation. This is due to factors such as weak governance, corruption, and poverty.

The Chinese government has taken some steps to address the problem of illegal logging, but more needs to be done. Chinese businesses are increasingly aware of the need to source wood products from legal and sustainable sources. This is due to the increasing demand from international buyers, who are subject to laws that require them to import only legally harvested timber.

The 2023 EU Deforestation Regulation (EUDR)[2] mandates extensive due diligence on the value chain for all operators and traders dealing with certain products derived from cattle, cocoa, coffee, oil palm, rubber, soya and wood. To address these concerns, China has taken a number of steps to improve the sustainability of its timber trade. These include:

- Enacting legislation to crack down on illegal logging,
- Investing in forest conservation and management,
- Working with timber-producing countries to promote sustainable forest management practices.

These efforts have had some success, but there is still more work to be done. China needs to promote the use of certified timber products by the importers (FSC, PEFC, etc.), and put more emphasis on raising awareness of the importance of sustainable forest management among businesses. Brand owners importing paper products and wooden products into the EU from Asia who cannot show certification that products are not the result of deforestation face the risk of fines up to 4 percent of their total annual turnover in the EU.

Printing inks and varnishes

Paper and pulp packaging relies on printing to distinguish one brand from another. There are many possible combinations of printing methods, printing inks, types of varnish, and varnishing methods. The choice of materials has consequences for toxicity and recyclability.

Inks

Printing inks contain three components: the vehicle, the coloring ingredients, and the additives. The vehicle, responsible for transferring the coloring ingredients from the ink fountain to the typeform, can be either a vegetable base (linseed, rosin, or wood oils), which dries by penetration and oxidation and at the same time ensures fixation, or a solvent base derived from kerosene, in which case drying takes place by evaporation. The coloring ingredients come in several forms: pigments, which are fine, solid particles manufactured from chemicals, generally insoluble in water and only slightly soluble in solvents; agents made from chemicals but soluble both in water and in solvents; and lacquers, obtained by fixing a coloring agent on powdered aluminum.

The specific ingredients used in printing ink vary depending on the type of ink and the printing process being used. For example, inkjet inks use a different set of ingredients than offset inks. The choice of ink ingredients is also influenced by the desired properties of the ink, such as its color, drying time, durability, and cost.

Varnishes

Varnishes come in all manner of variants. They are similar to printing inks but without colored pigments. The vehicle might be a solvent, drying oil, pre-polymer, or monomer. In addition to the vehicle, the varnish may contain resins, dryers, waxes, or photo-initiators.

Common types include over-print varnish, dispersion varnish, and UV varnish, which you may wish to investigate more in further reading after you finish this chapter.

Managing the growth of the paper and pulp industry

It is hardly surprising that with such a long history, a huge amount of paper material exists in the form of printed books, maps, documents, letters, pamphlets, and notebooks. Despite fears from the industry that paper would disappear in the digital age, the pulp industry has grown significantly during the twenty-first century.

In 2000, global pulp production was 191 million metric tons. By 2020, this number had grown to 273 million metric tons, an increase of 43 percent. This growth has been driven by several factors, including the expansion of the Chinese economy. This growth has led to an increase in demand for paper products, including those for packaging and printing. China is now the world's largest producer of pulp and paper, accounting for over 30 percent of global production.

Another major factor is the rise of e-commerce. E-commerce led to an increase in demand for packaging materials, such as cardboard boxes. This has boosted demand for pulp, which is used to make cardboard. When e-commerce experienced a sudden boom in the early months of the COVID-19 pandemic, there was a global shortage of corrugated cardboard boxes.

In the last decade, as more and more citizens begin to adopt toilet paper, this has been another principal driver of demand.

It's clear that a well-managed forestry and pulp supply chain is required to keep unfettered deforestation in check. Paper-based and pulp-derived packaging is very much in vogue in the 2020s, in part because these materials are renewable and recyclable. Government requirements for recyclable packaging are pressuring companies to move away from plastic, and paper is often the alternative of choice. It is useful to note that for applications that require protection from moisture damage, paper-based packaging often incorporates a layer of plastic.

Expanding the supply of wood fiber is paramount for the pulp and paper industry. It's in their interest to support investment in new forestry and plantations to increase the volume of wood available. Ensuring continuity of supply of material raw material is key, and allied to that is the need to produce an ever larger amount of recycled pulp. For more about the recycling process, see Chapter 9.

As mentioned earlier in this chapter, wood is far from the only potential source for making paper. We spoke with Neva Murtha of Canopy Planet, an NGO whose mission is to protect forests and advance the rights of Indigenous people, to get her take on the future of the pulp and paper industry.

Interview

Neva Murtha, Next-Generation Solutions Issues Specialist at CanopyPlanet

What are Canopy's ambitions for the paper and pulp industry for the next 5–10 years?

Canopy's ambitions are to scale up the use of alternative fibers. We envision 60 million tonnes of new alternative fiber production capacity coming online in a decade in order to protect Ancient and Endangered Forests globally.[3] Given the broad scientific consensus that conservation of primary and old-growth forests must be prioritized to address the climate and biodiversity crises, conserving Ancient and Endangered Forests is key, and therefore forest fiber sourcing needs to shift. The good news is that fiber for cellulosic fibers, paper, and paper-based packaging can be made from many alternative fiber feedstocks.

Mills are already investing in alternative fiber research and development as well as pulping capacity because there is an anticipation of wood fiber scarcity in the future. At least 33 mills in Europe are testing or scaling products with alternative fibers. Brands and producers need alternatives to both meaningfully reduce their carbon footprint and provide a secure supply. Many robust life cycle analyses show alternative fibers as a low carbon and low biodiversity impact source of feedstock as compared to fiber from Ancient and Endangered Forests.

What are some examples of alternative fibers for pulp, paper packaging and viscose?
Canopy's EcoPaper Database lists 70 types of alternative fibers already being used in paper and packaging. Approximately 11–12 million tonnes of alternative fibers are already going into pulp and paper on an annual basis. These include wheat straw waste left over after the grain harvest; sugarcane bagasse, food industry waste, dedicated crops (those that fix carbon in the soil and don't compete with food crops, are non-GMO and not invasive), and even grape skins and seaweed by-products.

These alternative fiber products have the dual benefit of taking the sourcing pressure for paper products off forests, and repurposing waste that is already in the system and in many cases would otherwise be burned or landfilled.

Given the anti-plastic sentiment globally, the paper packaging industry has been able to grow rapidly. Will that continue?
The United Nations Environment Programme, UNEP, did an assessment of single-use plastic and paper based on life cycle analyses (LCAs). The results determined that moving from plastic to paper just shifts the burden, and therefore suggests that circularity and multiple-use products are necessary. It's important to use a feed-stock with a smaller carbon and biodiversity footprint than fiber from most forests. Everyone working in this space needs to be aware of the full footprint of sourcing forest fiber and choose to support lower footprint circular solutions.

Are there any pledges and sector initiatives to help shift the logging and pulp industries?
Canopy Planet has nearly 25 years' experience helping over 900 companies make purchasing commitments to protect Ancient and Endangered Forests while sup-porting the use of recycled content and the scale up of alternative fiber solutions. We leverage this into conservation of what we call "Landscapes of Hope" in Indo-nesia, the Boreal and endangered Coastal Temperate Rainforests.

Corporate No-Deforestation Commitments are a good start, but they often still allow logging of Ancient and Endangered Forests, and fragmentation and degrada-tion in critical forests. We hope the 2023 EU Deforestation Regulations focused on deforestation and degradation will drive a big shift because of the requirement for tracking and monitoring.

Brand owners are looking beyond net zero to a full range of planetary limits. How does paper perform against those planetary limits (water consumption, carbon emissions, etc.)?
Traditional paper production is water, energy, and chemical intensive and not at all carbon neutral, despite claims to the contrary. Scope 3 supply chain emissions on average represent over 90 percent of a brand's carbon footprint.

Peer-reviewed studies have found that undisturbed primary forests contain 35 percent higher carbon stocks than logged forests and provide the fastest, cheapest, and most effective nature-based solution to preventing dangerous levels of warm-ing when protected. In all forest types, logging results in unavoidable forest and soil carbon losses at the time of harvest that add more carbon to the atmosphere at a time when science is telling us we urgently need do the opposite. Including biogenic carbon losses is fundamental to quantifying the full carbon impact of forest products. While some studies use default carbon neutral claims to avoid measuring biogenic carbon changes, life cycle assessments show that omitting such losses can dramatically underestimate net greenhouse gas (GHG) emissions by as much as 75–92 percent.

Paper/pulp recycling rates are high, but might they be jeopardized by pulp innovations such as novel fibers, bagasse, paper bottles, etc. getting into the waste stream and causing contamination? Do we understand the parameters?
Research shows that recycling rates really vary depending on the paper grade. While many newsprint and packaging grades have more than 50 percent recycled content, printing and writing paper has a global average of only 8 percent recycled content, so there is still much room for improvement.

I know of tests being done that show alternative fibers like wheat straw can be recycled up to 5–7 times and sometimes more than that. There may be the occasional short fiber that does not recycle as many times as other fibers. In the not-so-distant past, about 8 percent of all fiber getting into the system was alternative fibers like sugarcane bagasse, which has been used for decades.

When these papers got into the recycling systems, the feedstocks were not labeled and therefore not noticed and did not cause problems that we know of. Where recycling is really challenged is with plastic or other coatings and contamination. In this case, it's the product design and end of life, not the alternative fibers impacting recyclability. For example, paper bottles made from wood or alternative fibers lined with plastic, or other contaminants from municipal single stream recycling systems.

We think that over time, it will be shown that recycling of most alternative fibers will not be a problem, especially when dealing with feedstocks that have longer fibers than wood.

Notes

1 Titus, B. D. et al. "Sustainable Forest Biomass: A Review of Current Residue Harvesting Guidelines," *Energy, Sustainability and Society* 11 (2021): 10. https://doi.org/10.1186/s13705-021-00281-w.

2 European Parliament and the Council of European Union. 2023. "Regulation (EU) 2023/1115 of the European Parliament and of the Council of 31 May 2023 on the Making Available on the Union Market and the Export from the Union of Certain Commodities and Products Associated with Deforestation and Forest Degradation and Repealing Regulation (EU) No 995/2010," Pub. L. No. 2023/1115. https://eur-lex.europa.eu/legal-content/EN/TXT/?uri=uriserv%3AOJ.L_.2023.150.01.0206.01.ENG&toc=OJ%3AL%3A2023%3A150%3ATOC.

3 When this interviewee from Canada says tonnes, she means metric tons. We kept her wording.

6 Glass

A Brighter, Lighter Future?

Affordability is going to drive decisions around sustainability.
—Aston Fuller, Glass Futures

When I (Paul) was a child, all our milk was delivered to the doorstep in glass bottles with aluminum foil tops. As I got older, I was allowed to bring the milk into the kitchen, and that was a real treat. In picture books, we would see milk bottles on doorsteps, sometimes with birds pecking at the foil. My parents would dutifully put the cleaned bottles back on the doorstep at nighttime, and the "milkie" would arrive early the next morning in his electric vehicle to collect those and drop off more pre-filled bottles. It was the ultimate circular business back in the 1960s and 1970s.

Most exciting of all was when the main children's TV program on national TV (we only had three TV channels) launched a charity appeal, and we collected the aluminum foil tops and took them to school. Each school or community organization across the UK was collecting, and there was a huge board at my school with a running total. Every couple of weeks the school would post the collected bottle tops to BBC TV Centre, and the program presenters would announce the national total collected. As a child, this was the most exciting thing on TV—knowing that every top you collected was making a difference. The presenters explained that all the tops would be sold and converted into new items, raising money for charity.

But actually, the real hero was the glass—going round and round up to 30 times—no microplastics, no taint, in perfect condition with every fill. How innocent we were in those days. But how did milk come to be packaged in refillable glass milk bottles?

Refillable milk bottles

One of the most iconic containers to be made from glass is the refillable milk bottle. Between the 1860s and the 1890s, several experimental "jars" were used to carry milk in the US. In 1878, George Henry Lester patented the first glass jar intended to hold milk featuring a glass lid that was held on the jar by a metal clamp. In that same year, Brooklyn milk dealer Alex Campbell is credited with first selling milk

DOI: 10.4324/9781003409267-8

in experimental glass bottles. By the 1920s, glass milk bottles had become the norm in the UK after slowly being introduced from the US in the early years of the twentieth century.

The refillable glass milk bottle made a comeback in the UK in the last decade, but does switching to glass milk bottles offer an environmental benefit? When comparing glass to plastic, we need to consider several issues beyond the impact of producing the bottles. The first issue is the energy used to wash, rinse, and refill reusable glass bottles. The second consideration, and a critical one for any business thinking of making a switch, relates to how many times a glass bottle is reused.

A 2018 study by Zero Waste Scotland (now archived) noted that with growth in renewable energy generation, the Scottish energy grid decarbonized by 50 percent between 2010 and 2018. This improved the carbon competitiveness of glass, making the switch to reusable milk bottles a sustainable option. Also in 2018, a WRAP (Waste & Resources Action Programme, UK) spokesperson stated that glass milk bottles had to be reused at least 20 times to have a lower carbon footprint than single-use plastic, but without providing reference to that statistic. Milk suppliers' average reuse rate is 25 times and up to 30 times before recycling.

Even though milk delivery is by electric vehicles, it's also important to factor in the distance from the dairy to the filler to the point of consumption.

Milk bottles and other food and beverage packaging are, of course, only one of many uses for glass. Glass is one of the most versatile materials in the world. It is valuable in industries ranging from architecture to automotive to electronics. Toughened glass has become a prized material for industrial designers who have utilized it to make everything from chopping boards to shower tiles to homewares. Glass is a critical material for cell phone screens, which have become an essential part of everyday life since the launch of the iPhone in 2007.

This chapter answers questions people have about glass and clears up some misconceptions. Keep reading to learn about:

- Where glass comes from and how it is made,
- The history of glass,
- Types of glass for different applications,
- Advantages and disadvantages of glass for packaging,
- Efforts to decarbonize the glass industry.

Raw materials and glass manufacturing

Perhaps the most surprising thing claimed about glass is that it's a liquid. A very slow-moving liquid. People point to thicker-bottomed windows from previous centuries as evidence of "liquidity": there is more glass at the bottom. In truth, glass atoms move too slowly for changes to be visible, but decade by decade the bottom of the glass is perceptibly thicker.

Glass, however, is neither a liquid nor a crystalline solid. It is an amorphous solid—a state somewhere between those two states of matter. A more precise way to describe it would be as an inorganic solid material that has the atomic structure of a liquid, formed by cooling the molten liquid so that the atoms are prevented from arraying into a crystalline formation.

Scientifically, the term "glass" applies to a wide variety of amorphous solids that are liquids at high temperatures and solidify at their glass transition temperature. Practically speaking, when we talk about commercial glass, we mean silicate glasses. This is the category of materials we call glass in this book.

The primary component in glass is silicon dioxide (SiO_2), usually called silica. It comes from silica sand—highly pure sand that is nearly 100 percent SiO_2 and contains very low levels of contamination.

Silica makes up 70–74 percent of most commercial glass. The most common types of glass are made primarily with silica and soda ash, as well as other additives chosen to tailor the properties of the glass.

- Soda ash (sodium carbonate; Na_2CO_3) lowers the melting point of silica.
- Limestone (calcium carbonate; $CaCO_3$) is a stabilizer that improves the quality and physical appearance of the glass. Glass enriched with lime represents over 90 percent of the glass in use today.
- The addition of lead, barium, or lanthanum oxides increases the refractive index, making the glass more reflective and suitable for optical purposes (eyeglasses and lenses).
- Sodium sulfate, sodium chloride, or antimony oxide can be added to prevent the creation of air bubbles in the glass mixture.
- Recycled glass (cullet) is also often used in the production of new glass.

During glass manufacturing, the raw materials are collected in the appropriate proportions and mechanically crushed. These components are combined in mixing machines until a homogenous mixture is achieved. The batch, also known as frit, is a homogeneous mixture that is taken for further melting in a furnace.

The liquid is then cooled to form glass. The composition and the cooling method (more on that later in this chapter) determine the type of glass and its eventual application.

Variations in composition affect the material's properties, including the melting point of the glass. For example, clear, brown, and green glass bottles are made from glass with different melting points. To be recycled into new bottles, the colors need to be separated. We share more about glass recycling in Chapter 9.

Despite its recyclability, end-of-life building glass is almost never recycled into new glass products. Instead, it is often crushed together with other building materials and put into landfills or used in making roads. There needs to be a high visual quality for float glass to be reused, so it cannot be contaminated in any way when being recycled. Researchers are now looking to rectify this lack of recycling.

Fine crystal, especially that made centuries ago, often contains lead, which means it cannot be recycled. It also might be wise to keep the beautiful crystal glassware from your grandparents or great-grandparents on the shelf as a decoration instead of drinking from it.

The history of glass

Glass has been used since ancient times. Archaeological evidence suggests that the first true glass was made in coastal north Syria, Mesopotamia (present-day Iraq and Iran), or Egypt in around 3500 BCE.[1] There are theories that it was created accidentally during metalworking or the production of tin-glazed pottery. The first glass objects were vessels and jewelry.

Roman glassmakers made great advances in the first century CE, and what can be described as an industry underwent rapid technical growth. Windows made of *cast glass*, glass created by pouring molten glass into a mold, have been found in important buildings in Rome and Pompeii. Cast glass was the standard production method for over a millennium.

The Romans also advanced glassblowing, a glass forming technique that involves inflating molten glass into a bubble with the aid of a blow tube. The technique had been pioneered by the Syrians in the first century BCE.

Glass making evolved slowly beyond this point for over a millennium.

First devised and perfected in the 1320s in and around Rouen, France, the *crown glass* process for making sheets of glass remained in vogue for two centuries. In this process, a gob of molten glass was put on the end of a rod. The glassmaker then spun the rod and glass until it flattened into a disk. The disk was then cooled and cut into square or rectangular panes. This manufacturing method created a lot of optical distortions.

In the sixteenth century, glass makers began creating *plate glass* (in which molten glass was poured into a mold and pressed in between plates to create a flat sheet of glass) and *sheet glass* (in which ribbons of molten glass were extracted from a furnace and flattened by passing them between rollers). Both these techniques were time-consuming and a costly affair, not to mention the surface imperfection and inferior quality of the resultant glass.

The *float glass* process was invented by Sir Alastair Pilkington and his R&D team in Merseyside, England in 1952. It is a method of manufacturing glass that produces a continuous sheet of glass with a smooth, even surface. The process involves pouring molten glass onto a bath of molten tin, where it floats and spreads out to form a flat sheet. The glass then cools and solidifies, resulting in a high-quality product that is free of defects. The motivation was one of cost efficiency, as it avoided the need to grind and polish plate glass to make it clear.

The float glass process revolutionized the glass industry, replacing the older method of making plate glass, which was time-consuming and expensive. It is now the standard method for manufacturing glass for a variety of applications, including windows, mirrors, and automobiles.

There are 260 float plants worldwide with a combined output of about 41.6 million metric tons of glass per annum. Over 50 percent of float glass is made in China. Other major producers are located in the rest of Asia, Europe, North America, the Middle East, and Africa.

A float plant makes around 6,000 kilometers of glass a year in thicknesses of 0.4–25 mm and in widths up to 3 meters. A float line can be nearly half a kilometer long. Raw materials enter at one end and from the other plates of glass emerge, cut precisely to specification, at rates as high as 6,000 metric tons a week.

Over five millennia after it was first invented, glass is still in common use, with a renewed interest in glass for bottling and packaging in the twenty-first century.

Advantages and disadvantages of glass

Glass has been demonized by the plastics industry for decades, initially for its fragility, and more recently for its weight which results in an unfavorable carbon footprint.

There are several drawbacks commonly associated with glass. High energy consumption in its manufacture across the whole industry—as the tonnage required is far above that for plastics and aluminum—potential for injury when shattered and concerns about the availability of raw materials (silica) are among the most cited.

When it comes to packaging, glass has multiple benefits, especially when we consider our current understanding of health and environmental impact. Glass is benign and can hold food and liquids for years without taint or leaching. It does not convey a taste to food or beverages, which can be an issue with plastic and metal packaging. The FDA in the US rates packaging glass as GRAS, or "generally recognized as safe," the highest standard for food packaging and ingredients.

There is no leachate from glass in landfills or even in the ocean. As regards these aspects, it wins over polymers and metals.

Of all the advantages of glass for packaging, this is its principal one. Glass is inert and usually doesn't react with the product inside the pack. It doesn't degrade over time, which makes it suitable for wines and cognacs that may remain inside the bottle for decades. Baby food was packaged in glass jars for decades before the introduction of multilayer plastic pouches, and some brands still come in glass.

In plastic packs, cans, and cartons, the food contact material is a polymer, and often those polymers are problematic because of toxic additives in the plastics. (See our discussion of BPA and phthalates in Chapter 7.)

The non-reactivity of glass also makes it suitable for storing chemicals, including most acids and solvents. There are exceptions, namely hydrofluoric acid (HF). HF etches glass and must, therefore, be stored in plastic containers.

Glass also has the potential to become a vital part of a genuine circular economy. Glass has always been recycled, ever since the Roman era. Archaeologists find very few glass fragments compared to pottery shards, as broken glass was collected and remade into new items even two millennia ago.

Glass types and uses for glass

There are two primary methods of making glass today: the float glass process and the glassblowing process. Float glass is used to make glass sheets, and glassblowing produces bottles and containers. Figure 6.1 illustrates the two processes.

Prompted by discussions of recycling, we often think of glass as a packaging material, but the market size for flat glass is twice that of packaging glass (see Table 6.1).

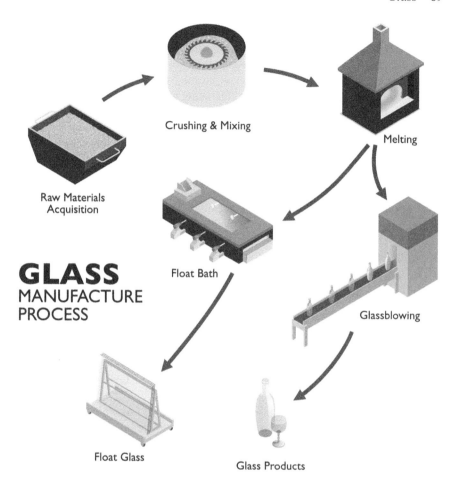

GLASS
MANUFACTURE
PROCESS

Raw Materials
Acquisition

Crushing & Mixing

Melting

Float Bath

Glassblowing

Float Glass

Glass Products

Figure 6.1 The manufacturing process for float glass and blown glass.

Table 6.1 Glass market size by type of glass. Data from ICG, International Commission on Glass, 2022

Glass Type	Primary Applications	Market Value (US dollars)
Flat (and fabricated) glass	Construction, automotive	$119 bn
Container glass	Food and beverage packaging	$53 bn
Specialty glass	Medical, lighting, flat-screen displays, fiber optics, and ophthalmic lenses	$37 bn
Domestic glass	Household (drinking glasses, appliances, etc.)	$11 bn

Flat glass (float glass)

Float glass is used by the construction industry for windows and doors, and in recent decades, architects have stretched the limits of structural glazing by creating extraordinary buildings with striking glass façades. It is even used in furniture as well as buildings. Some specialty glass (including tempered or laminated glass) is float glass that has been further processed.

Tempered glass is most commonly used for passenger side windows and the rear window on automobiles, while *laminated glass* typically is reserved for the front windshield. When tempered glass breaks, it is designed to shatter into small pieces that are less likely to cause added injury or damage. Laminated glass is a type of safety glass that is made by bonding two or more layers of glass together with a thin layer of polyvinyl butyral (PVB) or other polymer resin. The PVB layer acts as a cushion between the glass layers, which helps to prevent the glass from shattering into large, sharp pieces if it breaks. Laminated glass is also used for shower doors, skylights, security doors, and aquariums.

Other uses for glass

Lightbulbs

When incandescent light bulbs were invented, they needed an outer casing that was transparent (or partially transparent) to visible light, rigid enough to withstand having a vacuum inside, and resistant to softening when heated. Glass was the obvious choice given the materials available at the time.

Glass is strong, rigid, and transparent or translucent; can withstand high heat from a tungsten filament without melting; is easily blown into the required shape; and is easy to seal off after inserting a filament assembly and filling the interior with the inert gas argon.

Today's LED bulbs don't require all of those properties and could be made from high-performance polymers, but the market is still predominantly glass.

Domestic glass—glasses and plates

When used to make tableware, glass is vitrified or tempered to make it stronger and more hygienic, as it is not porous. It is also dishwasher-safe (up to 2,000 times potentially) and microwave safe.

There are two principal kinds of glass tableware: *tempered* and *opal glass*. Tempered glass undergoes a tempering treatment, which makes the material much more shatter-resistant. It is 3–5 times stronger than conventional glass. In addition, it does not break into shards when broken, which avoids the risk of injury. Opal glass is manufactured in the same way as clear glass, but opal is added, making it white and opaque. This type of glass has the same strength as tempered glass and has the advantage of being virtually scratch proof.

Decorative glassware

Decorative glassware, often just known as glassware, is a common feature in homes around the world. This is glass with no main utilitarian function which is used to decorate home interiors. It ranges from cut glass and glass art right through to items mass-produced in the millions, such as souvenirs made in factories from China to Italy.

The future of low-carbon glass manufacture

Since 2021, the glass packaging industry has been debuting carbon-neutral glass bottles, and much of the focus for this current decade will be on reaching carbon neutrality. We interviewed two representatives from the glass industry who elaborated on plans to decarbonize glass manufacturing.

We spoke with Aston Fuller from Glass Futures, a not-for-profit membership organization serving the global glass industry, with a mission of promoting research and innovation. To that end, the organization is building a large open-access glass melting facility in the UK. We also talked with Oliver Harry from Encirc, a glass packaging designer and manufacturer in the UK that produces 2.5 billion glass bottles and other containers annually.

Interview

Aston Fuller, General Manager, Glass Futures

I understand that Glass Futures is building an open-access glass melting facility. What is your intention and vision for this project?
We've never had a unified glass industry, so to speak. We've always had glass fiber, glass container, glass float industries, and they haven't really historically spent too much time collaborating and working together because glass manufacturers are competitive. So ultimately, the thing that unites them all is melting materials at high temperatures to produce glass. and in its current format, producing a relatively high amount of carbon. All manufacturers have the same issues, the same problems, and very similar solutions. And while there are a lot of parallels with steel and ceramics, where we can look at high-temperature fuel use, as an example, the ability for them to come together and collaboratively solve the problems is vitally important. What is also important is that the users of glass, e.g. everyone throughout society, also need the industry to become decarbonized.

Is decarbonization the only goal?
A sustainable future enabled by glass is the vision. There are two ways to decarbonize an industry. One is through efficiency improvements, do the same thing better, so you use less energy overall. And the other one is to find alternate ways so

we don't use any carbon in those processes as well. Ultimately, we've got six key technology themes focused around the fuels and energy that we use.

1 Alternative energy sources—reducing the carbon in our energy sources.
2 Carbon Capture and heat recovery systems to use our waste process gasses efficiently.
3 Secondary raw materials and driving a circular economy.
4 Digital technologies to make our processes significantly more efficient.
5 Technology used through supply chains. How do we ensure that we're tracking and we understand material flows in systems so you can get the raw materials back in the first place?
6 Skills and training. The industry can transform, but if it doesn't have the people and the skills and the necessary capacity to implement those technologies as they're developed, then it could struggle to embed changes.

Are there different challenges, for example, for plate glass compared to packaging glass compared to glass used in the medical industry? Do they have specific kinds of complex innovation challenges, apart from just the general ones that are in common?
The reality is that 80 percent of their problems are the same. Even if you look at digital technologies, you might apply them in a different fashion. Or you might have inspection equipment to look at defects in a container. It's basically the same inspection equipment on a float glass line, except the float glass line has to scan left and right. Or you put four cameras in a row that scan the sheet as it goes past as opposed to a camera taking pictures of every single bottle as they go past. With all of the technology in the backend around applying artificial intelligence (AI) and looking at automation across the line, it's a different application but it's the same challenges.
    The core of the difference between the sectors is the way that the supply chains work. And the way that the supply chains work will have a profound difference on the rate of change of those industries.

I read a lot about sustainable construction architecture every day and I rarely see anyone talk about the glass. Why is that?
Affordability is going to drive decisions around sustainability. And the reality is, the brands in the drinks industry can afford to do this, and they will do it, putting their money where their mouth is, and actually trying to make a difference because they know they need to. The construction sector is going to lag behind the container industry because it's a huge disparate set of tens of thousands of companies and individual players.

Is the glass industry really making use of the fact that it's a benign, nontoxic material, particularly for food packaging?
Glass Futures' ambition has always been to collaborate across the entire supply chain, from small-scale technology demonstration in academia, all the way through

to the products that we put on shelves for customers, including every company and every organization that's involved in that supply chain. For them to come together and to collaboratively co-fund the work that's required to really answer the big questions.

This is about promoting the values of glass. The glass industry has a standalone, relatively small footprint. The voice of the industry itself is significantly smaller than the voice of the other industries. And it's always gone under the radar, but I see a bright future considering the positive qualities of glass.

Interview

Oliver Harry, Head of Corporate Affairs, Encirc

What are the ambitions of Encirc between now and 2030?
Creating zero-emission glass and securing the future of glass as a sector is our biggest ambition. The work we do here will be used, I believe, as a blueprint for the entire glass industry nationally in England, and then perhaps globally. Decarbonizing glass, understanding all its benefits, and leading this effort for our material will have an incredible impact not just in glass but other packaging as well.

Tell me a bit more about your innovation work.
We have a history of innovation. We were the first to pioneer and help develop quad gob technology, where four bottles at a time are created on glass-making machines. We were the first in the world, and still remain the only in the world, to open a filling plant on the same site as our glass production plant, which has incredible sustainable benefits and has changed the way wine comes to market in the UK. And finally, we're leading globally in aiming to create zero-emission glass. We plan to re-build furnaces so they can run on hydrogen, green electricity, and other sustainable gasses. In 2023, we added The Park in Bristol, a global leader and specialist in wine filling, to our business unit.

What's the most pressing challenge for you now as a business?
Glass wins against all packaging on almost every sustainable and health metric, including recyclability, levels of recycling, the inertness of the material with no chemical leaching into products, and of course the taste (due to no chemical leaching). The issue at this moment is carbon. It can be more carbon-intensive to produce a single glass bottle than containers made from other materials. So as an industry, we need to solve that reasonably quickly. And I think the glass industry needs to be very disruptive and say, "We understand that as a concern, but here is the solution. This is the way forward." Acknowledging the carbon issue and saying

how we will solve it is probably something that the glass industry hasn't done very well up until now.

How important is legislation in comparison to pledges and sector initiatives?
At the moment, we have to decarbonize by 2050. I believe their glass sector needs to be far more aggressive than that. We're looking at creating zero-carbon bottles by 2030.
Legislation can do a lot of things to help. We have deposit return schemes coming to the UK that don't include glass, which is a good thing. In my view, glass just doesn't work in a traditional in-store scheme.

The government could support us more. But I am seeing a lot of progressive policies coming through now from the government in terms of the focus on sustainability. The support of hydrogen and green electricity in our economy will really support us going forward.

Of the different beverage sectors: wine, soft drinks, beers, waters, which is most supportive of glass?
I'd say probably spirits is near the top, because who wants to drink a glass of vodka out of a plastic bottle!? Certainly not me. You'd probably question the quality of that bottle of spirits. Glass is often seen as a premium material, and of course, it preserves the contents more effectively than any other, so wine is up there as well. Although I understand wine can be in cans and bags in some circumstances, primarily, wine is best in glass, and brands and consumers know that. By bulk shipping wine to us from all over the world, international wine brands can make huge sustainable savings and have a very simple route to market in the UK. It is a model we have helped to establish in the UK.

I understand cans have become more popular recently for beers, but I wonder if that is a trend that will last. The product tastes better in glass and consumers prefer it in glass.

What can the glass packaging industry offer in terms of pure innovation?
It's quite difficult to talk about glass in terms of new chemical makeup because broadly it's been a similar mix, with some additions, for thousands of years. It works. And it's infinitely recyclable. So I think in its purest form, glass doesn't need too much tinkering, but who knows what the future could bring there.

However, what glass does need to do is fit into a digital and modern world. If you're taking this ancient material, how do you make it this modern material for the future? In my view, glass needs to be digitalized. We want digital glass, or Smart glass as we call it at Encirc. On our Industry 4.0 bottling line, we imprint a QR code via laser on every bottle. And that allows it to connect to the digital world. All the source information of that bottle can go into the blockchain. The potential benefits of digitalizing glass are astounding. The dozens of benefits include making glass counterfeit-proof, preventing cross selling, reducing defects, supporting machine learning, and, of course, supporting digital deposit return schemes in the future.

There are so many benefits that digitalization and blockchain technology can bring, not just for glass, I think all materials need to be a lot more involved in that and they no doubt will be going forward.

Note

1 Henderson, Julian. 2016. *Ancient Glass: An Interdisciplinary Exploration*. Cambridge: Cambridge University Press.

7 Plastics
Wonder Materials or Global Disaster?

If there was a silver bullet, everybody would have done that already. We're trying to fix a very big system.

—Pat Teoh, Lean Giap

Plastics are everywhere

Plastics have become ubiquitous in modern civilization. Despite families in the developed world pledging to go a week or a month without buying any plastic and succeeding in this endeavor, those same families could not have separated themselves completely from the plastic they already own. As Susan Freinkel demonstrated in the introduction to her book *Plastic: A Toxic Love Story*, her attempt to avoid touching plastics for a day immediately evolved into tracking her interaction with plastics.[1] She discovered that she touched nearly 200 different plastic objects in a single day. Wherever you are reading this book, if you look around you, you will probably see many plastic objects.

Plastics can appear to be an ideal replacement for wood, metal, or glass, depending on the application. They are inexpensive, lightweight, and durable. When accidentally dropped, most plastic objects neither break nor damage the surface onto which they fall. Plastic can be easily formed into complex shapes using a variety of manufacturing methods. It can be injection molded, in which molten plastic is injected into a metal mold and quickly solidifies upon contact with the cold metal. Plastic is soft enough to be easily machined.

Some plastic materials are transparent to light, making them an inexpensive substitute for glass. Toughened or laminated glass—the glass used in car windshields and bulletproof windows—includes one or more layers of plastic sandwiched between panes of glass. These composite materials combine the shatter-resistance of plastic with the scratch-resistance of glass.

It is possible to infuse plastics with opaque color. Unlike with painted objects, the color does not rub off the surface during use. This feature is great for manufacturers wanting to produce long-lasting products in a wide variety of colors. LEGO bricks come to mind as an obvious example.

DOI: 10.4324/9781003409267-9

Plastics have clearly become an indispensable part of modern society. For better or worse, it is difficult to imagine any industrialized nation without plastics. But there are those who see plastics as an evil to be eradicated. This chapter delves into both the positive and negative attributes of plastics, answering questions that many people ask about plastics:

- What are plastics and how are they made?
- When were plastics invented?
- How are different plastics used?
- Which plastics are toxic?
- How much of a problem is plastic trash?
- How can society reduce the use of plastics?
- What are bioplastics and how can they help?

What are plastics?

Everyone is familiar with plastics, but what are they really, and how are they made? Here are some definitions from *The Merriam-Webster Dictionary*.

Plastic (adj): having a quality suggestive of mass-produced plastic goods; capable of being molded or modeled; capable of being deformed continuously and permanently in any direction without rupture; of, relating to, or involving plastic surgery; artificial or synthetic.

Plastic (noun): a plastic substance; specifically any of numerous organic synthetic or processed materials that are mostly thermoplastic or thermosetting polymers of high molecular weight and that can be made into objects, films, or filaments.[2]

In the context of plastic materials, "organic" means containing carbon compounds, molecules that are the basis of life on earth. All living things contain these molecules.

Polymers consist of long chains of atoms, often hydrocarbons, linked together to form large molecules. Polymers exist in nature. Cellulose, a fiber found in trees and other plants, is a naturally occurring polymer. Spider silk is also a polymer, one with an impressive strength-to-weight ratio that engineered materials struggle to achieve. Such biopolymers serve as an inspiration for the field of biomimicry, in which chemists and engineers endeavor to create manufactured materials that mimic the properties of these perfectly designed natural materials.

Plastics, however, are not naturally occurring or living materials, hence the phrase "synthetic or processed." Commercial plastics include polypropylene, polyethylene, polyvinyl chloride (PVC), and polystyrene, also known by the familiar trade name Styrofoam. Nylon is also a plastic. All of these materials are thermoplastics, polymers that soften when they are heated and harden when cooled to room temperature.

Thermosetting polymers achieve their properties through an irreversible chemical reaction. The most familiar example is epoxy glues. They come as a pair of liquids that, when mixed in the correct proportions, solidify within minutes at room temperature, forming a reliable, permanent bond to connect like or unlike materials to one another.

The remaining part of the dictionary definition defines plastics as being able to be formed into objects and films using multiple methods. This attribute is crucial to the prominent role plastics play in modern society. Plastics are extremely versatile and compatible with high-volume, low-cost manufacturing.

A brief history of plastics

Plastics are a relatively new class of materials. The first commercial synthetic plastic material dates to the early twentieth century. Leo Hendrik Baekeland created Bakelite, a thermosetting plastic formed by combining carbolic acid (also known as phenol) and formaldehyde. Baekeland founded the General Bakelite Company in 1910 to commercialize the product. It was marketed as a wonder material: hard, unbreakable, impervious to chemical attack, and fireproof.

Baekeland envisioned a world where nearly everything a person touched in daily life was made from Bakelite. While this has not come to pass, it is possible today to purchase a wide range of products made of Bakelite, from costume jewelry to cookware.

Many of the plastics in common use today were invented between 1930 and 1960. The 1930s saw neoprene, polystyrene, polyethylene, PVC, Plexiglas, polyurethanes, and nylon come to market. Polyethylene terephthalate (PET), polyimides, and polycarbonates followed in the next two decades. All these materials have valuable commercial uses. Reusable water bottles are made from PET. Polycarbonates are especially tough materials, used in eyeglasses and bulletproof windows. Figure 7.1 gives the approximate dates when select plastics were first patented or manufactured.

Conventional plastics start as hydrocarbon feedstocks derived from fossil fuels such as natural gas or crude oil. Polyethylene starts from ethylene, a hydrocarbon monomer (individual small molecule) that can be extracted from natural gas or by distilling crude oil. Similarly, propene is the basis for polypropylene. Combining

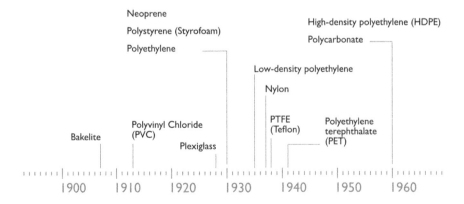

Figure 7.1 Timeline showing when various plastics were developed.

1950	2
1960	8
1970	35
1980	70
1990	120
2000	213
2010	313
2015	381
2020	420
2022	443

Figure 7.2 Increase in global plastic production from 1950 to 2022, millions of metric tons.[4]

ethylene and chlorine creates ethylene dichloride, which is converted into vinyl chloride to produce PVC.

It wasn't until around 1960 that the hydrocarbon feedstocks for plastics became readily available at low cost, greatly expanding commercial plastic production. Today more than 90 percent of plastics are made from virgin fossil-fuel feedstocks.[3]

The 60 years between 1960 and 2020 saw a more than 50-fold increase in annual global plastic production, which jumped from 8 million metric tons to 420 (see Figure 7.2). Despite efforts to curb plastics usage in recent years, global plastics consumption continues to rise. Much of this increase is due to rising populations and expansion of the middle class in China.

Hot polymers on a summer day

Polymers can be either thermoplastic or thermosetting. As mentioned earlier, thermoplastic polymers soften when they are heated and harden when they are cooled. When heated to a sufficiently high temperature, thermoplastics flow like liquids and can be poured into molds. At room temperature, most thermoplastics are stable and long lasting, although some can soften if left in the sun on a hot day. It is possible to melt and reshape thermoplastics multiple times. This property makes them easier to recycle than thermosetting polymers. Used thermoplastics can be cleaned, ground into pieces, and then reheated to make new plastic products.

For me (Julia), talk of thermoplastics often brings to mind a specific image. It's 95°F outside, even hotter in the lab, and I'm standing over a huge vat of black goo, wearing only a tank top and shorts under my lab coat to avoid getting heatstroke. The summer after graduating from college I worked at Raychem in Menlo Park, California. My official title was "technician," since this was just a temporary job before grad school and I suppose the company wanted to preserve the engineering jobs for permanent hires. I worked with a friendly applications engineer who knew I had an engineering degree and assigned me an engineering project.

My job was to test out different formulations of a specific thermoplastic material to determine which recipe would yield a material with the best match of properties for a particular application. I mixed translucent polymer beads with several additives in varying amounts and heated the whole mixture to melting, somewhere between 300 and 350°C (570–630°F), hotter than a household oven.

The ingredient list included carbon black, a powdered form of carbon much like purified soot. The carbon black colored the polymer and made it slightly electrically conductive.

Changing the amounts of the various additives affected the electrical conductivity and strength of the thermoplastic material I was making. In addition to a protective lab coat, goggles, and heat-resistant gloves, I also wore a mask to avoid breathing in the carbon black dust.

Once incorporated into the final thermoplastic material, the carbon black posed no danger. That is the case with many additives used in the chemical industry. So long as workplaces put appropriate safety measures in place, such as ventilating manufacturing labs and providing proper protective gear to employees, the additives are not hazardous to employees or customers.

Many producers of industrial chemicals like to advertise their materials as "safe when used as recommended" or similar language. But the manufacturers are not policing their customers' factories. Chemical suppliers hope that including appropriate usage directions, warnings, and safety recommendations will be sufficient to absolve them of legal responsibility should their industrial customers' employees become injured or ill after using their products.

Understanding common plastics

Polyethylene, polypropylene, and PVC are the most commercially important plastics. Chapter 9 revisits each of these materials, and other plastics used as disposable packaging, in the context of recycling.

Polyethylene

Polyethylene forms the basis for several common materials. In low-density polyethylene (LDPE), the molecules arrange themselves in a branched structure, with multiple small branches off of the primary chain. Like human hairs with split ends that branch off from the core, these molecules are not as strong as those where the hydrocarbon molecules arrange themselves in a single line. High-density polyethylene (HDPE) forms such a linear structure. The manufacturing process involves metallic chemicals called Ziegler-Natta catalysts, named after Karl Ziegler and Giulio Natta, who received the 1963 Nobel Prize in chemistry for their discovery. These catalysts allow the ethylene to polymerize at much lower pressures than those required to produce LDPE.

LDPE is a transparent material commonly made into films like plastic grocery bags. HDPE is opaque and is both denser and stronger than LDPE. Milk jugs are made from HDPE.

Linear LDPE, or LLDPE, is a material that may be considered an improved version of LDPE, combining the best features of both LDPE and HDPE. The structure is mostly linear, with occasional short branches, creating a material that is stronger than LDPE but still transparent to light. LLDPE can be stretched into very thin, relatively strong films.

PET is what plastic water and soda bottles are made from. PET is recyclable, and many clothing manufacturers have taken advantage of this to produce fabrics made from recycled water bottles.

Polypropylene

Polypropylene is known for having a high ratio of strength to density, making it useful for manufacturing both disposable containers and long-lasting storage bins. When woven into fibers, it's used to make strong ropes and indoor/outdoor carpet, the latter of which is usually made from recycled polypropylene.

Polypropylene has some disadvantages: it is flammable unless treated with potentially toxic flame retardants, and it degrades when exposed to sunlight.

Polyvinyl chloride

The hard plastic tubing used for water and sewage pipes is made from PVC. Commercial PVC includes additives known as phthalates, plasticizers whose purpose is to soften the plastic for easier processing. It is possible for phthalates to leach out of water pipes made from PVC. They can also be released into the air if PVC is incinerated.

Manufacturers of PVC argue that the material is safe when used as intended and are concerned about the difficulty of replacing it with something that works as well. Such claims provide yet another example of the underlying challenge in removing proven or suspected toxicants, fueled by the desire of companies with a profitable product to continue promoting it.

The US Centers for Disease Control and Prevention (CDC) conducted research showing the widespread prevalence of phthalates in human urine. At the same time, the CDC states that these results don't necessarily imply a public health problem and that "more research is needed to assess the human health effects of exposure to phthalates."

Public outcry against phthalates is, however, driving a trend toward PVC-free versions of consumer goods.

Additives and contaminants

All commercial plastics contain a complex blend of chemical compounds, some of which are potentially hazardous to human health. In the case of thermosetting polymers, the inhalation danger passes once the product cures fully and all solvents have evaporated. Some plastics, however, contain additives that are toxic not only during manufacturing but potentially to those who use products made from the materials. Research suggests links between exposure to these toxic additives and increased rates of cancer, genetic mutations, and diabetes.

Additives in plastics give the materials valuable properties. They may increase the fire resistance of plastics, help them flow better during injection molding, or infuse them with color that won't wash off. The manufacturers often prioritize the desired end properties without worrying much about safety and toxicity. Wouldn't it be great to find replacements for many of these additives that allow producers to create less-toxic plastics? Those efforts are happening, but the solutions don't always solve the whole problem.

When thinking of toxic additives to plastic, bisphenol A (BPA) tops the list. BPA is found in polycarbonate plastics and gained notoriety because of baby bottles made from these materials. Babies and young children are more susceptible to toxicants than older children and adults, so the presence of BPA in baby bottles was especially worrisome. Heating plastic food or beverage containers increases the likelihood of contaminants leaching out, and milk or formula is typically heated to body temperature before feeding to infants.

BPA is an endocrine disruptor. It mimics the hormone estrogen and is believed to affect brain and reproductive system development in those exposed to it early in life. A 2003 study showed that measurable levels of BPA in the urine of more than 90 percent of Americans.[5] The FDA banned the use of BPA in baby bottles in 2012, and the chemical now no longer appears in polycarbonates used in reusable bottles marketed to older children and adults.

The plastics industry responded to the demand for BPA-free plastics by substituting bisphenol S (BPS), a similar chemical that was believed to be less liable to leach into food or beverages stored in plastic containers. Unfortunately, it appears that BPS is risky as well and can cause the same type of health issues as BPA. Results from testing on animals, combined with data showing the presence of BPS in most Americans' urine, are frightening. Just because a container is BPA-free, it isn't necessarily safe.

What about just removing both BPA and BPS? That would create a safer polycarbonate, but such material could not be used for plastic bottles unless the industry can develop alternative plasticizers. Without a plasticizer, polycarbonate would be too brittle and susceptible to cracking during the molding process.

Some pigments used in labels contain lead or cadmium. These heavy metals are especially a problem in compostable plastics, since they contaminate the compost, potentially allowing the metals to enter the food chain when the compost is added to the soil. The presence of lead and cadmium also slows the process of bacterial growth in compost, which is essential to its function.

Certifications for compostable plastics specify strict limits on the acceptable level of heavy metals. The American Society for Testing Materials (ASTM) Standard D6400-12 states that for a plastic to be labeled compostable, it must contain less than half the EPA allowable concentration of toxic heavy metals. Is that sufficient to ensure safety and efficient breakdown of organic material in compost? We don't know. It would be best if manufacturers of compostable products could find 100 percent nontoxic inks for labeling.

Toxic additives hinder not only composting but also recycling. While these additives provide useful benefits when they are added to virgin materials during plastics manufacturing, they no longer improve material properties of the recycled plastics. Instead, they make these materials less pure and contribute to the perception that post-consumer waste is not safe. Removing the worst offending additives, if done while maintaining acceptable performance of plastics, improves the quality of recycled plastics and their economic value.

In an ideal world, it would be possible to replace all toxic additives with alternatives that are proved to be nontoxic while producing plastics that have equal or better performance and no increase in cost. But in the real world, alternatives that meet the toxicity criteria may not meet desired performance and cost goals. Unless public health is the top priority, rising above cost considerations, change will be slow.

Teflon as an example

Growing awareness of product safety and public pressure are pushing more companies to reduce toxicants in their products. The greater emphasis on safety helps companies that have long been promoting nontoxic products to have an increased presence in the global marketplace. This approach will only be successful, however, if the less toxic versions work as well as those they are replacing. Coatings on nonstick cookware serve as an example of the inherent challenge.

Polytetrafluoroethylene is better known by its acronym, PTFE. PTFE is the primary component of Teflon, trademarked by Chemours and originally developed by DuPont. The material has a very high melting point and low coefficient of friction, which means that coatings made from the material are extremely slippery. This property makes it desirable for coating nonstick cookware. Before 2015, nonstick cookware often also incorporated PFOA, the chemical that contaminated landfills and sickened cattle in West Virginia (see the story in Chapter 1).

The desirable properties of PTFE coatings are also what makes the material difficult to manufacture. It doesn't melt and flow easily like other polymers. Manufacturing processes use very fine powders of PTFE, potentially exposing workers to dust. Proper workplace safety procedures can reduce, but not necessarily eliminate, such exposure.

Teflon coatings on cookware don't last forever, and as they slough off, they can be ingested with food. Concern about the toxicity of Teflon coatings, especially the toxic fumes that can be released if the coating is heated above a safe temperature, has led to a market for "greener" nonstick cookware.

Early attempts were not especially successful. In 2009, *Cook's Illustrated* magazine tested "green" skillets, those free of PFOA. The skillets were coated with either PTFE-based materials, polymers containing silicone, or ceramics. PTFE produced the best nonstick surface. Testers found the ceramic coatings to be severely lacking when it came to durability and nonstick performance. The article concluded that customers wanting a chemical-free nonstick skillet should buy a cast iron pan, a product they call "the original green skillet." It's heavy, but it's safe, and it works.

A decade after *Cook's Illustrated* tested nonstick skillets, the latest trend in nonstick cookware was pots and pans coated with a copper-infused ceramic that gives the cookware a distinctive reddish-brown copper appearance. The core is aluminum, just like in previous generations of nonstick and regular cookware. These pans are free from PFOA and PTFE, but reviews suggest that the nonstick performance isn't as long-lasting as promised. Perhaps *Cook's Illustrated* is still right about cast iron. Meanwhile, concerns about plastic reach beyond PTFE coatings.

The plastic trash problem

In addition to concerns about toxicants, another problem with plastics is what happens to them after people discard them. Plastic packaging is the largest source of plastic trash, because these are products designed to have a very short useful life, less than a year from when they are manufactured and sometimes less than an hour from when they arrive in a consumer's hands. Though their useful life is short, disposable plastics can last on this planet for over a century.

The plastic grocery bag stands as the prototypical example of plastic trash. Americans use 100 billion plastic bags each year (that's more than 250 million per day), and the United States is not even close to the worst offender worldwide when it comes to sources of plastic trash.[6]

Mentioning plastic bags, especially when associated with the word "ban," is a surefire way to start a spirited discussion. Some environmental groups have made enacting plastic bag bans a key element of their platform. They are certainly tackling other issues, but plastic bags get people's attention.

Public opinion on plastic bags primarily falls into two camps: those who believe bags are a danger to the environment and should be banned, and those who think the government has no place regulating what types of bags their local grocery store should be allowed to carry.

Those against banning plastics bags often point out their usefulness. They are effective for carrying groceries, with convenient handles that make it easy to carry several bags in one hand. They handle wet groceries without breaking or disintegrating. Once the bags are home from the grocery store, they come in handy for lining trash cans or disposing of used cat litter. Why buy new bags for that purpose rather than reusing those from the store?

Even though some tout the benefits of plastic bags, the tide is turning against single-use plastics. More and more cities are banning various types of disposable plastics, from grocery bags to drinking straws.

Despite the efforts of those who reuse plastic bags and dispose of them properly, far too many plastic bags—and other types of plastic trash—are ending up in the oceans. It is the presence of plastic trash in rivers, lakes, and oceans that is causing the greatest concern.

There is debate and disagreement about where the plastic in the oceans comes from. Multiple authorities, including WWF and the U.S. government's National Ocean Service, state that abandoned fishing nets are responsible for much of the plastic in the ocean, but without quantifying the amount. There has been even more debate about the origin of microplastics. The Marine Institute at the University of Plymouth refers to three sources that are widely accepted. These are particles resulting from tire abrasion, microfibers shed from garments during washing, and particles arising from the breakdown of larger items of plastic litter. There is little agreement on the percentage or quantity of each, either among NGOs, academics, or manufacturing corporations.

According to the Ellen MacArthur Foundation, at least eight million metric tons of plastic enters the oceans each year, the equivalent of a garbage truck full of plastic trash every minute. This has not been challenged. The economic impact of ocean plastic is astounding. Globally, the presence of plastics in the oceans costs tourism, fishing, and shipping industries $13 billion per year.[7]

The statistics are alarming, but for citizens in North America and Europe, it may seem far removed from our own lives. It is easy to get complacent if we don't personally see the damage. From our viewpoint, the trash seems to be under control. In many cities, curbside collection is inexpensive and reliable.

We spoke with Pat Teoh, who works for a plastics trading company in Malaysia that acts as a distributor for plastics manufacturers around the world.

Interview

Pat Teoh, Lean Giap

What got you interested in the plastics industry?
Lean Giap is my family's business. It wasn't by choice, it was more of an obligation. That is the conversation that probably a lot of Americans wouldn't understand. Since I was in, I thought, I'm going to look at ways to be proud of that.

Climate change is a very big problem. The fact that there is much less denial now makes my conversation a lot smoother. Ten years ago, when I talked about climate change or decarbonization or circular economy, it was as if I was speaking a foreign language. For the longest time, a lot of my partners thought that I wasn't interested in the business. Now, I guess they do see the value of having that knowledge and being able to implement it.

Tell me more about your work. What has happened since we last talked two years ago, in 2021?
All the conversations that I have now with the petrochemical plants, all the partners, suppliers, it's all about sustainability, which is very refreshing. It's great to hear that a lot of them have been doing quite a bit in the past few years. Everybody

worried about things being leaked out, worried about not being able to fulfill what they promised. So a lot of things have been going on behind the scenes. Finally in my post-COVID visits with them, they have shared their plans.

These are companies that are producing plastics. What are they actually doing?
I can't speak on their behalf, but I can speak on behalf of my company. The last few years, we have set up new class of solutions to look at closing the loop for waste in general, and circular economy in particular, for the industry. There's a lot of infrastructure to be set up. It's a learning curve for all of us, because it's something completely new.

I remember talking with someone else I know in Malaysia, and she was saying, North America and Europe, they're dumping all their trash here, so why does it matter what we do? What is your perspective, living in that part of the world?
I think that there have been a lot of challenges when it comes to plastic waste in general. And like, we're all we're all very aware that one of the biggest challenges is actually the infrastructure. And I think in the past few years, we're seeing a lot of investment into recycling technology. You have petrochemical plants investing a lot of money into chemical recycling, which I think is very progressive news. The real challenge is, where is that raw material going to come from? It has got to be clean, segregated, and it's got to be within reach. It's got to make sense in terms of the logistics. So I think that's the infrastructure challenge that I foresee. Not just in Malaysia, it's everywhere.

What is the role of your company in this whole system?
We've been in plastic trading for the past 40 years. We are looking at designing a way to get back the waste after delivering the raw materials so that those can actually get to the recyclers. It's a very big project, it's also it requires a lot of planning, because it's all a volume game. And on top of that, we have to do a lot of education awareness to the stakeholders that this is something that's a win-win solution for everybody.

Compared to the conversation that we had two years ago, sustainability is going mainstream. The backlash against the plastics industry is definitely not helping, because I think that also discourages a lot of risk taking. There's a lot of trial and error, let's face it, right? If there was a silver bullet, everybody would have done that already. But there isn't. We're trying to fix a very big system.

Regardless of how bad you think plastic is, everybody benefits from it. And I think people need to be able to respect that. And then let's work on it. Because I've seen initiatives attacked for no reason. That is counterproductive, in my opinion. Because that's just going to make a lot of people within the industry who actually want to make a difference, who actually have the market knowledge as well as the technical experience to be able to do something, not want to do anything because of the fear of backlash.

What do you think that readers need to know about the reality of working in the plastics industry in Malaysia?
First, we are well aware that resources are finite. Sustainability is a business opportunity. And right now is the best time for you to jump on board and maximize this

opportunity. For sure there is risk. But how do you turn that risk into something that will future proof your business?Have conversations like I'm having with you. That changes the mindset. The knowledge gap needs to be closed immediately, then everyone's on the same path, In my opinion, it has got to be a motivating, and also a very encouraging movement, as opposed to a lot of fear or threats. Because I just don't see how that's going to work out, with all this unnecessary pressure that's been put onto something that is already a very challenging task.

I've been expanding the team in sustainability because we're moving towards Circular Economy implementation. I'm not expecting people to have knowledge in it, which is fine. But the attitude is really critical. Because it's not just a trend.

Does your circular economy work focus just on recycling plastics? Or is there more to it than that?
We're also approached by a lot of companies who are looking at lowering their carbon emissions by switching out different types of materials. But at the end of the day, you need life cycle analysis. The alternative may not be exactly what you're looking for because plastic as a material is very durable, cost-effective, lightweight, etc. You name it, you got it. So it's more about creating an infrastructure, which is what I mentioned earlier, to ensure that it doesn't go into landfill and doesn't become waste.

The best people to actually look at sustainability transformation are within your organization. And that is something that I hope business owners are going to realize and start investing in. The first step is to invest into that closing that knowledge gap within your organization.

An island of plastic

The Great Pacific Garbage Patch is somewhat of a misnomer. Despite the image the name may suggest, no large plastic island in the Pacific Ocean can be seen from space, or even from an airplane. The Pacific Garbage Patch is, however, real. Most of the trash lies beneath the surface, and much of it consists of microplastic.

Plastic fragments less than around 5 mm in size—there is no agreed-upon exact cutoff—are termed microplastic, while larger pieces are called macroplastic. Macroplastic debris is an eyesore and can pose a suffocation or strangling hazard to marine animals.

While plastic debris exists throughout the world's oceans, currents concentrate it in specific regions, such as the two large collections of debris in the North Pacific Gyre. Coastal areas also exhibit a much higher concentration of plastic debris than the open ocean.

Henderson Island, an uninhabited, remote island in the South Pacific, stands as a prime example of the prevalence of macroplastic. The island made international news headlines in 2017 when Australian researchers published results of a study showing that Henderson's beaches are covered in more than 37 million pieces of trash. Much of that is discarded plastic. Henderson is only 14 square miles.

Currents have been washing trash ashore from locations as far-flung as China, Japan, and Chile.

Trash-strewn beaches around the world provide a visible reminder of the problems that plastic trash is causing and make for compelling photographs. But microplastic is a problem that is just as worrisome, if not more so.

When plastic packaging starts to degrade as a result of exposure to sun and oxygen, it breaks down into small fragments. This process is part of the reason that concentrations of microplastics in the oceans have increased significantly since the 1960s. The plastic trash that has been accumulating for decades continues to break down into smaller pieces. At some point, these microplastic bits do not further degrade but are small enough for fish and other marine animals to eat. This type of debris is called secondary microplastic.

Primary microplastics are posing a growing concern. These are from sources that are manufactured as small plastic particles. One example is so-called microbeads or microexfoliates, synthetic alternatives to ground almonds or pumice in facial cleansers. Plastic microbeads are made from polyethylene, polypropylene, or polystyrene. These plastic particles, which range from under 0.1 mm to around 5 mm in size and enter waterways when washed down drains, are a growing source of microplastics in the oceans.[8]

Heavy industry creates another source of microplastics in the ocean. Acrylic, melamine, or polyester particles are sometimes used in air blasters to clean paint or rust off of machinery, engines, or boat hulls. The paint residue may contain heavy metals, especially if it dates from the 1960s or earlier, causing not only microplastics but toxic metals to contaminate waterways.[9]

The concentration of microplastics in the oceans increased significantly in the second half of the twentieth century, but accurately measuring it presents a challenge. The oceans are incredibly vast, and distribution of microplastics is not uniform. Concentrations in local regions increase after storms or hurricanes, for example.

Concentrations can be measured directly by taking samples of ocean water or sediment from the sea floor. Results depend on the size of the mesh used to trap microplastics. In one study, an 80-micron mesh resulted in a concentration 100,000 times that obtained with a 450-micron mesh in the same region at the same time.[10]

Another common approach to measuring microplastic concentrations gives some alarming results. Examination of the gut contents of fish or seabirds shows an incredibly high percentage of creatures with ingested plastic. Plastic fragments were first observed in seabirds back in the 1960s, and a 2011 study of fulmars, an ocean-foraging bird species, showed an average of 26 plastic fragments in the gut of each bird.[11] The fact that this value has remained stable since 2000 is slightly encouraging. At least it isn't still increasing.

Multiple studies have confirmed that microplastics ingested by marine animals move up the food chain when other animals eat the seafood.[12] At present, it appears that the presence of mercury in fish is more of a danger than plastics, at least from the viewpoint of those eating the fish.

Goal: reduce plastics usage

Project Mainstream, an initiative developed by the World Economic Forum and the Ellen MacArthur Foundation, published a report in 2016 called The New Plastics Economy. This report lays out the organizations' vision—a world in which plastics are never sent to landfills nor end up in the oceans but are continually recycled until the point where they have outlived their usefulness and can biodegrade. This vision will be easier to achieve if fewer plastics enter the world in the first place.

Several approaches can be considered to reduce the amount of plastics being produced. These include:

- Reducing the weight of existing plastic products by changing the design. Plastic water bottles demonstrate an example of this approach. Over the years, the layer of plastic has become thinner and caps have become smaller. (We would argue that getting rid of disposable plastic water bottles entirely would be a better solution.)
- Replacing plastics with materials that were in common use before plastics became so pervasive. For example, glass storage containers are becoming more popular, although they do sometimes come with plastic lids.
- Improving recycling rates so that more products are made from recycled plastic rather than from virgin material. Such efforts should ideally be combined with improving recycling technology.
- Replacing conventional plastics with polymers produced without fossil fuels. This action doesn't reduce the total amount of plastic being produced but may reduce the carbon footprint associated with plastic production.

All these approaches have their benefits and drawbacks, not all of which are obvious at first glance.

Design changes aimed at reducing the weight of a product may cause problems with performance. Thinner water bottles are much flimsier than the previous generation of bottles they replaced.

For durable goods, reducing weight may make them less durable, causing them to be replaced more frequently and negating any benefits. Small plastic parts that break and render a product useless are not just annoying, but wasteful. 3-D printing, discussed in more detail in Chapter 11, presents a possible solution. Simply print a replacement part, and the product is as good as new.

Switching out plastics for other materials may come with unintended consequences. Replacing the plastic grocery bag with a paper or reusable bag, for example, would seem to be an environmentally sound decision, but that is not necessarily the case. Plastic grocery bags were first introduced in the US in 1979 and became popular more than a decade later, helped by a marketing strategy that promoted them as being less expensive and stronger than paper bags. Unlike plastic, paper bags can disintegrate when exposed to water.

The environmental benefit of replacing plastic bags is not obvious when considering the energy and water used to produce various types of bags. Paper bags are usually made from virgin sources rather than recycled paper because recycled paper is not as strong. As noted in Chapter 5, the production of paper requires resources: trees and water, plus the energy needed to process the wood into pulp and then process the pulp into paper. Producing a paper bag requires four times as much water as producing a plastic bag.

This calculation, however, does not consider the fact that the same groceries when bagged in paper typically use less than half the number of bags they would if bagged in plastic. Unless, of course, baggers double-bag the paper because they don't think it's strong enough to carry heavy groceries.

Improving rates of plastic recycling is helpful, but there are limits to the effectiveness of recycling. Replacing conventional plastics with those not made from fossil fuels makes a lot of sense. This approach doesn't solve all the problems inherent in using plastics, but it is worth considering.

Biodegradable plastics are not all the same. Some biodegrade much more rapidly than others. In order to be industrially compostable, materials have to meet several criteria.[13] They must:

- Degrade at least 90 percent by weight within six months at an industrial composting facility,
- Contain at least 50 percent organic matter,
- Contain no more than a specified concentration of heavy metals,
- Disintegrate into fragments smaller than 2 mm within 12 weeks under controlled composting conditions,
- Create compost that is nontoxic, meaning that it will create no negative health effects when used as a soil amendment for food crops.

The performance and price of compostable materials have improved significantly in recent years. Compostable bags, plates, and utensils are sufficiently strong to withstand use, allowing them to fulfill their purpose and help return nutrients from food waste back to the soil.

Industrially compostable bioplastics generally require a combination of water and heat to decompose properly. PLA, the material most commonly found in compostable plastic cups, falls into this category. The requirement of adding water and heat is an important concept, since PLA may not decompose if discarded into the trash, nor will it degrade in rivers or oceans. Cups made from PLA will best serve their intended purpose if discarded with food waste into bins headed for commercial composting facilities. They should not be placed into recycling bins, where they will contaminate the recycling stream if not segregated.

The availability of curbside composting for residents in some communities has created a market for compostable bags for collecting food waste. These bags are "certified compostable" and can be deposited into containers intended for compost. A box of such bags from BioBag Americas claims to use resins sourced from Italy, made with "starches from renewable crops free from GMOs."

In some communities, food waste bagged in compostable bags joins yard waste in a single, large bin. Increasing adoption of composting is an especially effective way to reduce the volume of waste being sent to landfills since uneaten food makes up the largest single component of municipal solid waste. Of course, larger-scale adoption relies on the availability of local industrial composting facilities. This availability is sorely lacking.

Compostable products extend well beyond bags for collecting food waste. An entire new industry is developing with compostable products meant to replace plastic flatware, Styrofoam takeout containers, and more.

Toward better compostables

Not all compostable flatware is of the same level of quality. I (Julia) recall a lunch event where all the forks were falling apart as we tried to cut our chicken. Tines were breaking off, and handles were breaking in two. It was both amusing and frustrating. The chicken wasn't especially tough, but the forks just weren't up to the job. There is some benefit to flatware that composts, but not if it falls apart when we're using it. Products that create less waste to landfill are wonderful in theory. But if they don't perform, no one is going to buy them.

Part of the issue is that using more material—making fork tines thicker— makes a product more expensive. In a niche where products are already more expensive than the conventional plastics they are replacing, this can put the supplier in a difficult position. The more material used, the longer a product will take to compost as well. The trick is finding the right balance. Plant-based PLA can produce strong flatware that is no thicker than conventional plastic products and serves its purpose well, but it needs to be properly designed.

In addition to concerns about the performance of compostable plastics, their environmental benefits are not clear cut. The Oregon Department of Environmental Quality (DEQ) compared the life cycles of compostable and non-compostable food-service products by reviewing scientific literature and came to some counter-intuitive conclusions. A DEQ report cited a study showing that composting compostable food packaging (primarily PLA) created a greater negative environmental and health impact than either using non-compostable packaging or recycling compostable packaging. The issues stem from the resources needed to make compostable products and the cross-contamination that occurs when people accidentally put non-compostable packaging into a compost bin.

Not all compostable products degrade as quickly as assumed. Even for those that do, compostable service ware does not improve the quality of compost because, unlike food waste, most degrade to carbon dioxide rather than useful biomass. The presence of food waste, however, helps food-service ware degrade in industrial composting facilities.

Context is critical. At large public events, providing 100 percent compostable serving ware and replacing trash cans with compost bins reduces food waste because people aren't tossing leftover food into bins destined for the landfill. This only works, of course, in regions where industrial composting exists. Also, staff or volunteers need to make sure the containers get to the composting facility after the event.

In this use case, the environmental benefit of less food waste probably overrides the impact of producing the compostable plates, cups, and forks. Offering compostable packaging for customers to take home is different. That approach relies on customers having access to compost collection and knowing to toss the packing in the right place. Establishments that offer a mix of compostable and non-compostable packaging will likely have confused customers who don't know what to toss where and aren't going to take the time to figure it out.

Replacing Styrofoam packaging

Plant fibers make an effective substitute for Styrofoam clamshell food packaging and might eventually completely replace it. The reason they haven't already is an all-too-common problem: cost. Styrofoam is very inexpensive, and alternatives haven't reached the volume production necessary for costs to come down. With pressure from consumers and regulations at the city level, however, there may soon be enough businesses willing to buy plant-based clamshell packages and other containers at a premium. When that happens, the packaging industry should be able to bring costs down and mass production may become a reality.

Styrofoam is used in many more applications than just clamshell packaging. It's used to protect items being shipped. When replacing Styrofoam packing "peanuts" or solid forms shaped to protect furniture or electronics, stiff plant-based fiberboard will not do the job. Product shipping requires a different type of plant-based product to replace Styrofoam.

Compostable versions of Styrofoam "peanuts" have existed for years, in the form of cornstarch-based pellets. These aren't as sturdy as Styrofoam, but they serve their limited purpose. They can protect items that aren't especially fragile, and when they are no longer needed they quickly dissolve in water.

Cornstarch-based pellets aren't strong enough to replace Styrofoam in custom-molded shapes designed to protect delicate products during shipping. This application needs a more out-of-the-box alternative. One such option now exists.

Ecovative, based in Green Island, New York, makes a mushroom-based product that takes compostable packing material a step further. The material is grown from waste feedstock, in a new twist on additive manufacturing. Products are made from mycelium (mushroom roots) and agricultural fibers and take about a week to grow. Ecovative is gaining traction, having been awarded a contract from Dell to protect its computers for shipping. Still, its slow manufacturing process is likely to limit mass adoption at a global scale.

The next chapter offers many more examples of bioplastics, some of which are commercially available and others that have yet to reach mass adoption.

Notes

1 Freinkel, Susan. 2011. *Plastic: A Toxic Love Story*. Boston, MA: Houghton Mifflin Harcourt.

2 Merriam-Webster, Incorporated. "Definition of PLASTIC," Merriam-Webster, 2019, https://www.merriam-webster.com/dictionary/plastic.

3 World Economic Forum, Ellen MacArthur Foundation, and McKinsey & Company. "The New Plastics Economy — Rethinking the Future of Plastics," 2016, https:// emf.thirdlight.com/file/24/_A-BkCs_skP18I_Am1g_JWxFrX/The%20New%20 Plastics%20Economy%3A%20Rethinking%20the%20future%20of%20plastics.pdf.

4 Sources: Geyer, Roland, Jenna R. Jambeck, and Kara Lavender Law. 2017. "Production, Use, and Fate of All Plastics Ever Made." *Science Advances* 3 (7). https:// doi.org/10.1126/sciadv.1700782 [1950-2015 data]; OECD. 2022. "Plastics Use by Type." OECD ILibrary. Paris. 2022. https://www.oecd-ilibrary.org/environment/data/ global-plastic-outlook/plastics-use-by-type_ad13eab0-en?. [2020-2022 data].

5 United States Department of Health and Human Services, Centers for Disease Control and Prevention, and National Center for Health Statistics. "National Health and Nutrition Examination Survey (NHANES), 2003-2004," www.icpsr.umich.edu, 2016, https:// www.icpsr.umich.edu/web/NACDA/studies/25503/versions/V7.

6 Worldwatch Institute. "New Bans on Plastic Bags May Help Protect Marine Life," Worldwatch Institute, March 8, 2017, https://web.archive.org/web/20170308074520/ http://www.worldwatch.org/node/5565.

7 United Nations Environment Programme. *Valuing Plastic: The Business Case for Measuring, Managing and Disclosing Plastic Use in the Consumer Goods Industry*, 2014. https://wedocs.unep.org/20.500.11822/9238.

8 Science Advice for Policy by European Academies, *A Scientific Perspective on Microplastics in Nature and Society* (Berlin: SAPEA, 2019), https://doi.org/10.26356/ microplastics.

9 Okoro, H. K. et al. "Sources, Environmental Levels and Toxicity of Organotin in Marine Environment—a Review," Digitalknowledge.cput.ac.za, 2011, https://digitalknowledge.cput.ac.za/handle/11189/4749.

10 OSPAR, "Marine Litter in the North-East Atlantic Region: Assessment and Priorities for Response" (London, United Kingdom: OSPAR Commision, 2009), https://qsr2010. ospar.org/media/assessments/p00386_Marine_Litter_in_the_North-East_Atlantic_ with_addendum.pdf.

11 van Franeker, Jan A. et al. "Monitoring Plastic Ingestion by the Northern Fulmar Fulmarus Glacialis in the North Sea," *Environmental Pollution* 159, no. 10 (October 2011): 2609–15, https://doi.org/10.1016/j.envpol.2011.06.008.

12 Cverenkárová, Klára, Martina Valachovičová, Tomáš Mackuľak, Lukáš Žemlička, and Lucia Bírošová. "Microplastics in the Food Chain." *Life* 11, no. 12 (2021): 1349. https:// doi.org/10.3390/life11121349.

13 CEN, EN 13432:2000/AC: 2005 Packaging—Requirements for Packaging Recoverable through Composting and Biodegradation—Test Scheme and Evaluation Criteria for the Final Acceptance of Packaging, 2005.

8 Material Innovations and Future Materials

Can Performance Improvements Make Them Mainstream?

Cellulose is already built into nature's regeneration cycles, so nature can adapt and reuse it.
—Jen Keane, Modern Synthesis

An introduction to novel materials

The last ten years have seen many new materials coming to market. Mass-market bioplastics (see Chapter 7) are already on shelves and in cupboards in our homes. We have seen an explosion of innovation in the 2010s and 2020s, with billions of dollars already invested in bioengineered materials, mycelium-based materials, materials derived from pulp co-products, plus nanomaterials and nanotech metallurgy. These materials will play an essential role in our lives and will begin to replace fossil fuel-based polymers and natural materials such as cotton, leather, and wool.

What makes a material novel or innovative? The materials covered in the previous four chapters were all innovative at some point. Now we are looking at the recent past, at materials that are so new that they didn't exist when we authors began our careers several decades ago. We are also looking into the future to predict which materials currently in research and development will turn into commercial products.

Some of the novel materials covered in this chapter have been used for decades. Others are barely out of the laboratory but are experiencing rapid uptake as businesses look for less toxic, more regenerative alternatives.

We believe that these novel materials will become key to a circular future, as is evidenced by growing multinational investment in existing plants to take bio-based polymers and other materials into global markets and new sectors.

This chapter covers information that has been documented in academic papers and at professional conferences over the past decade. Little of it has ever been written in a way that those without doctorates in chemistry or materials science can understand. We aim to change that, beginning with defining relevant terms.

Chemical, biochemical and biological, processes: a quick primer for non-scientists

Chemical processes

We discussed chemicals in Chapter 2. Chemical processes involve chemical reactions, which are mostly irreversible changes in non-living organic or inorganic

DOI: 10.4324/9781003409267-10

elements and compounds. Examples include oxidation, polymerization, chemical vapor deposition of metallic oxides, and reactions of liquids or gases that change the properties of surfaces.

Toxic chemicals continue to pose a wide range of health hazards (such as irritation, sensitization, and carcinogenicity) and physical hazards (such as flammability, corrosion, and explosibility). "Green chemistry" aims to replace hazardous substances with safer alternatives. As noted in Chapter 2, it is a challenging process that often takes many years of research and development.

Biochemical processes

Biochemistry is the application of chemistry to the study of biological processes at cellular and molecular levels. The word "biochemistry" was coined in 1903 by a German chemist named Carl Neuber, and it emerged as a distinct discipline around that time.

Biochemical processes are chemical reactions that occur in living organisms. For example, the way the body converts food into energy is biochemical. From a materials science perspective, biochemistry can include the design of bio-inspired materials, the use of new classes of catalysts, right up to cosmochemistry and its application to terrestrial materials development.

Biochemical engineers can translate discoveries in life sciences into practical materials and processes using biology to make products such as biofuels and new materials that don't rely on petrochemicals as a raw material.

Biological processes

Biological processes are those that occur naturally in living organisms. Biomimicry aims to leverage these processes to inspire new and better solutions to technological and environmental problems. These can range from exploiting a better understanding of interactions between organisms to using biotechnology to enhance photosynthesis to increase crop yields without increasing chemical inputs or land use.

Biomanufacturing relies on naturally occurring processes and reactions to produce a material, product, or chemical that would otherwise be produced through a synthetic process. The biological process on which nearly all biomanufacturing is based is fermentation, which makes use of naturally occurring microorganisms and enzymes to carry out reactions.

A brief history of bioplastics

What we now call biopolymers or biomaterials pre-date fossil-fuel plastics. Rubber made from a rubber tree was the first true bioplastic, but when people talk about bio-based plastics, they usually aren't referring to natural rubber. The very first commercial plastics were bioplastics derived from cellulose in cotton. Biomaterials, as such, have a somewhat long history, dating back to the 1850s and 1860s.

The invention of celluloid has been attributed to English chemist Alexander Parkes, who in 1856 was granted the first of several patents on a plastic material that he called *Parkesine*. Parkesine plastics were made by dissolving nitrocellulose (a flammable nitric ester of cotton or wood cellulose) in solvents such as alcohol or wood naphtha and mixing in plasticizers such as vegetable oil or camphor (a waxy substance originally derived from the oils of the Asian camphor tree).

Parkesine was not without its problems, however. It was flammable and could easily be melted or dissolved by certain solvents. It also tended to discolor over time. Despite these drawbacks, Parkesine was a significant breakthrough in the development of plastics that paved the way for the invention of more durable and versatile plastics such as Celluloid (mentioned below) and Bakelite (discussed in Chapter 7).

The Parkesine Company struggled financially and went out of business in 1868. Parkesine was later produced by other companies, but it never achieved widespread commercial success. Around that time, two other bioplastics came out. John Wesley Hyatt made a breakthrough in the US with his first natural polymer, which his brother dubbed Celluloid (meaning like cellulose).[1]

In 1867, Daniel Spill patented *Xylonite*, a more stable improvement upon Parkesine. It was a cellulose nitrate plastic, made from cellulose and nitric acid. Xylonite is similar to Celluloid, but it is made with a different type of plasticizer, which gives it a different set of properties.

However, Xylonite is also flammable and can be dangerous if it is not handled properly. In the early 1900s, there were a number of fires and explosions caused by Xylonite products. As a result, Xylonite use declined, and it was eventually replaced by safer plastics.

Parkesine, Xylonite, and Celluloid were made from plant-based materials. Once fossil-fuel plastics were invented, the scientific community abandoned the work that had been done to develop commercial plant-based plastics. By the mid-twentieth century, the whole focus switched to fossil-fuel plastics, which were cheap and plentiful at a time when no environmental risks were perceived. These risks only began to be highlighted many decades later.

Since early in the twenty-first century, we have seen a growing recognition that fossil-fuel plastics are worrisome from an environmental viewpoint. Images of trash-strewn beaches and frightening warnings about microplastics abound. As noted elsewhere in this book, the additives in plastics pose serious health risks, particularly the many chemicals of concern used as plasticizers. Moving forward, will bioplastics be the path that solves the problems with conventional plastics? Keep reading and draw your own conclusions.

Bioplastics: the wave of the future?

For some applications, people much prefer a product that looks, feels, and works like plastic. Paper isn't water resistant, and going back to metal or glass creates a heavier product that doesn't always meet customer expectations and may require more energy to produce. Glass is susceptible to breaking, and metal is susceptible to rusting. How about instead creating a "better" plastic?

Bioplastics provide one route to addressing the carbon footprint and waste associated with conventional plastics. To better understand the term "bioplastic," it is helpful to look at two more definitions: bio-based and biodegradable.

- Bio-based plastics are plastic materials made from recently living organisms (biomass) rather than fossil fuels. Corn, wheat, and sugarcane are possible sources.
- Biodegradable plastics are compostable and can degrade relatively quickly into simple elements and compounds.

A plastic can be bio-based and not biodegradable. Many commercial bio-based plastics are chemically the same as the conventional plastics they replace. For example, ethylene is the same compound whether it is derived from natural gas or ripening bananas, which emit ethylene gas. Bio-polyethylene and bio-PET are the most prevalent bio-based plastics on the market, with 2.02 million metric tons produced in 2014.[2] These materials are no more compostable than conventional polyethylene or PET.

Even though fossil fuels are not the feedstock for bio-based plastics, the energy needed to manufacture plastics from agricultural sources likely comes from fossil fuels. These bio-based plastics also require farmland and the associated water for irrigation. Land used to produce bioplastics exclusively is not available for food crops. The goal of agriculture is supposed to be to feed people, not to feed our ever-growing desire for more plastic stuff.

We can look at this problem in several ways. What about all the agricultural land that's being used to grow feed for cattle? If global beef consumption were to plummet as a result of advocacy for a more plant-based diet, then farmers could convert their land to crops grown to produce bio-based plastics or biofuels. They could, of course, choose to grow food crops for human consumption. In reality, they would probably take whichever route was most likely to allow them to stay financially solvent.

The methods of producing bio-based plastics matter—agriculture using large quantities of water and pesticides can have a more negative environmental and human health impact than producing plastics from fossil-fuel feedstocks. The Oregon Department of Environmental Quality (DEQ) evaluated results from scientific studies and concluded that just because a plastic is bio-based doesn't mean that it is a better choice from a safety and environmental standpoint.

Biomass does not need to be created from crops planted for that purpose, nor should that be the first approach. The inedible parts of plants that often become compost could instead be sources of biomass.

What about all the produce that farmers and grocers discard every year because it is blemished or otherwise can't be sold to consumers at a reasonable price? Sometimes it becomes animal feed. There is a growing movement to sell "ugly" produce at discounted prices rather than tossing it in a trash heap or compost bin. But scrap from food crops can be used as a source of biomass, alleviating the concern about dedicating acres of land to produce plastic.

Non-food plants can also be a source of plastics created from biomass. Cellulose from trees could be once again processed into commercial plastics. Startups such as Bloom Materials have developed methods to make plastics derived from algae. Such efforts have yet to hit mainstream commercial adoption.

Researchers are also developing another option: bioplastics sourced from captured greenhouse gas emissions. Methane can be recovered from landfills and coal mines. Industrial processes, such as metal and cement production, create carbon dioxide. Capturing the methane or carbon dioxide represents a new opportunity in the search for new sources of bioplastics. Several companies are working to bring such bioplastics out of the lab and into commercial production. All bio-based plastics sourced from greenhouse gases are entirely new polymers.

Polylactic acid (PLA) and polyhydroxyalkanoate (PHA) are common bio-based plastics. PLA is gaining attention for its use in compostable serving ware designed to replace disposable clear plastic cups. As we will see later in this chapter, however, PLA is not necessarily as environmentally friendly as many people believe.

Many inside and outside the bioplastics industry have focused on these materials' utility for food-grade packaging. Given EU legislation in the 2020s, European manufacturers have begun to pivot towards other sectors, where the emissions reductions and life cycle analysis (LCA) benefits are much more clearly appreciated as valuable.

This pivot stems from the actions of the European Commission and also the clauses contained in the 2022 Circular Economy Action Plan (CEAP).

Clause 3.3 of the CEAP relates to packaging. It encourages less complex packaging consisting of fewer different materials and reducing polymer usage.

The European Union is more concerned with removing complexity (encouraging the mechanical recycling of polymers invented in the middle of the last century), than encouraging the development of new polymers, which may have better properties and zero microplastic shedding.

Compare this to the March 2023 announcement from the Environmental Protection Agency in the US that announced a goal to replace 90 percent of plastics with biomaterials by 2043. The statement was met with mixed reviews, with some calling it a step in the right direction while others question the plan's feasibility.

Bio-based plastics produced using sustainable feedstocks and nontoxic production methods are a good alternative to conventional plastics. Given the huge amount of biomass (in the form of agrowaste), which is currently burned or ploughed back into the soil, before we even consider other bio feedstocks such as forestry, mycelium, and algae, opportunity abounds. The pessimism about the EPA announcement may be overstated.

Practical uses for bioplastics

From a manufacturing perspective, it makes sense to understand bioplastics from an end use viewpoint. Figure 8.1 gives an overview of the commercially available options.

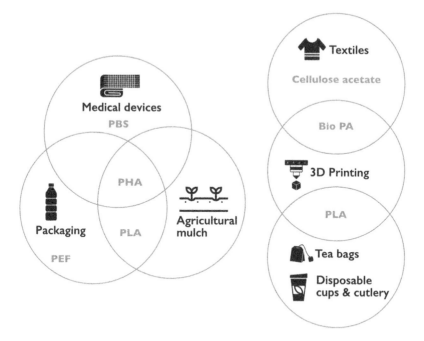

Figure 8.1 Classification of common biomaterials by application.

Some of these bioplastics are industrially compostable, and some of them are proven to be recyclable or are in recycling trials. Early proponents of bioplastics focused on their biodegradability and nontoxic properties compared to fossil-fuel plastics, but as circular economy proponents have advocated for reuse and longevity, more focus has been placed on durability and recyclability. We now share more information about specific bioplastics.

Polylactic acid

PLA is the most widely produced and widely used bioplastic. It is a thermoplastic polymer derived from renewable, organic sources such as corn starch or sugarcane. PLA is industrially compostable and is used in food-grade flexible packaging films and increasingly in rigid packaging and disposable cutlery. PLA is also used to coat the inside of paper drink cups and soup containers. It is nontoxic, in contrast with many fossil-fuel plastics.

While PLA coatings can withstand hot tea or coffee, PLA has a lower heat deflection temperature (HDT) than other plastics. HDT is the temperature at which a plastic bends a specific amount under load. It measures how much the plastic softens as temperature increases. PLA's low HDT makes pure PLA unsuitable for use in most building construction applications or for garment textiles.

The low HDT makes PLA an excellent material for 3D printing, as it doesn't need a heated bed. For more on 3D printing, see Chapter 11.

Polyhydroxyalkanoate

PHAs are linear polyesters produced in nature by bacterial fermentation of sugar or lipids. These plastics are biodegradable and can be either thermoplastic or elastomeric materials. Thermoplastic materials have linear polymer chains that are held together by weak intermolecular forces. These forces can be broken by heat, which allows the material to be melted and reshaped. Elastomeric materials, on the other hand, have polymer chains that are cross-linked together by strong covalent bonds. These bonds cannot be broken by heat, so elastomeric materials cannot be melted and reshaped.

Owing to the diversity in PHA structural properties, they can be used in both packaging and medical applications. Examples include biocompatible implants, bone replacements, blood vessel replacements, and scaffolding material in tissue. But manufacturing industries now see PHA principally as a replacement for fossil-fuel based packaging plastics.

Polyethylene furanoate

Polyethylene furanoate (PEF) is a recyclable polymer produced from plant sugars. It is used to package alcoholic beverages, fruit juices, milk, soft drinks, iced tea, and water. It is considered by many in the bioplastics industry the polyester of the future and a completely bio-based alternative to petroleum-based PET. Two major businesses in the Nordics are planning to build major facilities if the demand is certain.

PEF exhibits an intrinsically higher gas barrier for oxygen, carbon dioxide, and water vapor than PET and can therefore be considered an interesting option for packaging applications such as bottles, films, and food trays.

Some major consumer brands are convinced that PEF should replace PET because of its superior barrier and thermal properties. However, with so much existing consumer confusion around plastics, this seems unlikely to happen based purely on technical reasons.

An LCA study published in 2020 found that replacing purified terephthalic acid (PTA) in the production of PET with bio-based furandicarboxylic acid (FDCA) for the production of PEF could significantly reduce greenhouse gas emissions.[3] The study found that the use of bio-based FDCA could reduce greenhouse gas emissions by up to 70 percent compared to the use of fossil-based PTA. FDCA can be derived from many kinds of biomass such as fruit waste or forestry waste.

Polybutylene succinate

Polybutylene succinate (PBS) is a thermoplastic biodegradable aliphatic polyester.

In the early 1990s, after being forgotten for more than 40 years, PBS received a renewed interest due to the increasing demand for biodegradable and bio-based polymers. It is more brittle and less versatile than polyethylene and polypropylene, but biopolymer scientists are working to improve those qualities, driven by customer demand for broader range of bio-based materials.

PBS can be used either as a matrix polymer or in combination with other biopolymers such as PLA. Possible applications include food packaging, mulch film, plant pots, hygiene products, fishing nets, and fishing lines.

Bio-based polyamides

Polyamides (PAs), also known as nylons, play an important role in the manufacture of high-quality structural components. They strong and resist damage from abrasives and solvents. They are useful for items that require both strength and flexibility, including fishing line, electrical connectors, gears, guitar picks and strings, and medical implants. Polyamides are common in textiles like athletic and outdoor clothing and carpets.

Bio-based PAs are a class of polyamides that are derived from renewable resources such as natural fats and oils. The majority of these bioamides are based on sebacic acid with the exception of PA 11 (also called Nylon 11 or Polyundecanolactam), which is based on undecylenic acid, a fatty acid derived from castor oil.

Cellulose acetate

One of the most widely used bioplastics is not a novelty at all, having been mass-produced through most of the twentieth century up to today. What is commonly known as cellulose acetate is usually cellulose diacetate, made by treating cellulose with acetic acid. It consists of two acetyl functional groups on each unit of D-anhydroglucopyranose of the cellulose molecule.

Cellulose acetate has a wide range of end uses including textiles, X-ray films, cigarette filters, artificial heart valves, lacquers, coatings, adhesives, sealants, and membranes for dialysis machines.

Petroleum-derived compostables

There are a number of compostable plastics derived from petroleum, which may seem counterintuitive to those using or studying bioplastics for the first time. But there are many countries with zero recycling infrastructure, where compostables are seen as one of the solutions, even if the feedstock is fossil fuels.

There are dozens of fossil fuel-based plastics (fossil plastics) that have been designed to be biodegradable both for packaging and for textiles. These plastics are made from modified petroleum molecules that are easier for microorganisms to break down. They may also contain additives that help to speed up the biodegradation process.

The biodegradability of fossil plastics depends on a number of factors, including the type of plastic, the additives used, and the environmental conditions. In general, fossil plastics will biodegrade more quickly in warm, moist environments with a high concentration of microorganisms, as will bio-based biodegradable materials.

The principal petroleum-derived compostable in widespread use is Polybutylene Adipate Terephthalate (PBAT). PBAT is a biodegradable copolymer, where biodegradability comes from its chemical make-up, as opposed to non-degradable polymers such as polyethylene. PBAT-based products are used in many applications such as packaging, mulch film, and cutlery.

Polycaprolactone (PCL) is a widely used biodegradable polyester derived from the chemical synthesis of crude oil. PCL is an FDA-approved material that is used in the human body as a drug delivery device, suture, or adhesion barrier.

Starch-based biopolymers

Starches, polymers that occur naturally in plants, can be a source for bioplastics. Starch is made up of two types of molecules: amylose and amylopectin. Amylose is a linear molecule, while amylopectin is a branched molecule. The properties of starch-based biopolymers depend on the ratio of amylose to amylopectin in the starch.

Starch-based biopolymers are biodegradable and non-toxic. They are also relatively inexpensive to produce. However, starch-based biopolymers also have some disadvantages. They are not as strong as petroleum-based plastics and can be more susceptible to moisture damage.

Some of the most common starch-based biopolymers include:

Thermoplastic starch (TPS): TPS is a starch that has been modified to make it able to be melted and molded into different shapes. TPS is used in a variety of applications, including packaging, disposable utensils, and food service products.

Starch blends: Starch blends are made by mixing starch with other polymers, such as PLA or PCL. This can improve the strength and toughness of the starch, while still maintaining its biodegradability. Starch blends are used in a variety of applications, including packaging, textiles, and compostable cups.

Starch composites: Starch composites are made by mixing starch with fillers, such as cellulose fibers or wood pulp. This can improve the strength and stiffness of the starch, while still maintaining its biodegradability. Starch composites are used in a variety of applications, including packaging, automotive parts, and building materials.

Starch-based biopolymers still need to be developed further to improve their strength and moisture resistance. If those hurdles can be overcome, they have the potential to play a major role in reducing our reliance on petroleum-based plastics.

For a view on the future of biomaterials, we spoke to entrepreneur Jen Keane, She mentions AIMPLAS, an organization we feature at the end of this chapter.

Interview

Jen Keane, Co-founder | CEO at Modern Synthesis

Please describe what Modern Synthesis does and the materials you produce.
We're a London-based biomaterial company and we're crafting the next generation of materials with biology, specifically microbes. We're creating a new, circular textile manufacturing process that utilizes microbes that feed from waste feedstocks, such as agricultural waste to produce nanocellulose—nature's strongest, finest form of cellulose. Combining biology, material science, engineering, and design, we form these nanofibers into a novel class of non-woven textiles that are aimed at displacing things like animal leather, synthetic leathers, and other synthetic textiles. We want to not only help industries like fashion and automotive reduce their dependence on petrochemicals and plastics to lower emissions but also help bring down plastic pollution.

What are the ambitions of Modern Synthesis for the next five to ten years?
In the long run, our aim is to deliver an entirely new breed of biomaterials that can fulfill the performance standards that we have today, while also unlocking performance potential that we haven't even imagined yet. We want to build this new class of biomaterials that enables us to design, create, and live better in harmony with the planet.

In the short term, over the next five years, our focus is on how we take this concept, which was first materialized in the shoe that I grew as part of my Masters' research, and scale the process to a point where it evolves for maximal impact. For start-ups like us, it's a challenge building out these new supply chains and working with partners to integrate these materials into existing products and existing supply chains so that we can accelerate the transition to this new circular bioeconomy that we're building.

How does your product fit into the circular economy?
We're aiming to close the loop on both ends of the material lifecycle. One way we do this is utilizing biomass better. One of the reasons we are so excited about this bacterium is that it's a very efficient bug. It transforms all sorts of energy or sugars into quite a lot of material with less inputs. If you think about the energy required for producing traditional materials, like growing a cow for leather, our microbial processes require way less energy. First, we are more efficient in where we source our inputs and where we grow our materials. On the other end, at the end of the product's life, it's cellulosic and therefore naturally biodegradable.

There have been a lot of important efforts within cellulosic recycling over the last few years because cellulose is the most abundant polymer on the planet. It is already built into nature's regeneration cycles, so nature can adapt and reuse it. Also, it's a polymer that we've shown can be chemically and mechanically recycled fairly easily. These systems are already being built out within fiber recycling, enabling us to tap into and join forces with recyclers to create a fully circular material that can feed back into not only our own production but potentially other streams as well.

What are the environmental benefits of your product?
A major benefit is the potential to displace plastics and, therefore, reduce plastic pollution and microplastic shedding. One of the hero qualities of the nanocellulose fiber is that it's a very strong fiber that binds to itself really well. Because of that innate quality and natural strength, we can get around the need for some synthetic binders, which has been a big challenge in biomaterials. It can also remove the need for harmful chemical processes, like tanning.

The other big win in the long run is its positive impact on land use. If we're looking at legacy natural fibers like cotton and hemp, which are better from a pollution standpoint, they're not necessarily the environmentally friendly option in terms of land and water use. What we are able to achieve with our materials is to radically reduce the footprint of manufacturing into a more compact process. Using waste feedstocks as the material input frees up land that we could be using for farming, or other purposes like rewilding [letting land return to its natural state], which is game-changing in terms of reducing emissions overall. Rewilding and improving biodiversity is actually a huge contributor to carbon reduction. Our material process allows those lands to be used for that purpose rather than for the production of materials.

Do you envisage a time when fossil fuel materials are outlawed?
This is certainly my hope. Honestly, I think that we're unfortunately still a while off. However, I do think that we're already starting to see a huge shift in mindset and intent from both brands and consumers, particularly in the last couple of years. There's going to be increasing incentive for all product categories to move away from that, and we're excited to be here to help them along on that transformation.

What else can you achieve as you scale up?
I think it is important to start thinking holistically about material design. Not just from the level of displacing polymers but thinking about how a combination of different natural polymers (or in our case nanocellulose) and other things create these new material systems as opposed to just thinking about it on a single mono-material level.

Look at recycling today, it's an absolute mess. I think we need to urgently improve our cellulosic recycling systems, so that we capture a lot more of this biomass to return to the loop. And in case it doesn't end up there, we need to mitigate the harmful effects of its disposal as much as possible with considered design from the start.

Collaborations between manufacturers and research institutes can advance the adoption of new materials. AIMPLAS, the Plastics Technology Centre, is a research center in Spain that works with companies on a variety of projects. One involves making a PHA film from used restaurant coffee grounds to be used in flexible packaging applications.

This example is part of a broader program that seeks to promote the importance of urban biowaste as a resource and create new value chains to expand to an industrial scale. The project has also reprocessed waste from fish, meat, and cooking oil into new bio-based products, including bioethanol, biosolvents, food additives, condiments, and insect protein.

Compostability versus recyclability

Compostability is one factor that has spurred brands and businesses to embrace bioplastics. Growing evidence of uncontrolled plastic pollution in oceans and on land encouraged bioplastics producers to expand their offerings. They pointed to the fact that bioplastics (under the right industrial conditions) degrade into simple compounds, including carbon dioxide (CO_2) or methane (CH_4) and water.

The EN 13432 Industrial Compostability Standard must be met in order to claim that a plastic product is compostable in the European marketplace. In summary, it requires multiple tests and sets pass/fail criteria, including disintegration (physical and visual breakdown) of the finished item within 12 weeks, biodegradation (conversion of organic carbon into CO_2) of polymeric ingredients within 180 days, no plant toxicity, and limited presence of heavy metals.

It is important to clarify that many packaging materials that are suitable for industrial compost facilities will not degrade in home or community compost systems. Industrial facilities grind the waste into small pieces and expose it to the right combination of temperature and humidity so it will degrade within the required timeframe. Chapter 7 explained the requirements for materials to be industrially compostable.

Many so-called compostable items do not degrade as quickly as expected, especially in less-than-ideal conditions. The EU Circular Economy Action Plan points out the lack of infrastructure for industrial composting. Because of increased awareness about these issues, there is a growing movement to test materials for home compostability and develop packaging that is home compostable.

Manufacturers are also looking to introduce fully recyclable biomaterials after decades of work on compostability. They are concerned about the potential for bioplastics to contaminate well-established recycling streams, such as that for PET. From the viewpoint of circularity, a material that is no longer available for reprocessing or reuse at end of life is wasteful and adds unnecessarily to the emissions of those businesses that use it in their supply chain. So after a decade of growth, there are several factors that restrict the growth of compostables.

This has encouraged biopolymer scientists to pivot toward materials that can be recycled or can be used in products for multiple reuse.

Trends in composite materials

The term "composite" means that the material is made from two or more different materials fused together. Composite materials are generally stronger for their weight than any of the individual components, and hence are attractive options for lightweighting products. Composites aren't new, but there is a new emphasis on the sustainability advantages and drawbacks of these materials. I (Julia) attended the Society for the Advancement of Material and Process Engineering (SAMPE) Conference in 2023 and learned about what is happening in the composites industry.

There is tremendous interest in recycling of composites. The student poster session featured the following topics:

- Demonstration of successful recycling of a polymer used in aircraft interiors,
- Synthesis of bio-based thermoset materials,
- A process for upcycling polypropylene that increases the strength of the material,
- Methods to recycle plastic filaments used in 3D printing,
- Additives that improve properties of mixtures of recycled polypropylene and polyethylene.

I asked one of the students whether anyone had asked them to focus on recycling or sustainability. No, that's just what drew their attention.

From toy boats to real ones

When you think of balsa wood, what comes to mind? Perhaps you might recall kits from your childhood to make toy boats or planes from balsa wood. Balsa is a soft, light wood that is easy to machine.

Sandwich composites made from balsa wood cores and fiberglass face sheets were first used in aircraft in the 1940s. The desire to reduce the use of polymer foam cores has spurred renewed interest in balsa. Synthetic cores require between 5 and 25 times the energy to produce compared to balsa cores, with a similar advantage in carbon footprint. Research, however, suggests that the natural variations in the mechanical properties of balsa wood can make it a risky choice for high-performance applications like aerospace.[4] And although balsa wood is biodegradable and compostable, the resins that fill it are generally not.

Several companies have commercialized balsa-based composites that are finding their way into sailing yachts and vehicle floorboards. According to SAMPE exhibitor 3A Composites Core Materials, the yachts use "sustainable and recyclable raw materials like volcanic fibers, biologically safe epoxy mix," and balsa cores.

Bio-based resins

The bioplastics discussed earlier in this chapter are thermoplastics. Composites designed to withstand heat are instead filled with epoxies, thermosetting resins historically sourced from fossil fuels. (For more on thermoplastic versus thermosetting plastics, see Chapter 7.)

Bio-based sources of thermosetting resins include plant oils and rosin acids from pine trees.

Entropy Resins, one of the exhibitors at the SAMPE conference, makes epoxy resins. The resins are designed for use in fiberglass and carbon fiber composites. The company sources its materials from industrial and agricultural waste. A life cycle analysis showed that this product is less detrimental to the environment than a conventional petrochemical-based epoxy.

Most of the health hazards associated with skin contact or inhalation of uncured epoxy resins and hardeners, however, still apply. Just because it is bio-based doesn't mean it's safe. Also, it's interesting to note that the products contain just 30 percent bio-based content, which is enough to earn recognition from the U.S. Department of Agriculture (USDA) as "Certified Biobased Products."

Interview

Chelo Escrig and Elisa Cones, AIMPLAS

How do you see the possibility of biopolymers replacing conventional plastics?
Chelo: From my perspective, the main problem lies in our tendency to generalize everything. It is not feasible to replace all plastic materials. While biopolymers can be good choices for certain applications, they cannot (and should not) replace all polymers. They represent one more alternative on the market. Biopolymers have limitations in terms of transparency, mechanical properties, thermal resistance, and chemical resistance. It is not easy to replace commodity plastics or technical plastic materials in many applications. Thus, biopolymers have their limitations.

Biopolymers are a good alternative for products such as bags, mulch films, single-use packaging, etc. However, they still require proper end-of-life management and cannot be discarded under uncontrolled conditions.

Elisa: We strongly emphasize that each material has an ideal application. For example, a coffee capsule or an onion mesh bag can be composted at the end of its life, but there are cases where the material should instead be recycled.

At AIMPLAS, as part of our mission toward raising awareness in society, we keep insisting that the idea is not that you end up throwing it away or that the end of life of any plastic should be in the environment. Rather it is very important to make the user aware of each product, so that in the end, they make good use of each material. It is true that the administration is helping more in so far as there is a collection circuit for compostable material, but if it is recyclable, then the citizen or the user also has part of the responsibility to get it to the recycling container.

How do bioplastics fit into the recycling system?
Chelo: There are polyethylenes, polypropylenes, and other thermoplastics derived from renewable sources that are not biodegradable or compostable. They can still be recycled just like fossil-based polymers.

If we consider compostable or biodegradable biopolymers, their end-of-life management is not designed for post-consumer recyclability, but they are being recycled within the production process.

As an example, let's consider a company that manufactures biodegradable bags. If any non-conformities are found during quality control, these bags can be crushed and reintegrated into the production process without any issues. To achieve post-consumer recycling of these bags, we would need a separate collection management system from the current one, which is not easy to envision at the moment.

The proper solution in all aspects would be social education. From an R&D standpoint, the development of new materials and products with proper design and end-of-life management is crucial. Where does this material come from? What I am going to manufacture with it? When this product's useful life ends, what should I do with it? If this is considered from the beginning, it will be easier to transfer the knowledge to the rest of the society, so there is proper engagement in the end-of-life management to close the loop.

Elisa: Let's not forget how much it costs to manufacture each product. Because many times, and here we are going to talk about greenwashing, sure it may be manufactured with cardboard or paper, but have you calculated how much water was needed? If it's made of glass, how much energy do you need to spend in transporting and recycling? All these points need to be considered. More and more, the carbon footprint also points to being the other major problem.

Chelo: Each material has its own market niche, and there are packaging options where it is worth using glass, while others are better suited for aluminum, such as cans. Some others require plastics, and others biodegradable plastics. The problem lies in generalizing and stating that certain materials are better than others. This depends entirely on the application and the end-of-life management.

For example, if cardboard is used for certain food contact applications, it would not be suitable unless coated with a polymer. In consequence, doing this hampers the recyclability of the product and would not be environmentally suitable.

Therefore, it is important to objectively evaluate and eliminate prejudices when introducing something new to the market. It is important to ask ourselves: What is this for? What application will it have? What are its requirements? What is its lifespan? How will its end-of-life be managed? And based on that, select the best option.

I don't want to end the interview without talking about what my colleagues are doing with polymer synthesis. They are developing new biopolymers using agricultural waste, sugars from agri-food waste, or starches. This way, they are eliminating a waste stream that currently ends up in landfills, causing significant environmental pollution.

For example, PHA, PLA, and low molecular weight biopolymers, etc., for use in coatings are being obtained. All of this is an immeasurable source of raw material that is being wasted and could be used.

The ideal plastic

The ideal plastic material of the future would solve all the problems with conventional plastics. It would be strong, durable, formable, and possess all the desirable properties of the best-performing plastic materials in common use today. It would be easily recyclable, enabling it to be recycled many times while maintaining the properties of the virgin material. This hypothetical ideal plastic would be made from renewable resources and produced in a manner that would not negatively impact the growth of food crops.

The ideal plastic would be bio-benign, causing no harm to the oceans or sea creatures if accidentally released into waterways. Creating a bio-benign plastic that degrades in marine environments is especially challenging. Such a material must disintegrate rapidly into small fragments, less than 2 mm in size. The small size reduces the risk of entanglement or strangulation of marine animals, but that feature alone is not sufficient. These plastic materials would have to be nontoxic, containing no additives that would endanger marine life in case of ingestion.

Methods of producing the ideal plastic would need to consider multiple potential issues, including energy use, water use, human health risks, and the effect on lakes and oceans. Not only should the end product be nontoxic and bio-benign, no step in its production should pose a health risk and emissions should be kept as low as possible.

This hypothetical ideal plastic material remains elusive and may never come to fruition, but biopolymer scientists are getting closer. Biomimicry is one promising path.

The Biomimicry Institute, a leading organization in the field of biomimicry, is helping to create a more sustainable future by encouraging scientists to design solutions that are inspired by nature. One of its principal activities to incentivize scientists working on nature-inspired solutions is the Ray of Hope Prize, a competition that awards $100,000 to the most promising biomimetic startup.

Notable winners include:

- GreenPod Labs (2022) for developing a biomimetic air purifier that uses plant-based materials to remove pollutants from the air.
- Spintex Engineering (2021) for developing a biomimetic process for spinning silk at room temperature without harsh chemicals.
- NexLoop (2017) for developing a biomimetic material that can store energy more efficiently than batteries.

Notes

1 Freinkel, Susan. 2011. *Plastic: A Toxic Love Story*. New York: Houghton Mifflin Harcourt, 18–19.

2 Facts and Statistics—IfBB—Institute for bioplastics and biocomposites. Biopolymers facts and statistics. (2015). Ifbb-Hannover.de. https://www.ifbb-hannover.de/en/facts-and-statistics.html

3 nova-Institut GmbH. "New Bio-based Polymer PEF Shows Low CO2 Footprint—Peer-reviewed LCA Study with In-Depth Assessment of Industrial PEF Production and Its Use as Raw Material for Bottles." Petnology.com. September 5, 2022. https://www.petnology.com/online/news-detail/new-bio-based-polymer-pef-shows-low-co2-footprint-peer-reviewed-lca-study-with-in-depth-assessment-of-industrial-pef-production-and-its-use-as-raw-material-for-bottles.

4 Galos, Joel, Raj Das, Michael P. Sutcliffe, and Adrian P. Mouritz. "Review of Balsa Core Sandwich Composite Structures," *Materials & Design* 221 (September 2022): 111013. https://doi.org/10.1016/j.matdes.2022.111013.

Part III

Rethinking the Product Life Cycle

9 Reduce, Reuse, Recycle

People's perception is if it has the recycle symbol on it, it can be recycled. That's a big misconception.

—Smokey Peck, Pro Recycling Group

You can't take plastic and recycle it back safely into new food-grade plastic.
—Jan Dell, the Last Beach Cleanup

Recycling in context

How can our society use less material? The "reduce, reuse, recycle" mantra lays out a path. The order is critical. We cannot recycle our way out of the excessive consumption problem.

The options in Figure 9.1 represent possible strategies, all of which we delve into in this chapter.

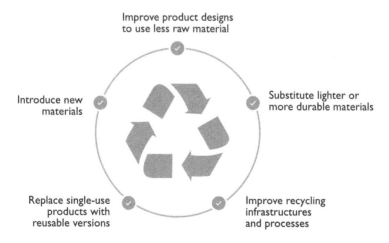

Figure 9.1 Possible strategies to reduce materials use.

DOI: 10.4324/9781003409267-12

Reduce

The first step, and perhaps the hardest, is to reduce consumption. It is hard because it requires wealthy individuals, companies, and countries to cut back. Those of us who have benefited from capitalism (which includes both your authors) are often reluctant to make do with less. Less stuff, less profit, less spending.

There are various ways to reduce our need for more raw materials. One is to produce smaller quantities of products. When companies prioritize quality over quantity, each product might cost more, but it also lasts longer.

Improve product design to use less raw material
Consider the evolution of beverage cans. Aluminum cans for beer and soft drinks were first introduced in 1959, but it took a few decades to completely replace steel. During this time, manufacturers replaced virgin aluminum with recycled aluminum and redesigned the can to use less material. Early versions required 85 grams of aluminum per can.[1] By reducing the thickness of the can body and shrinking the lid, engineers were able to create a perfectly functional can with less than 13 grams of aluminum.

Substitute lighter or more durable materials
Replacing steel with aluminum or switching from metal or glass to plastic reduces weight. This approach requires caution to avoid creating more waste or using more energy. Lightweighting isn't equally helpful for all applications. Sometimes a more durable material is a better choice even if it isn't the lightest. A thorough analysis needs to consider the resources required to produce the raw materials, make the product, ship the product, and dispose of it at the end of its life cycle.

Make products last longer
The less often a customer replaces a product, the greater the effective value of the raw materials used to make it. Designing for sustainability encompasses product durability, including awareness about which parts or components are most likely to fail first. If those can be replaced, the product lifetime will increase. This approach, unfortunately, can be a hard sell to companies used to building cheap products that need frequent replacement to boost sales.

Introduce new materials
Scientists are continually working to develop new materials and chemicals that can provide a safer or less wasteful substitute for those in use today. Chapter 8 presented many examples.

Reuse

The second step is to reuse as much as possible. Scrap materials, broken products, and items that customers no longer want can all find a second life. *We advocate replacing single-use products with reusable versions.* This is especially true for packaging. Reusable packaging harkens back to a time before inexpensive disposable packaging became readily available. Reversing habits in the other direction will not be easy, but it is possible and is already happening. We hinted at progress in reusable packaging adoption in the earlier chapters.

It is important to design products and packaging with reuse in mind. Reuse extends beyond packaging. One example is stainless steel safety razors instead of disposable plastic ones. Designers of all sorts of products can think up creative ways to reuse packaging, parts, and materials either in-house or by collaborating with other companies that can use the items.

Recycle

Recycling is the last step to consider, but it is one that attracts a lot of attention. This chapter explains why recycling is valuable, dives into the recycling process, and dispels common myths about recycling. Possible actions include improving recycling infrastructure and increasing recycled content.

Recycling rates improve when collection is easier and more convenient for residents and business owners. Advances in recycling technology increase the variety of materials that can be economically recycled, and policies such as container deposits encourage consumers to return cans and bottles to stores.

When manufacturers use more recycled content in their products, that provides a market for the recycled materials and makes collection more economically worthwhile. There is a caveat: prioritizing recycled content can give producers an excuse to keep creating more virgin raw materials that can then be recycled to meet the demand for recycled content.

Not all recycling processes are equally effective, nor are all materials equally recyclable. This chapter delves into the challenges of recycling the materials covered in the previous four chapters.

Reasons to recycle

The motivations for recycling seem obvious: reduce carbon footprint, trash, and pollution.

Emissions

Recycling reduces the carbon footprint of manufacturing by reducing the carbon emissions associated with producing raw materials. Products made from recycled materials take less energy to produce than those made from virgin materials extracted from the earth. As Figure 9.2 shows, the percentage of energy saved varies by material. The values in the figure are medians, as there is variability for each material class depending on production processes.

Trash

Recycling can result in less trash cluttering up our streets and waterways. Deposit systems in which consumers get cash back by returning cans or bottles encourage people to return these items rather than discard them, hence reducing trash.

Plastic	25
Glass	30
Paper	52.5
Steel	60
Aluminum	95

Figure 9.2 Percentage of energy saved by replacing virgin materials with recycled.

Depositing packaging into recycling bins often diverts these materials from landfills (but not always—keep reading to learn more). Strategically placed recycling bins may increase recycling rates.

Pollution

Recycling ideally reduces pollution in two ways. It extends the lifespan of landfills. Increased recycling of products should lead to reduced raw materials production, eliminating the toxic byproducts of producing those materials. That doesn't happen to as great an extent as people assume because materials sent for recycling are not always properly recycled.

The recycling process

Many people don't know what happens when they toss items into a recycling container, nor do they necessarily understand which materials are recyclable. This section will clear up some of that confusion.

What is recyclable?

Waste haulers collect some combination of paper, metal, glass, and plastics through residential and commercial municipal recycling programs. Many of these programs offer convenient regular curbside or on-site pickup. Figuring out exactly which items in each category belong in a recycling bin is not straightforward.

People are often surprised by what is and isn't recyclable. For example, most store receipts made from thermal paper aren't recyclable. The paper is coated with bisphenol A (BPA) or bisphenol S (BPS), the same toxic additives that caused health alerts for reusable plastic bottles.

Certain items, such as plain paper and aluminum cans, are universally recyclable. Others cannot be commercially recycled at all. Many materials and products, however, fall into a gray area. Regulations vary from place to place depending on existing technology and practices. Something that is recyclable in one city may not be recyclable in an adjoining city in the same metropolitan region.

Single-stream or dual-stream

The reason for the variability in recycling rules lies in differences between processes, equipment, and budgets at various recycling facilities, also known as material recovery facilities (MRFs). This variation starts at the collection step.

Collection at the curbside or in commercial dumpsters can be either single-stream, in which people dump all their recyclables into one bin, or multi-stream, in which some degree of sorting takes place during collection. Typical dual-stream processes differentiate between paper and all other recyclables.

Decades ago, homeowners in many U.S. cities were given three plastic recycling bins. In this triple-stream process, one bin was for paper, one for plastic, and one for metal. Local hardware stores sold carts on wheels that held all three bins, making it easier to get all that recycled material to the curbside. The bins were open, so haulers could see inside and tell whether residents had sorted their items properly.

At some point in the early 2000s, cities all over the US transitioned to a single large cart for all recyclables, a huge garbage can on wheels. It made recycling easier.

Now most U.S. cities offer single-stream recycling, but there are holdouts. In 2021, I (Julia) gave a virtual presentation about recycling and composting to an audience in Shrewsbury, Massachusetts, where residents can recycle paper one week and everything else the next week. Participants reported that the system was working well.

The single-stream approach promotes increased recycling rates, which is one reason many cities have migrated to this type of collection. It also is more efficient for collection trucks to have one compartment for recyclables. With multiple compartments, trucks need to empty their loads once one fills up.

However, easier recycling comes at the expense of a less efficient process once the materials reach a recycling facility. More varied contents on the trucks that transport recyclables to recycling facilities for sorting and processing translates to a greater number of machines required to separate out the various materials. It takes energy to run these machines, reducing the energy savings of producing products from recycled materials rather than virgin materials. It also takes time, both to run the machines and to hand sort to remove items that don't belong in the recycling stream. All this reduces the value of the recyclables.

Contamination is also greater in facilities that use single-stream collection. Reducing contamination to desirable levels, 10 percent or less, requires an investment in more staff to hand sort materials and a willingness to run conveyor belts at a slower speed.[2] This makes the process more effective, but also more expensive.

Once materials arrive at a MRF for single-stream or dual-stream recycling, they go through the following basic steps:

1. Trucks dump materials into a holding area.
2. Materials move onto feeders and conveyor belts.
3. Staff hand sort to remove large items that will jam equipment. These items typically go to a different facility.
4. Materials are separated into categories: paper, cardboard, plastic, ferrous metals (iron and steel), aluminum, etc. A variety of equipment automates the sorting process.
5. A baler machine compacts each separate stream of materials into bales for further processing, usually at a separate facility.

In *Material Value*, recycling industry executive Smokey Peck told a story about a meeting at the Utah state capitol regarding curbside recycling. One of the representatives stood up and said he was not going to force his constituents to participate in such a program. Smokey explained how recycling would help some of those people financially. They would avoid the extra fee they were being charged for having two garbage cans. He further explained that cities are motivated to charge residents less for a recycling can than for a trash can because by reducing the amount of garbage, it prolongs the life of a landfill and saves money in the long term. In the end, the state representative relented.

We spoke to Smokey again to get his perspective on recent changes in the recycling industry.

Interview

Smokey Peck, Pro Recycling Group

You've been in waste management for a long time. What attracted you to the waste management and recycling industry in the first place?
I actually grew up in the business. My dad had a company that did recycling on the side. When I went to work for Waste Management, I just could see recycling taking off. I used to tease all the operations guys at Waste Management that one day recycling was gonna have as many trucks as the trash side. When you look at municipalities, they now do. It's not quite 50/50, but it's close.

You're primarily working in commercial recycling. How have you seen things evolve in the last few years?
In Salt Lake City, they have an ordinance where they require all businesses to recycle up to 60 percent of their waste stream, in some shape or form. I don't know how they monitor that, but it's helped us on the other end of selling a baler to a company, because it gets them closer to that goal.

A lot of manufacturing here has a lot of scrap plastics, whether it be containers, or scrap bottles, or byproducts of their whole process. So we grind a lot of plastics. Those are industrial plastics, not the curbside type. We have some residential customers in Wyoming, where they have really good programs and drop-off sites. We manage all their paper and plastics and some of their metals. But their landfill rates are up around $100 a ton.[3] It helps them incentivize recycling versus landfilling. Here in Utah, it's still around $38 a ton.

But a lot of the businesses that have been moving to Utah are European based. So it's been a little bit easier to help them, even though recycling is more costly than going to the landfill. They have some corporate mandates that say zero waste to the landfill.

There are various ways to achieve zero waste to landfill. Do you have strategies to help your customers?

We have our on-site services, a program called Bridge to Zero. We place our employees on site and help them segregate, so the customers can focus on their core business. A lot of places will have their janitorial company just haul it from point A to point B, but it's never segregated, it's dirty, so we end up charging them on the other end.

Our job is to help them see that we're showing them some value, and help educate the plant employees to segregate. If you put it in this container, it's going to be clean, you're going to receive some revenue. If you put trash in there, then it's going to cost you.

We had a mattress company that had us in there to test it out. A new manager came in and said, no, I don't want to do it. We saw their latest trash bill, and it's tripled since we left. So which way do you want to go? Do you want to be zero waste? Or do you want to be 50 percent waste?

I see this with all kinds of sustainability measures. People are worried about costs, but they're not looking at the long term. Do you say, here's the five-year story if you bring in our people, versus if you keep landfilling the way you're doing right now?

We try to let them know that you can use this as a selling point when you're selling your product that you're zero waste to landfill. But I think it's just dollars and cents, depending on the manager at the site. We've got a couple of sites that trust our input and they understand that there's a cost associated with it. It costs them less by having us help them segregate and use the right equipment. Having the right equipment cuts labor, which is going to save them money, even though they've got some upfront out-of-pocket cost. But long term, it's going to help them on their bottom line. This mattress company, we've been telling them they've needed this larger baler for probably six, seven years. And they finally got it approved because it made sense, it's gonna reduce their labor. You have corporate mentalities that are either positive or negative toward these programs.

What is your view on how the pandemic has changed and affected recycling practices?

The pandemic hasn't affected us negatively because it's produced more waste, more boxes.

The inflation that's coming down is reducing a lot of that because nobody's buying anything. They're not buying like they were, anyway. Except for food and the necessities. I just had lunch with one of our trucking companies here. They had to invoice a dollar store distribution center here in Utah $500,000 for trailer rental, because they had no room for all the products they had bought, because nobody was buying.

It's interesting how the dynamics change. Amazon built a new distribution center here, just north of Salt Lake. They fast-tracked it, and it's been sitting empty ever since. I guess they saw what was coming down and they had built enough of them here in Utah that they didn't need it.

In fact, my wife bought something from Amazon, and I'm sure you've seen a lot of this, where they'll ship a box inside of a bigger box so you've got all this packaging. It blows me away. A lot of companies try to put out that they're doing the green thing. I understand it's hard, especially for a company like Amazon, you've got all these different products that you're trying to ship with your logo. And it'd be impossible to have a box size for everything. It's just comical all the packaging waste that happens, even though it's good for us.

I don't think you're going to go out of business because people stop recycling. What about from the point of view of a manufacturer that's sending out products and dealing with packaging and waste? Do you have advice or best practices for collecting and processing their recyclable packaging and other materials?
Investigate how recyclable it is. Just because it has a recycle symbol on it doesn't mean every location can manage it right and recycle it correctly. There are some manufacturers of plastics that had to put a disclaimer. People's perception is if it has the recycle symbol on it can be recycled. That's a big misconception, which is not true. It'd be great, but it's not reality.

Do you think there's a role that city and local governments can play?
They're just disseminating the information as best as they can. But like you said earlier, the plastics manufacturers push that symbol out there. Each material is different. Just because they have the same symbol doesn't mean they can be mixed. Mixed paper, you can have really any kind of paper. Plastics, it's harder because the manufacturing process is way different than paper.

What creative ideas have you seen for manufacturers or retailers to reduce their packaging waste?
So there's a box manufacturer called Packsize. They make a machine so you can make the size of box you need on demand. And so you're not buying pallets and pallets of boxes that you may or may not ever use again. A lot of companies here have bought these machines. So when they're shipping a particular product, they can make the exact size of box they need and the exact quantity and not waste.

I wish Amazon could do that. But again, that's kind of difficult because they've got so many different SKUs. It'd be impossible, I think, but who knows? Or why couldn't they just use the box that a product comes in and just put a label on it?

And maybe they can tell us, we do it that way, because... But to me, it just makes no financial sense. Why box up a box? Why not just slap a different label on it? You reduce your cost, and you can become more efficient because you had labor to put that box inside a box.

Here's an example of too much packaging. This is an antacid. There's three little bottles in here. I opened all three bottles, and I dumped them into one bottle. And it created a half full bottle out of these three. If you think about it, trucking wise, you've got these three bottles and a whole case, and now you've just used up all this room on a truck, which costs money. Why not just market that you're gonna get the same amount in a third of the cost? It just blows my mind.

Is there anything that you wish I'd asked that you want to talk about?
I guess just to get the message out that recycling is a good thing. We had a billboard here in Salt Lake that said recycling plastics is a sham, which was misinformed. No, not all plastics are going to the landfill. It's just that you've got to be careful. Hopefully people can understand that not all plastics are recyclable. It all depends on the type of packaging.

Recycling various types of packaging materials

Recycling rates range from nearly zero for plastics in the developing world to 80 percent or higher for metals in some U.S. cities, but low rates are the norm.[4] There are many factors at play, from the economics and technology of recycling to the difficulty in changing human behavior. Figure 9.3 shares published recycling rates for common packaging materials.

The following sections outline the processes and challenges associated with recycling common packaging materials.

Paper recycling

Regulations, like the European Union's target for 90 percent of all paper and cardboard to be recycled, are fueling demand for increased collection and recycling of

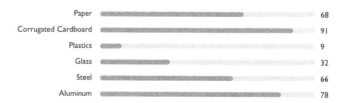

Figure 9.3 Published global recycling rates for different packaging materials, percentage of material recycled.

paper and cardboard. The recycling process for paper is similar to the latter elements of the pulp making process as described in Chapter 5.

Recycling process

Paper is taken to a recycling plant where it is separated into different types and grades.

The separated paper is then washed with soapy water to remove inks, plastic film, staples, and glue. The paper is put into a large holder where it is mixed with water to create a slurry. By adjusting the slurry composition, different paper products can be created, such as cardboard, newsprints, or office paper.

The slurry is spread into large thin sheets using rollers, left to dry, and then rolled up. At this point, it's ready to be made into new products.

Carbon benefit

Manufacturing one metric ton of 100 percent recycled paper emits 38 percent less CO_2 than paper produced from virgin pulp. The emissions saved is the equivalent to driving from Paris to Moscow in the average European car.

Recycled paper has a lower carbon footprint than virgin paper because of reductions in energy, water, and land use.

It takes at least 35 percent less energy to produce recycled paper than virgin paper. This is because recycled paper does not require as much energy to harvest, transport, and process the raw materials.

Recycled paper production uses about 47 percent less water than virgin paper production. This is because recycled paper does not require the same amount of water to pulp the fibers.

Recycling paper helps to conserve land resources. In addition to saving space in landfills, the more paper we recycle, the fewer trees need to be cut down to make paper.

Despite the advantages of paper recycling, there are limitations. Recycling shortens the fibers, and after a few cycles, the poor quality of the recycled product makes it not worth producing.

Glass recycling

Glass is recyclable, reusable, and refillable. It can be recycled endlessly without losing any of its quality or purity. There are caveats, however. As noted in Chapter 6, because of differences in melting point, glass containers of different colors must be recycled separately.

Packaging glass is one of the most recycled products in the world. Recycling rates for glass are on a level with metals and paper in most countries and several times those of plastics. The global recycling rate is estimated at between 21 and

46 percent. Regionally, the rate is 74 percent in Europe[5] and 31.3 percent in the US.[6] In the US, the situation varies state by state. States with container deposit laws have an average glass container recycling rate of just over 63 percent, while non-deposit states only reach about 24 percent.[7] Globally, higher recycling rates seem possible, as in some regions, there is an excess availability of waste glass or recovery rates are low.

The benefit of using recycled glass, also called cullet, to produce new jars and bottles is that melting and shaping uses around 30 percent less energy than for virgin materials. Increasing the amount of cullet that goes into production conserves natural resources and energy. Every 10 percent increase in cullet results in a 3 percent reduction in energy consumption.[8]

Metal recycling

Like glass, metals can be recycled over and over while maintaining the same quality and properties. The relatively high cost of virgin materials, in terms of both monetary value and energy cost, provides an incentive to recycle various metals.

The most cost-efficient way to recycle metals is to do so where metal products are manufactured. Such recycling is a common practice. As the plant tour with Nucor Steel (Chapter 4) demonstrated, steelmaking plants in the US incorporate recycling throughout their facilities.

Manufacturers that make metal products often remelt scraps or faulty parts and send the material back into production. Machine shops can either sweep metal shavings into a trash bin or save them. If the floor is kept clean and areas for machining different types of metal are separated, it is easy to create a high-purity supply of metal shavings that can become new blocks or bars of metal.

Recycling products made from metal is cost-effective as well, especially for steel and aluminum. Metal is easy to separate from the rest of the recycling stream. Magnets pull out ferrous metals like iron and steel, since they are magnetic.

An eddy current separator, a machine with a magnetic rotor that spins at high speed, is used to filter out other metals after the steel is out of the way. The rotor creates an electric current in anything conductive that passes over the rotor. This current produces a magnetic field in the opposite direction from the field of the rotor. Much like two magnets with opposite poles repel each other, the force pushes the metal bits away from the rotor and into a bin. Materials that aren't electrically conductive, such as plastic, simply pass over the rotor and drop, via gravity, into a separate bin.

Aluminum is the one of the most heavily recycled materials in the world. More products are made from recycled aluminum than from virgin aluminum. As the data on the energy cost of materials show (see Figure 1.1), the reason is obvious.

I (Julia) have fond memories of my first foray into aluminum recycling. When I was in elementary school in San Diego, California, seamless aluminum cans were newly recyclable. The going rate for empty aluminum cans was 17 cents per pound. Each can contained a lot more aluminum that today's cans, so it look less time to collect a pound of cans than it would now.

My elementary school started an annual contest, rewarding the classroom that brought in the largest number of cans. Although Mr. Riley's fifth/sixth-grade class was small, his class won every year because of Mr. Riley's unique strategy. He took us on a field trip to the beach to collect cans. All 18 of us loaded into his VW Bus—this was in the days before seatbelt laws—and, armed with giant trash bags, gathered hundreds of discarded cans to bring back to school.

We had to examine the cans carefully and only take the aluminum ones. The steel cans had a telltale seam on the side, so we could distinguish them fairly easily. Although several soft drink companies started producing aluminum cans in the 1960s, it wasn't until 1996 that steel cans were entirely phased out in the US. Changing an industry takes time.

Much of the aluminum that has been extracted since the beginning of the twentieth century is still in use today, thanks to the ability of aluminum to be recycled over and over. There are limits, however, especially for specialty alloys that contain a variety of other elements. Refining these alloys for recycling requires separating out the various metals, which consumes time and energy and makes recycling less efficient. Those specialty alloys are often found in automotive and aerospace applications, where the combination of strength and light weight is critical.

The challenge of recycling plastics

Plastic's durability, which makes it desirable during use, is why disposal of plastic products is creating a growing environmental disaster. Plastic materials last centuries, far longer than the useful lifespan of a plastic product.

Many plastics are recyclable, but recycling rates are low. Of the estimated 9.2 billion tons of plastic produced since the early twentieth century, 7 billion tons have become waste.[9] Most discarded plastic in the US ends up in landfills. The US buries 73,890 tons of plastic in landfills every day.[10] Much of the remaining plastic produced worldwide is still in use, or sitting unused in homes, garages, and commercial buildings. A relatively small amount—less than 10 percent—has been recycled.

Some countries do not have an infrastructure set up for recycling. But even where recycling is well established, several factors conspire to limit the recycling of plastics.

Economics. Compared to glass and metal, plastics are relatively low-value materials. It is often less expensive to throw them away and buy new raw materials than to recycle. Compared to aluminum, the difference in energy required to produce plastic from virgin materials instead of recycled materials is much smaller, lowering the incentive to recycle.

Diversity of plastics. Plastics form a diverse waste stream made up of many dissimilar materials that cannot easily be separated, especially if plastics are embedded in products made from layers of different organic and inorganic materials.

Confusing messaging. Regulations regarding what types of plastics and plastic objects can and cannot be recycled vary tremendously from place to place. Citizens are confused about what to toss in a recycling bin and are more likely to discard plastic into the trash than attempt to recycle it.

Toxicity. The recycling process concentrates toxic compounds, including those from printing ink and contaminants that get into the mixed recycling bins. When everything gets ground up and melted, new toxic compounds can form. Jan Dell, founder of The Last Beach Cleanup, shared her perspective. We feature a more extensive interview with her in Chapter 14.

Plastic is fundamentally not recyclable. It has no material value. This big study just came out about microplastics. Six to 13 percent of PET bottles when they're recycled become microplastics that end up in our waterways and onto our farmland. The other issue is toxicity, and this is the true deal killer. You put a plastic bottle in your curbside bin, it has now slept with the malathion bottle and it is now toxic. The best that can happen is maybe to get down-cycled into a rug or something.

The only reason seven PET recyclers operate in California is because they're taxpayer funded. It is it is a money losing business. They're not making clean, safe plastic, and they're generating tons of microplastics along the way.

Plastic packaging makes up the largest component of the plastics waste stream. These are products designed for single use, as opposed to durable goods made out of plastic designed to last many years. One way to reduce waste is by reducing the use of excess packaging of consumer items.

We can reduce the amount of packaging being used without compromising the ability to safely ship products around the world. Recent years have seen a resurgence of interest in reducing disposable packaging. Even companies that make disposable packaging are getting on board to reduce the amount of plastic used per unit of product packaged. This is incremental progress, though. A better option is to replace disposable plastic packaging with another material or no packaging at all.

Still, packaging is not going away. Disposable packaging protects products during shipping while minimizing excess weight. In the health care field, disposable packaging guarantees sterility of medical instruments. The risk of contamination and infection is a greater concern than the packaging waste. Even in a hospital setting, however, it is possible to set up systems that encourage plastic recycling and to use metal instead of plastic for tools and equipment.

Numbered plastics

Plastic packaging containers are often labeled with a number from 1 to 7 that indicates the type of plastic (see Table 9.1). Number 7 covers everything other than the materials of types 1–6. Recycling programs often accept packaging labeled 1, 2, or 5. Some cities or counties further limit what they take by shape in addition to material to make it easier to sort and more likely that they can sell the resulting bales.

Even the best-designed recycling facilities manage a waste stream made up of at least a handful of different plastic materials. Because of confusion over what to toss into the recycling bin, plastic and nonplastic contaminants abound. Some contaminants are relatively easy to separate. Steps in which materials are sorted by density, for example, will quickly filter out materials that are much denser than plastics. But many plastic materials have very similar density, and unwanted plastics contaminate the recycling stream for recyclable plastics.

The presence of a single PVC bottle among a batch of 10,000 PET bottles being melted for recycling will ruin the melt. The acids in the PVC break down the PET. The result is a yellowish and brittle material, whose poor strength and unsightly appearance make it unsuitable for reuse. Because of these types of difficulties, as well as concerns about toxicity, consumer product companies are moving away from PVC. Unilever, for example, has removed PVC entirely from its packaging.

PET bottles are the most commonly recycled plastic packaging product in the US, with a recycling rate of around 27 percent.[11] According to the European Union's Plastics Europe, the recycling rate of PET plastic packaging in the EU27+3 (EU member states plus Iceland, Liechtenstein, and Norway) increased from 46 percent in 2020 to 51 percent in 2021.[12]

There are a number of factors that have contributed to this increase, principally more stringent recycling regulations in some countries, improved recycling infrastructure (up 21 percent between 2020 and 2022) and above all increased demand for recycled PET plastic from manufacturers.

High-density polyethylene (HDPE) can be recycled into a variety of products, including drainage pipes and plastic lumber as well as the same types of containers that are made from virgin HDPE.

Table 9.1 Types of plastic packaging

Number	Material	Examples
1	Polyethylene terephthalate (PET)	Water bottles, some clamshell containers
2	High-density polyethylene (HDPE)	Milk jugs, bottles of cleaning products
3	Polyvinyl chloride (PVC)	Plumbing
4	Low-density polyethylene (LDPE)	Grocery bags, reclosable baggies
5	Polypropylene	Yogurt tubs, takeout containers
6	Polystyrene	Foam cups, takeout containers
7	Other	Nylon, polycarbonate, compostable plastics

Low-density polyethylene (LDPE) is especially troubling. Plastic bags clog up the machinery at recycling facilities, and they have no end market for selling it. Despite being told not to discard plastic bags into recycling bins, lots of individuals and businesses in the US and Europe are doing just that, creating a headache for recyclers.

Polystyrene often appears in its expanded form. Expanded polystyrene (EPS) is used in egg cartons, meat trays, hot beverage cups, clamshell packaging for takeout foods, and packing "peanuts" that protect items being shipped.

EPS is often contaminated with food, which is part of the problem with recycling it. The other problem is that the material is very bulky for its weight. As a result, the collection and transportation costs are high compared to the value of the material being collected. Some cities have enacted bans on EPS. In response, restaurants have been replacing EPS with PET, polypropylene, or polylactic acid (PLA) materials. McDonald's got rid of its EPS clamshells for packaging burgers in 1990 and replaced them with cardboard ones. Unfortunately, their action did not result in a cascading trend in the fast-food industry.

Sorting technology: plastics recycling

Once the plastics are separated from paper and metal, various techniques exist to further sort plastics into specific materials, creating separate streams for PET, HDPE, polypropylene, and other plastics. Technology for sorting plastics to be recycled falls into one of three basic categories: optical sorting, image recognition, and markers.

In optical sorting, near-infrared spectroscopy remains the industry-standard method. Near-infrared spectroscopy analyzes the reflection from an illuminated piece of plastic to identify the type and grade of polymer, and state-of-the-art machines achieve nearly 100 percent accuracy. Each machine identifies one specific polymer to separate, though, so a recycling facility needs quite a few machines to sort all the materials they receive. This gets very expensive.

Image recognition involves automatically recognizing items by their shape or size. The problem here is that some containers arrive crushed or deformed, making it difficult for the machine to distinguish one from another. An ideal image recognition system might even be able to identify a brand by reading a logo, but this level of sophistication doesn't yet exist.

Brand identification would be helpful, though, especially if the system collected data on the number of different specific packages recycled and relayed that information back to the companies whose brands are being processed. Such a system could help support Extended Producer Responsibility requirements.

The next level of sorting technology relies on bar codes or invisible chemical markers that machines can read. Patents exist to cover chemical markings and detection systems, but no commercial products for the recycling industry currently use this technology. If such products were developed, they could replace the near-infrared machines that are used for optical sorting.

Toward higher-quality recycled plastics

Even with advances in sorting technology, sorting will probably never be 100 percent accurate. It's also hard to remove all contaminants even if materials are properly sorted. For effective plastics recycling that works, we need a process that creates higher-quality recycled plastics. As mentioned earlier, once MRFs sort incoming materials, they compact them into bales for further processing. The next step for plastics is either mechanical or chemical recycling.

Mechanical recycling breaks the plastic into tiny pieces but keeps the polymer itself intact. This technique is most efficient for closed-loop recycling, in which a material is recycled into the same type of object as that made from the virgin material. For example, used PET bottles would be recycled to make new PET bottles. Quality can be lost in this type of process through contamination. Contamination standards are strict. Batches of PET with more than 100 ppm (0.01 percent) of foreign particles aren't suitable for recycling into new bottles. Improved sorting and cleaning processes can help to reduce contamination.

In open-loop recycling, the material that is ground up is used in a lower-value application. A PET bottle, for example, turns into carpet fibers or plastic lumber. This allows bales of plastic with higher levels of contamination or made from mixed plastics to find new uses in long-lasting products. These materials cannot be economically recycled again, however. Once the plastic carpet or lumber is discarded, it goes to landfill.

Chemical recycling, also called advanced recycling, is another option. In this case, solvents break the polymers down into individual monomers (the small molecules from which the polymers were originally made), which can provide feedstock to make new materials. The recovered monomers are chemically identical to conventional monomers made from fossil fuel sources, so they produce polymers of similar quality.

Nylon 6 is an example of a thermoplastic material that can be recycled many times using chemical recycling. This was the first material to be economically recycled using a chemical recycling process, beginning back in the 1990s. Aquafil, a global company based in Italy, makes a polymer called Econyl that's composed of entirely recycled nylon 6. Around half of the incoming material is scrap from nylon production, and the other half is post-consumer waste. The post-consumer waste stream includes nylon fishing nets. Any nets brought in for recycling don't end up contributing to plastic trash in the oceans, providing an added benefit.

Clothing companies have jumped at the opportunity to use recycled nylon for everything from yoga pants to swimwear. Calling this clothing "sustainable" oversimplifies things, however. If boasting about recycled content allows manufacturers to sell more clothing, they aren't saving the planet. Also, there is no further market for clothing made from recycled nylon once it wears out. It is a single recycling loop with a dead end.

Companies are working on improving chemical recycling processes so that they can efficiently recycle a greater variety of plastic materials, including the most common thermoplastics used in disposable packaging. One problem with this process is that it can be hard to remove pigments and additives.

For decades, waste processors in the US and Europe shipped bales of recyclables to China for mechanical or chemical recycling. Without strict limits on contamination rate, these bales often contained 10–20 percent contaminants.

In 2017, the Chinese government announced that it was changing the game. China was no longer going to serve as the world's trash compactor and would refuse to accept highly contaminated bales of materials for recycling. The US-based recycling industry viewed this turn of events as both a challenge and an opportunity. Without the option of sending bales overseas and shutting their eyes to the bales' eventual fate, companies needed to improve their waste processing so more material could be recycled locally.

Chemical recycling looked like a plausible solution to the problem of poor-quality recycled plastics. Multiple startups, often supported by giants in the plastics industry, proposed new technologies. But the promise of high-quality recycled plastics that rival the performance of virgin plastics has not come to pass. Plastic recycling remains difficult, which is why reducing the amount of disposable plastic needs to be a higher priority.

The role of product design

Improving product design is another way to create a better recycling infrastructure. Although it has not historically been the norm, products can be designed with reuse and recycling in mind. For example, manufacturers can avoid the use of inks or glues that impede recycling. Design changes are not easy since they require cooperation between many different companies throughout the supply chain. Limited availability of replacement materials that are compatible with commercial recycling often stands in the way.

Product labeling also plays an important role in designing for recycling. Product designers unintentionally create recycling roadblocks when they only consider how a product will look on the store shelf. Full-color plastic sleeves on bottles attract attention, but they create sorting errors in systems that use optical recognition to sort different types of plastics. Paper labels pose another problem. They disintegrate when the plastic bottles are being washed, and they also leave behind an adhesive residue that can contaminate the recycling stream. Possible solutions include replacing paper labels with plastic ones for plastic bottles, getting rid of plastic sleeves, or using water-soluble glues that can be washed off easily.

Product design can help with the sorting process at recycling facilities, in addition to its role in creating products that are recyclable. Compostable plastics like PLA should not be part of the recycling stream, but when consumers see a cup or fork that looks like plastic, their instinct is often to toss it into a recycling bin. People want to do the right thing, but if labeling isn't clear, they can end up contaminating the recycling stream by mistake.

Manufacturers of compostable products are addressing this. Compostable flatware from World Centric has a cut-out in the handle in the shape of a leaf. This feature reminds consumers that this isn't an ordinary plastic utensil. The hole can tell a sorting device that the object doesn't belong in the plastic recycling. The machine then diverts it to a composting facility. This concept, while helpful in theory, will only work if recycling facilities are equipped with machines that can distinguish between flatware with and without holes.

Some compostable cups and containers made from PLA are marked with a green band that helps visually identify the product so that optical sorting systems can separate it from plastic recycling streams. This labeling isn't consistent, limiting its practical usefulness.

The compliance problem

Recycling initiatives face a challenge in convincing citizens to comply. When recycling and composting are inconvenient and confusing, people lack the incentive to do their part unless they have a personal conviction that overrides the challenge of complying.

A financial incentive to recycle always helps. Programs that involve container deposits are very effective in increasing recycling rates. In the state of Michigan, for example, stores collect ten cents for every container and return the fee when the consumer brings the container back. In 2016, the overall recycling rate in that state was 92 percent. Programs in the ten other states with deposit laws can't claim quite those results, but the states of California, Iowa, and Oregon all achieved relatively impressive recycling rates of more than 60 percent for plastic containers in 2017.

In the absence of financial incentives, the secret to getting consumers to recycle and compost regularly is to make the process easy and automatic. Labeling plays a role. Fast-food or quick-serve restaurants provide a perfect opportunity to serve food with compostable plates, cups, spoons, and forks. Some are doing this already, either because it ties into their corporate culture or because regulations are forcing their hand.

Taco Time in the Pacific Northwest uses nearly 100 percent compostable serving ware in its restaurants. The restaurants post clear signs indicating which items aren't compostable and provide a small bin in which to toss these. In Molly Moon's, a popular chain of Seattle-area ice cream shops, every food-service item in the stores, from bowls to napkins, is compostable. The stores provide one bin for everything, making compliance simple.

On the surface, you might think that requiring all service ware and to-go containers to be compostable and encouraging customers to deposit these items in provided bins is the best approach for sustainability. Unfortunately, it isn't that simple. As mentioned earlier, compostable packaging does not necessarily use fewer resources or have less environmental impact than other options. In addition to concerns about land and water use for producing PLA, some paper-based compostable containers are coated to minimize leakage, and these coatings often include toxic compounds. If a cardboard container is shiny on the inside, the compost bin isn't the right place to toss it unless it is clearly labeled as compostable.

Unless more stringent standards are put in place to guide the design of compostable food-service ware, it's hard to know how to proceed. Meanwhile, encouraging clearer signage should, in practice, limit cross-contamination of waste headed for recycling or composting.

In reality, compliance remains difficult. The Climate Pledge Arena in Seattle aims to be the most sustainable sports and music venue in the country. They have separate containers for trash, recycling, and compost, all clearly labeled. Announcements alert fans and concertgoers about what to toss where. Despite all this effort, a staff of four to six people works two eight-hour shifts after each event to sort everything before sending recyclables to a local transfer facility and organics for composting.

If an organization called Climate Pledge can't encourage people to toss the right stuff in the right place, how can a municipal curbside collection program expect to receive clean recycling and composting streams?

Geographical focus: United Arab Emirates

Opinions about recycling and recycling practices vary depending on geographical location. The United Arab Emirates (UAE) is one example where policies have affected the recycling industry.

There has been a dramatic change to recycling infrastructure in UAE since 2015, when the Emirate of Sharjah laid down a mandate regarding zero waste to landfill. There is no legal backing to the recycling efforts blossoming in the UAE, but over 200 companies are providing recycling services.

The providers initially had support only from brand-conscious multinational companies. Interest in recycling is now widespread across all businesses. There continue to be numerous discussions around pricing, as businesses think that the recyclers should pay to take the refuse, not the other way around.

This increased collection has, in turn, encouraged an influx of buyers interested in buying different materials. They buy via a trading platform where prices are dynamic, and buyers are able to purchase by the ton.

Most of the recyclables are cartons and boxes. There is plenty of availability in the market, and there's a strong demand for it. In 2023, PET has become a focus as an additional waste stream with initial demand exceeding hundreds of tons.

There is low demand for glass in the UAE, and a low sale price. Someone we spoke with feels that there needs to be a separate collection process for glass under a government-sponsored program to scale the collection and processing of packaging glass.

The Sharjah Waste-to-Energy Plant opened in 2022. It is the region's first commercial project of its kind. The plant powers 2,000 homes in the emirate by connecting them to the Sharjah Electricity. We say more about waste to energy in the next section.

Multiple ways to "recycle"

The umbrella of recycling incorporates several types of reuse: reusing materials from a discarded product to build new products, extending product lifespan, or creating energy from burning discarded materials.

Recycling of materials

The first type of reuse is the most common interpretation of recycling. Materials in discarded products are recycled by crushing and melting them (or washing and drying, in the case of paper) to create materials for use in other products. Much of the reuse falls into the category of downcycling, where the products made from recycled materials require a lower grade of material and have less economic value.

Recycling of products (reuse)

Using entire products or components more than once extends their lifespan. This benefit extends the life of a product by days, for a plastic grocery bag reused as a trash bag, or years, for a cell phone donated to an organization that provides free phones to victims of domestic violence.

The examples above involve the consumer's decision to reuse a product, but companies should consider product lifespan when designing products or buying the supplies they need to run their businesses. Such decisions do not always tilt toward choosing products with a longer lifespan, of course, since longer product lifespan isn't necessarily the least expensive option, or the one that creates the most income for the company.

The concept of Life Cycle Assessment—evaluating a product throughout its life cycle, from raw materials sourcing through production, use, and disposal—incorporates the value of increasing product lifespan. Life Cycle Assessments are critical to understanding the most efficient ways to reduce waste. The results of these assessments are sometimes counterintuitive, leading companies to make changes that they had not previously considered.

For example, consider crates used to transport fruits and vegetables. Plastic crates weigh 2 kg, compared to less than 1 kg for wooden or cardboard boxes. But the energy required to produce enough cardboard boxes to ship a million boxes of produce per year is more than twice that required when using wood or plastic boxes. Making cardboard requires more water and heat than making wood slats, but that isn't the main source of the difference. Cardboard crates don't last more than one or two shipments, whereas wood and plastic crates can be used dozens or even hundreds of times before they break.

Plastic crates are the most durable option because they are resistant to damage from moisture. If made from recycled plastic, the choice is by far the most environmentally friendly.

Recovering energy

As an alternative to recycling, recovered materials are sometimes burned to create energy. This type of reuse replaces other sources of energy such as fossil fuels.

Burning materials for energy is not the same as replacing landfills with incinerators. The path to zero waste to landfill cannot involve merely incinerating the waste. Incinerating mixed garbage releases toxic dust and creates ash. In addition to the environmental risks of incineration, incinerators that do not capture the energy from burning material do not recover the monetary value.

Waste-to-energy plants, as opposed to incinerators, create value by converting waste materials into useful energy. It is often more cost-effective to burn materials for energy than to separate streams of multiple recyclable materials for use in low-value applications.

If a recycling stream is contaminated with many different types of plastics, for example, it requires more energy to make a product from recycled plastic than to make one from new materials. In this case, burning the plastic, if done safely, makes more sense. Safely is the key here. The toxic fumes released from burning must be captured to avoid endangering the health of workers and the local community.

Environmental regulations in many countries govern the filtering of airborne toxicants and disposal of any hazardous waste, which adds cost. The common alternative used to be sending waste—either garbage or low-value mixed materials from recycling facilities—to countries without such regulations, where there is no requirement to capture the toxic dust.

China used to be among those countries, but with its new policies restricting imported garbage, waste handling companies face fewer options. Without an inexpensive way to dump excess plastic waste generated in North America and Europe, recycling facilities will need to adapt quickly to avoid being inundated with materials that they cannot sell locally or ship overseas. There will be a greater incentive to improve recycling in the country where the waste is generated or to send more material to waste-to-energy plants.

Recycling processes, infrastructure, and practices need to improve in order to achieve the EU's binding target to reduce landfill to a maximum of 10 percent of municipal waste by 2035. Incremental change in all these areas is happening, but that isn't enough.

What about composites?

Given the high amount of energy required to produce many composite materials, recycling them sounds like a good idea. Unfortunately, composite materials pose a unique challenge when it comes to recycling. Recycling requires separating the various materials from each other so that they can be reused. It is not as simple as grinding and melting a product made from a single type of metal or plastic.

One material that comes to mind is Trex, a composite material used to build decks. It supposedly provides the best of both worlds, being a wood-like material that doesn't rot. Trex doesn't require the regular maintenance that wood decks demand to withstand exposure to rain and variations in temperature through the seasons. What happens to Trex decks, however, when they are no longer needed?

The planks of wooden decks will decompose once the nails and screws are removed, especially once any stains or paints have worn away. Trex, however, must be eventually destined for landfills. Still, composite decks last 50 or 100 years, a factor that must be considered. For a wood deck to last for decades, it needs a fresh coat of stain or paint applied every year or two. A thorough analysis needs to include the production and disposal of the chemicals in these protective coatings.

Manufacturers in the composites industry are investing research funds into evaluating potential methods to recycle these materials. High-performance composites hold enough economic value to provide an incentive to reuse them. Successful separation of the various components, if possible, allows each component of a composite material to find new uses in a completely different application than that of the original material.

Carbon-fiber composite materials, commonly used in sporting goods and aircraft, contain carbon in the form of graphite fibers. These are woven into a mat to form a fabric, and epoxy is used to glue the fibers together. At this point, the composite fabric is called a "prepreg," meaning that it has been pre-impregnated with epoxy but is not ready for final use.

Prepreg carbon-fiber sheets are relatively soft and flexible. They can easily be cut into any desired shape and layered to form a structure. Once cured at high enough temperature to solidify the epoxy, the resulting structures are strong, tough, and lightweight. This combination of properties makes them especially desirable for building sporting goods and aircraft. Carbon-fiber composites are also of interest for automotive applications and building wind turbine blades.

There are two points during the life cycle of carbon-fiber composites when they get discarded. The first occurs during manufacturing, when cutting out pieces of prepreg sheets creates scrap waste. The second is at the end of life for objects made with carbon-fiber materials.

Carbon-fiber composite recycling methods do exist. Most methods use pyrolysis, in which cured material is heated to a sufficiently high temperature that it decomposes. The epoxy resin is burned off, and the carbon fiber remains. During pyrolysis, it is important to handle emissions appropriately so that no toxic fumes are released into the air. The companies doing this work understand that requirement.

The carbon fiber that remains after recycling cured composites is in the form of discontinuous threads, unlike the continuous woven threads in virgin composite material. The mechanical properties of sheets of material made from recycled carbon fibers are therefore compromised, which limits the applications for the recycled material. It can be reused, but the resulting product will not be as strong as a composite made with woven carbon fibers.

There are ways to effectively reuse recycled carbon fibers. 3-D printing (more about this in Chapter 11) poses one such possibility. Adding carbon-fiber reinforcement to thermoplastic filaments creates a stronger, tougher material for printing. This application doesn't require long, continuous threads of carbon fiber.

A resurgence of reusable packaging

Earlier in this chapter, we mentioned replacing single-use items with reusable versions as a good strategy for reducing waste. This is possible in practice, but it requires undoing decades of ingrained habits. Reusable packaging is no longer common in products sold directly to consumers, at least in urban regions of the developed world. Decades ago, people used to get their food more directly from the farm.

It now seems quaint thinking of a time when milk was delivered daily in glass bottles to the door, like Paul's childhood experience (see Chapter 6). But as of June 2023, there are an estimated 670,000 households in the UK that get milk delivered to their doorstep. This represents a 21 percent increase from the number of households that got milk delivered in 2019.

Some stores sell premium brands of milk in glass bottles. The store charges a deposit on the bottles, which customers get back when they return the bottles to the store. The milk manufacturer is responsible for cleaning and refilling the bottles.

Stores in communities with many environmentally oriented residents have tried other approaches, such as having customers refill reusable containers that they bring from home with bulk goods ranging from food to laundry detergent. Zero-waste grocery stores are becoming more common, but these do not always stand the test of time. Without enough customers, they cannot stay in business.

It's hard to know whether the desire to use less packaging will win out over the desire for the convenience of disposable packaging. It may take regulation to force the issue.

Tossing mountains of used packaging materials into recycling bins and assuming that they will magically be turned into valuable new products is naive. Still, infrastructure for recycling is moving in the right direction. New technologies for sorting and processing waste are coming.

How much difference will these changes make? It's hard to say. Ingrained habits are hard to break. The hard truth is that businesses will not shift their practices unless it saves them money or allows them to break even while improving their reputations with customers. Very few individuals will change their practices unless doing so is easy and convenient. But if we continue to educate ourselves and those around us about effective recycling practices, progress will occur.

Notes

1 Can Manufacturers Institute | Washington, DC. Renewable Can. 2020. www.cancentral. com. Retrieved February 18, 2023, from https://www.cancentral.com/can-stats/ history-of-the-can/renewable-can-0.

2 Ullo, F. J. Single Stream Recycling Contamination. Florida Department of Environmental Protection, 2015, https://floridadep.gov/sites/default/files/Single-Stream-Recycling-Contam-Memo_21Dec15_0.pdf.

3 This US-based interviewee means a short ton (2000 lb).

4 Duong, T. "Recycling in the U.S. Is Failing, But These 7 Cities Are Doing Things Right," *EcoWatch*, April 21, 2021, https://www.ecowatch.com/best-cities-for-recycling-2652630134.html.

5 European Container Glass Federation (FEVE), 2022.

6 United States Environmental Protection Agency, 2021.

7 Glass Packaging Institute.

8 European Container Glass Federation (FEVE), 2022.

9 Geyer, R. 2020. "A Brief History of Plastics," in *Mare Plasticum—The Plastic Sea*, 31–47. https://doi.org/10.1007/978-3-030-38945-1_2.

10 US EPA, OLEM. "National Overview: Facts and Figures on Materials, Wastes and Recycling | US EPA," US EPA, October 2, 2017, https://www.epa.gov/facts-and-figures-about-materials-waste-and-recycling/national-overview-facts-and-figures-materials#Landfilling.

11 NAPCOR. 2020. 2020 PET Recycling Report [Review of 2020 PET Recycling Report]. National Association for PET Container Resources, https://napcor.com/reports-resources/.

12 Plastics Europe. 2021. "Plastics—the Facts 2021 an Analysis of European Plastics Production, Demand and Waste Data," https://plasticseurope.org/wp-content/uploads/2021/12/Plastics-the-Facts-2021-web-final.pdf.

10　Tackling the E-Waste Monster

A battery is a highly engineered product. When we call it dead in a car, it still has 80 percent of its ability to store energy.

　　　　　　　　　　　　　　　　—Dan Schwartz, University of Washington

It's ridiculous that we still extract metals that are abundantly available above ground.

　　　　　　　　　　　　　　　　—Joost de Kluijver, Closing the Loop

Mountains of cell phones

"Mom, how old were you when you got your first cell phone?"

I did a quick mental calculation. "Thirty-three."

My son seemed momentarily astounded, as though he had forgotten that cell phones have not been around forever. To someone born in the late 1990s, however, it may seem that way. Around 1.4 billion smartphones were sold worldwide in 2021.[1] There is something wrong with a world where more people own cell phones than have access to running water. Our communities need to work harder to provide more people with safe running water. The production and disposal of consumer electronics contribute to pollution in waterways, so the smartphone explosion and water access are connected.

Any effort to shift away from the disposable society will face tremendous resistance. Electronic products are designed with frequent replacement in mind. Marketing campaigns are designed to convince consumers that they must have the latest and greatest version.

Bernard London's 1932 book *Ending the Depression Through Planned Obsolescence* lamented peoples' insistence on using items until they were worn out rather than replacing them with newer versions. London spoke out in favor of planned obsolescence and wanted the government to mandate that consumer products like appliances come with expiration dates. Once items had expired, consumers would turn them in for a rebate on the sales tax they had paid when they bought the items.

London's vision didn't come to pass, but many industries adopted products that were "good enough" to function for a limited length of time. Products are no longer

DOI: 10.4324/9781003409267-13

built to last generations. They are built to last only long enough to give the manufacturer time to release a new version.

Planned obsolescence does drive innovation—one of the positive effects that manufacturers are touting—but also creates a great deal of waste. An obscenely high number of phones are discarded every year, not because they no longer work, but because people buy newer models to replace them. Cell phones contribute a significant portion of the growing electronic waste (e-waste) problem because of the vast number produced and market forces telling consumers that their phones need to be replaced every year or two. Billions of phones are discarded every year.

These discarded cell phones contain a wealth of materials that could potentially be reused. These materials include metals, semiconductors, glass, plastics, and ceramics. Cell phone manufacturing requires up to two dozen different metals. Some, such as aluminum and copper, are used in significant quantities in a single phone. Others are present as trace elements in alloys or as minute additions to the glass or plastic of the phone's screen and casing. Gold is the most valuable metal inside phones, and the most likely to be recovered when phones are recycled, but all metals in the phone have economic value.

An experiment in 2017 shredded an iPhone 6 to discover what it was made of. The phone contained 129 grams of metals, including more aluminum than any other metal, and only 0.014 grams of gold. Figure 10.1 gives more details.

Among the many materials in cell phones are small quantities of toxic metals such as lead, cadmium, and mercury. If we ship our e-waste to countries where environmental regulations aren't as stringent as they are in North America and Europe, we are subjecting workers to toxicants and also leaching those toxicants into their communities' water supplies.

The standard method for processing e-waste involves smelters, which are furnaces that burn up the circuit boards inside electronic devices and recover the

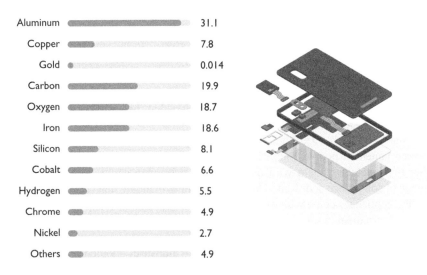

Aluminum	31.1
Copper	7.8
Gold	0.014
Carbon	19.9
Oxygen	18.7
Iron	18.6
Silicon	8.1
Cobalt	6.6
Hydrogen	5.5
Chrome	4.9
Nickel	2.7
Others	4.9

Figure 10.1 Weight of materials in an iPhone 6, grams.

precious metals. Smelting creates toxic particles and releases these highly carcinogenic particles into the air. At responsible recycling facilities, the workers wear respirators to protect themselves, unlike at unregulated places where workers wear no protective gear whatsoever. Still, tiny particles that cannot be captured are released into the air surrounding the processing plants.

Repairability and product lifespan

What should we do about the e-waste problem? Stemming the flow of e-waste is extremely difficult in the current consumer environment. The companies that produce electronics benefit from encouraging increased adoption worldwide, and their customers in regions with limited resources benefit as well from access to global information.

There is a movement toward making electronic devices last longer and become easier to repair. Repairability is key to extending the lifetime of electronic devices and reducing the mountains of e-waste. The mission of iFixit is to promote the repairability of electronics. The website includes repair guides for everything from phones to kitchen appliances. The company sells tools to help people repair their stuff at home. iFixit posts repairability ratings for smartphones, tablets, and laptops on a scale of 0 (unrepairable) to 10 (easy to repair).

In March 2022, an amendment to the EU's consumer rights directive was proposed which would oblige traders to provide consumers with more detailed information on products' durability and reparability.

For tech products like smartphones, consumers would have to be informed about software updates provided by the producer "in a clear and comprehensible manner"—either on the packaging or online.

A digital product passport will be introduced for a wider range of products, with the "A to G" rating set to become the norm in upcoming product-specific rules. This refers to energy efficiency, where A is the lowest and G is the highest energy consumption.

The UK announced more decisive action one year earlier in 2021: manufacturers were now legally obliged to make spare parts for products available to consumers for the first time—a new legal right for repairs—so that electrical appliances could be fixed easily.

The move was expected to extend the lifespan of products by up to ten years—preventing appliances from ending up on the scrap heap sooner than they should and reducing carbon emissions at the same time. The UK generates around 1.5 million metric tons of e-waste every year.

Replacing electronic devices less frequently is part of the solution, but that alone won't fix the e-waste problem. We, as a global society, need to increase collection rates and process our e-waste in a less toxic manner.

Worldwide e-waste regulations

It may surprise some people that in the US, there are no federal laws regarding e-waste. Regulation occurs at the state level. California was the first to enact such a law, back in 2003. By 2011, all the U.S. states that are shaded in Figure 10.2 had e-waste laws in place. No new laws have come since then.

Worldwide, 57 countries, covering every continent except for Antarctica, have national e-waste regulations. Figure 10.3 shows where these countries are located. The US is shaded in the figure even though half of the U.S. states have no e-waste regulations whatsoever.

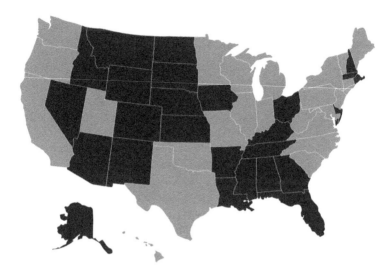

Figure 10.2 Map showing the 25 U.S. states (shaded in gray) with e-waste regulations as of 2023.

Figure 10.3 Map showing countries (shaded in gray) with e-waste regulations as of 2022–2023. The list includes Australia, 10 countries in Africa, 10 countries in Asia, 25 countries in Europe, 4 countries in the Middle East, 3 countries in North America, and 5 countries in South America.

"Responsible" e-waste processing

Unfortunately, laws do not guarantee that e-waste will be recycled properly. Electronics being sent to so-called responsible e-waste recycling companies are not always handled in a truly responsible manner.

Breaking news in September 2016 told the story of Total Reclaim, a Washington state "responsible" recycler that was illegally dumping e-waste overseas rather than processing it locally, as its certification as a green recycler required. The state fined Total Reclaim, Washington's largest recycler, almost half a million dollars. Oregon, a state in which Total Reclaim also operated, followed suit in 2017 by imposing a fine and banning the company from collecting e-waste.

This story is just another example of consumers being duped, thinking we were doing the right thing by bringing our old electronics to an e-waste facility. Since the story aired, Total Reclaim claims to have taken multiple steps to improve its recycling processes and try to regain the public's trust as an "environmentally responsible recycler."

Smokey Peck, the president of Pro Recycling Group who we interviewed in the previous chapter, told the story of Stone Castle, an e-waste recycler that was facing fines from the EPA and potential jail time for its executives. The owner had fled the area, leaving behind mountains of e-waste at several facilities that "magically" kept catching fire.

Putting our heads in the sand is the easy way out. We drop our e-waste off at what looks like a legitimate recycling location and assume it will be dealt with properly. In the best case, the e-waste will be processed locally at facilities where the workers wear suitable protection from lead, cadmium, and the toxic dust and fumes created by grinding and incinerating the circuit boards from old cell phones and computers.

In the worst case, e-waste will be shipped to facilities where workers are subjected to dangerous conditions every day. In countries without strict labor laws, children work dismantling computers and tossing circuit boards into smelters.

Until electronics companies demand better e-waste recycling or regulations require it, truly responsible e-waste handling remains elusive. The best way to ensure that a so-called responsible e-waste recycler is doing what it says is to physically go into a plant and audit the recycling company's practices.

Companies that collect used electronic devices from customers can choose an e-waste recycling facility that calls itself responsible and hope for the best or look deeper to find the facility most likely to process the e-waste safely. They have other options as well: the landfill or incineration.

Sending e-waste to a landfill is, surprisingly, a more responsible choice than shipping it to unregulated recyclers overseas. Laura Turbini at Georgia Tech researched landfill management and concluded that no measurable amount of lead was leaching into soils from electronics discarded into landfills. From the perspective of protecting people from lead poisoning, dumping e-waste into landfills is a much better option than sending it to unregulated disassembly and incineration facilities overseas. While Turbini's research focused on lead, presumably the results for cadmium and mercury would be similar.

What about the batteries?

Recovering valuable metals like gold is standard practice in e-waste processing. Metals that command lower prices per ounce haven't historically been recovered because the cost of extracting them from e-waste is too high given their resale value.

Meanwhile, some relatively low-cost metals are facing potential shortages as demand escalates. Shortages will drive up metal prices and motivate greater recovery and recycling efforts. Lithium, a crucial component of batteries, is one of these metals.

Lithium-ion batteries are removed before consumer electronics are processed at e-waste recycling facilities and recycled independently. Battery recycling comes with a set of unique challenges. At present, recycling lithium does not make sense economically. Lithium is much less valuable than the cobalt or nickel inside lithium-ion batteries, and it is present in such small quantities that the cost of recycled lithium is much greater than that of virgin lithium. Today's lithium battery recycling efforts are directed at keeping batteries out of landfills and recovering the more valuable cobalt and copper inside them to resell.

In the future, however, soaring lithium prices could make recycling the metal worthwhile. Lithium prices tripled from 2001 to 2011, reaching $6,000 per metric ton. By 2017, lithium carbonate was selling for $20,000 per metric ton in China. After a peak in late 2022 to $83,000, 2023 prices are closer to 2017 values. Increasing demand for lithium-ion batteries for both consumer electronics and electric vehicles, combined with limited resources concentrated in South America, is expected to keep prices relatively high.

Lithium-ion battery recycling is being done, just not with the recovery of lithium as the primary goal. Umicore has been providing lithium-ion battery recycling services since 2006 and claims to have a unique recycling process. The company also recycles lithium polymer and nickel metal hydride batteries.

Umicore's "pyrometallurgical treatment" is a fancy way to say that it incinerates the batteries in a high-temperature furnace. But there is more to it than that. The company claims to use the energy present in the batteries to power the process, reducing total energy consumption. Following incineration, Umicore refines the alloy using a "hydrometallurgical process" that involves water.

Umicore's recycling process reclaims cathode materials—cobalt, nickel, and copper—to be used to produce new batteries. The company has a large facility, with the capacity to handle 7,000 metric tons of materials per year. That's the equivalent of 250 million phone batteries or 35,000 electric vehicle batteries.

Li-Cycle Corporation, a startup in Ontario, Canada, is tackling lithium recycling directly. It claims to have created a process to safely and profitably recycle lithium from lithium-ion batteries. Its process also recovers nickel, cobalt, and copper. Li-Cycle boasts low energy consumption, low carbon emissions, and zero waste to landfill, which sounds impressive compared to existing industry-leading battery recycling processes.

In September 2023, Li-Cycle opened its latest battery recycling facility in Saxony-Anhalt, Germany. The facility can process up to 20,000 metric tons of lithium-ion battery material per year. Like Li-Cycle's four facilities in North America, it can handle everything from cell phone batteries to full EV battery packs with no need for disassembly in advance.

Reuse before recycling

Better battery recycling is encouraging. As with the materials we discussed in previous chapters, though, recycling should not be the top priority. Reuse needs to happen first. We spoke with Dan Schwartz, director of the University of Washington Clean Energy Institute (CEI), a research facility that spans multiple departments at the university. The CEI focuses on three areas—solar energy, energy storage, and grid integration—chosen because of their importance to society and their ability to translate research into commercial products.

CEI is an excellent example of university-industry collaboration, something that has become more prevalent in recent decades. It started as a research institute solely for faculty and students, but Dan saw an opportunity to connect with commercial clean energy efforts in the surrounding region. CEI includes the Washington Clean Energy Testbeds, a warehouse-like space occupying an old sheet metal manufacturing plant near the university. The facility provides the missing link: manufacturing at a scale that is compatible with commercial business. Materials and processes that work well in the lab, at a small scale, will likely face different challenges when they are transferred to real-world scenarios.

The cross-pollination makes sense, especially for engineering departments. There is certainly a place for research for research's sake, work that expands human knowledge about the world around us. However, applied research, aimed at uncovering the link between scientific discovery and the ability to use that knowledge to create products that benefit society, is at the heart of graduate research programs in engineering.

Interview

Dan Schwartz, UW Clean Energy Institute

What do you want people to know about batteries?
The issue about batteries that most of the general public asks me about is recycling and reuse. There's a lot of popular press, especially about cobalt, but also lithium as a resource. It's the area of greatest public interest right now, as people hear the proclamations about ground transportation, and what they are seeing in some of the popular or the mainstream press.

Now, suddenly, everybody is worried that we're going to run out of the materials needed to make batteries. Tell me your perspective and what got you into researching batteries.
One of the key spaces for opportunity is information about batteries. A battery is an archaeological object after it's been used. It's got history embedded into its

chemistry and materials. Every battery is unique. Even batteries in the same vehicle, depending upon where they are relative to the cooling systems, can experience slightly different things. Subtle differences add up so that even a cell in the same vehicle that has been driven on the same course has slightly different archeology embedded into it.

Something my group has been looking at is better ways to diagnose that archaeology. We don't want to unearth it by destroying the batteries because then they lose their value. Within the reduce, reuse, and recycle world, reduce is best, reuse is second best, and so on. Recycling is, in my opinion, a distant third best for a battery. A battery is a highly engineered product. When we call it dead in a car, it still has 80 percent of its ability to store energy. But it's like the gas tank has shrunk by 20 percent. And we don't like that because our range goes from 320 to 250 miles.

Or from 100 to 70. I own a 2016 Leaf, and its battery capacity has dropped significantly. It's still great for driving around town, but it's not as good as it used to be. What can we do about that?

There are companies like Recurrent. I'm on the Scientific Advisory Board and have a small financial interest. I invested in that because they're adding value to the resale of electric vehicles with their program to assess the value of the battery.

The value of a used EV is the value of the battery. After the Bolts had all their batteries replaced, it didn't matter what the odometer said. It mattered how long the new battery had been running.

The Bolt story was a total recall nightmare. Bolt EVs had a manufacturing defect in their battery packs that increased the risk of a fire during charging. People were told to charge outside, not in their garage. Then there were some software upgrades to make it so you could park it in your garage and charge.

Once those batteries were replaced, the cars were like new. It doesn't matter how many miles were on the odometer. If you were part of the recall and replacement, you had a new car. The mechanical systems don't really wear out that much. It was really about the battery pack.

The highest value reuse of batteries is something that my group is really interested in. How do we run non-destructive diagnostics that can really elevate our understanding of that archeology? How do we do archaeology with radar instead of picks and shovels?

Getting more information from a sealed battery is a non-trivial thing. And it's worth a lot to decide what is the best future use of a battery. Even with new batteries, they still grade them by different qualities. Every manufacturing process has a bell curve. Subtle differences get amplified as a battery is used. To resell a battery and have confidence in it, instead of sending it to be ground up and recycled or thrown to the landfill requires validated methods of diagnosing its current state of health, and then deciding its best future path.

I believe there will be a battery economy. Ideally, we'll get more standardization, more standard testing, more validation. Because the more that we integrate the information about batteries, the more we can reuse them in their highest value. We want to keep them out of landfills and out of recycling. Eventually, they will need to be recycled, and there's work going on in that. But I think in most EV applications, which is the driver for the volume of batteries, reuse is the way to go.

The volume of EVs will increase. In California, there's a mandate coming that all the cars will have to be electric. What do you think about that?
GM said their cars will be only electric in 2035. Volkswagen will only be electric. The billions of dollars that are being invested in that are real. I think the pendulum, from not paying attention to what goes into a battery to paying attention, has swung a little too far.There's a lot of focus on cobalt. It's a bad actor, it's super expensive. It's dug by artisanal miners in the Democratic Republic of Congo. Artisan mining means people with no safety regulations, children working in the mines, no environmental standards. And that is a major global source, but we've already eliminated 90 percent of that from batteries.

Are you saying that the newer generation of batteries won't have cobalt at all?
Yes. Batteries are being replaced now. That will reduce cobalt by 90 percent. The trend over the last ten years has been to say, we know cobalt is a problem. Whether it was motivated by human rights or the environment, it's a problem in the supply chain. Cobalt is being eliminated because as the demand rises, if you don't drop cobalt content, battery prices will do something other than what they've been doing, which is going down, 10–15 percent a year, on average. The price for a cell has been dropping, and the energy storage capacity, the energy density of those cells has been going up by 8 percent a year. You can't have a price drop like that when you've got unstable sourcing of materials and or no way to scale the manufacturing of those materials. And so it's getting eliminated.

One concern about EVs is longevity. There are old cars that have 200,000 miles on them, or even more. They've been going for decades, and they will continue to run. But if EVs are down to a terrible driving range in less than ten years, what's the plan? Is it so expensive to replace the battery that people will buy a new car?
In ten years, if costs continue to decline 10–15 percent annually, think how much cheaper that battery is to replace. The mechanical systems in EVs will last so much longer. Even the brakes last longer, because you're regenerating the energy rather than just rubbing things together to make heat. So the mechanical systems are so much better.

Those 300,000 miles of the Toyota, or whatever they tout? Consider all those tons of oil extracted from the earth to put fuel into it for all those miles and the damage from the emissions. A battery pack requires a one-time extraction of materials. It is not a balanced perspective to think that battery manufacturing extracts

X amount and to forget that an internal combustion vehicle continually extracts a fossil resource and throws every bit of it away into the air we all breathe.

To answer your question, the battery will be replaced by a much cheaper battery. And if you like the car, and you want to keep it, you'll replace the battery. That battery that you remove will get used in the stationary application somewhere. This is the battery economy I envision.

The electronics industry and mining

As the stories in Chapter 4 demonstrate, the mining industry has been changing for the better in recent years. Companies are prioritizing worker safety and developing ways to reduce environmental harm. Electronics companies are also reconsidering the source of the metals they use.

Apple made an audacious announcement in 2017, publicly stating a goal to eliminate mined rare earth elements from its iPhones. Stating such a goal, without a concrete plan in place to achieve it, was unheard of from the usually secretive Apple.

It is not clear at this time how Apple will manage to remove mined metals from its phones, especially given the relatively short timeline of product development. Apple has set up a system where consumers expect a new phone every couple of years. The technology to produce rare earth metals without mining is not ready to handle the huge volume of materials that a company like Apple requires.

Any solution that reduces the amount of mining required automatically addresses conflict minerals, so Apple's goal is laudable. Urban mining, which keeps electronics out of landfills and sends the items to e-waste recycling facilities, is going to be the route that enables such a shift. The trick is to improve the e-waste infrastructure and create economies of scale so that all the metals needed to make the next generation of electronics can be recovered at a reasonable cost.

Ideally, electronics manufacturers will become vocal advocates of the circular economy. They will migrate toward corporate policies that support best practices for choosing the materials that come into their factories, how they process these materials, and the eventual fate of the products they produce. They will encourage their customers to return electronic devices and consumables like ink cartridges for recycling.

Some prominent companies are taking action or making public statements that demonstrate their concern about toxic manufacturing or disposal of their products. Takeback programs are becoming more common. Multiple device manufacturers and retail stores offer credit toward a new purchase when customers turn in their old devices. Some old devices get refurbished and sold at a discount.

A shift toward different models of producing electronics will help reduce the need for mining. Fairphone, a niche player in the electronics industry, promotes the idea that cell phones should be modular, allowing customers to replace and upgrade individual components instead of discarding a phone for a new model. The phones are much more repairable than devices from more popular companies. iFixit, the company mentioned earlier in this chapter, rates several Fairphone models as 10 out of 10 on repairability.

As of 2023, Fairphone's modular cell phones are only available on a small scale in Europe, limiting the company's potential impact.

Modular cell phones can only become mainstream if suppliers offer a product that people want to buy. Some people, like Alexis Eyre whom you will meet in Chapter 13, love Fairphone. It meets their needs. At present, Fairphone has proponents, but not enough of them to make a real dent in the market. Reinhardt Smit (see interview in this chapter) is not a fan.

One idea is for companies like Fairphone to partner with major manufacturers such as Apple and Samsung. They can leverage streamlined software while promoting modular hardware and repairable devices. Niche players struggle to compete head-to-head with the giants, but maybe a collaboration could offer true choice to consumers.

Apple hasn't committed to any specific deadline regarding its goal of eliminating mined metals, but the statement itself says a lot. HP is another company making strides toward better e-waste management with its comprehensive inkjet cartridge recycling program.

The shift in attitude is happening because of both economic and social pressure. Reclaiming metals from electronics creates a new stream of materials that cost less than metals mined from the earth. In affluent countries, consumers are more likely to want to buy from companies that are trying to minimize the negative environmental impact of their products.

Improving e-waste collection rates

Joost de Kluijver is one of the entrepreneurs whose story appeared in *Material Value*. Joost believes that cell phones are vital for communication, entrepreneurship, and sometimes even for human rights. He notes that digital access supports several of the United Nations' Sustainable Development Goals, especially in emerging markets. But Joost became concerned—rightly so—about what was happening to cell phones at the end of life. In response, he founded Closing the Loop as an NGO in 2012, with the ambition of collecting scrap phones in emerging markets. He discovered instead that there was a financial opportunity related to old phones and reorganized the NGO into a social enterprise organization in 2014. Closing the Loop is based in Amsterdam, The Netherlands.

Closing the Loop participates in two primary endeavors:

1 Running a "One for One" waste compensation program. A tech brand sells a new phone and Closing the Loop links that new device to one scrap device. Joost's company collects and recycles that broken device on behalf of the tech brand. Closing the Loop's customers pay a fee for the service and can claim their new phones are now "waste neutral."
2 Collecting cell phones from countries in Africa and shipping them to the nearest responsible recycler (which for Africa, is in Europe). This work

focuses on countries where there are no convenient recycling facilities and phones typically end up in landfills.

The compensation program is attractive to companies wanting to deliver on the growing customer demand for greener tech in a pragmatic and engaging way while funding Closing the Loop's collection efforts. The concept is similar to carbon off-sets, where companies pay to balance their carbon dioxide emissions with projects that, for example, plant trees to sequester carbon dioxide. This service does not focus on the complex and elusive concept of carbon but instead on a very tangible and commonplace item—a (broken) phone.

Joost pointed out that steps that people are willing to take now, even if limited in scope, are more effective than more ambitious concepts that appear too complex or expensive or will require efforts that people aren't willing to make.

Closing the Loop relies on partners to support its vision. One of those is Voda-fone Germany, which promotes the concept that cell phones should never end up as waste and encourages its customers to repair and upgrade their phones rather than discard them after a year or two. Vodafone's partnership with Closing the Loop has made over one million devices "waste neutral."

We spoke with one of Joost's colleagues about the company's goals and the ongoing challenge of e-waste collection.

Interview

Reinhardt Smit, Closing the Loop

What got you interested in Closing the Loop and the type of work you do?
I'm the supply chain director at Closing the Loop. I do everything that's opera-tional within the company.

Why work for Closing the Loop? The fact that it deals with Africa is the honest answer. I'm from South Africa and grew up in Ghana. I've always done a lot of work in Africa. That's where my heart is. When this opportunity came, I realized I could use my cultural knowledge and my cultural experience, plus my project management skills and communication skills. So that kind of all came together in this job.

You told me that you are working on expanding operations to deal with different types of e-waste beyond phones. How is that going?
We're doing a pilot in Nigeria with computer monitors to prove that our model works for any sort of waste stream in the electronics industry.

We started with mobile phones for two reasons. First, simplicity in selling the concept. Everybody has a mobile phone, it's a topic we can talk about easily. Sec-ond, from the operational side, one mobile phone is very similar to another mobile phone. Whether it's Nokia, or Samsung, or Apple, whether it's ten years old, or five years old, or from last year, it's still quite comparable.

Computers or monitors or printers are less homogenous products. One laptop is not the same as another laptop because it has a much bigger housing or is made of plastic instead of aluminum. There are so many completely different printers. When you're buying by weight, it becomes more complicated. What it's worth when you recycle the product is also less clear. One kilogram of phones is not going to differ much from another kilogram of phones. That's not true with other kinds of electronics.

A mobile phone goes directly into a smelter so long as there's no battery in it. You don't need to do anything to it, you don't need to dismantle it or anything. For most other products, you do need to dismantle it. When we moved to monitor recycling in Nigeria, we needed an in-between step and that's the dismantling. The monitor needs to be taken apart. The glass goes to one place, mercury-containing fluorescent tubes in some of the old monitors have to be taken out, there's a circuit board inside, etc. You need a preprocessing step before it gets to the smelter. That was a learning experience for us. But that also means there's a new step in the process for the model of waste compensation. It was much more complicated than we expected but still successful. So it is looking good for the industry in that sense.

One of the issues with e-waste is making sure that it gets processed properly and you recover as much as you can from it without harming people. How do you deal with that challenge?

We try to keep people in the industry in the countries where we collect, like Ghana and Nigeria, to minimum standards. If they stick to those standards, it means they have to avoid the bad ways of recycling. So in terms of getting the maximum out of something, we don't really focus on that. We just make sure that what happens happens in a good way. So for example, if we're talking about the mobile phones, we make sure they don't dismantle them. You could get more out more per kilo out of it if you take off the covers. We tell them to leave the covers on, because by taking the covers off, you're creating hazards down the line. By keeping the covers on, we are recycling less per kilogram of waste, but that's because there's also more in there. Rules like keep the covers on or, bring us the batteries and we'll store them separately, or make sure that it ends up with recyclers that are certified recyclers that are incentivized to do things correctly, and not to do things as fast as possible. That's a way that you improve the industry as a whole.

When it comes to the companies that do the recycling, their business model is that they earn from what is in the materials. So the more they get out of the material, the more money. There's already an economic incentive for them to recycle as much as they can. Because doing anything less would not make business sense.

How do you ensure that the responsible recyclers are actually behaving responsibly?
All of our recyclers are in Europe for now, so certification means a lot. You can't get a license to build a facility that deals with high-temperature burning of waste

without sticking to some certain minimum standards in terms of emissions in Europe. We also make sure that the recyclers have other voluntary certifications that prove that they're going a little bit beyond the minimum. If not, then we help them get there. The recycler we're working with currently in Italy, they weren't originally registered with the Responsible Jewellery Council, for example. They are now. We ask them to get registered because there are extra checks. Where do your metals come from? Do you also source from non-recycled sources? In that way, we encourage our suppliers to improve.

What is your perspective on the state of the e-waste recycling industry?
My perspective will be based purely on Africa. Africa is really good at recycling stuff. They are very, very good at using things as long as they can. People have less, and so therefore, they make more of what they have. So in terms of the repair industry, the sharing industry, all of that, we don't need to help them. They're doing a good job. In fact, if I need something fixed, and I travel to Africa, I take my stuff with me that I need to fix because I can get it fixed quickly and cheaply.

The problem is that there's a lack of environmental awareness. That's where improvement is necessary. The easiest way to do things, the quickest way to do things, is not necessarily the most environmentally friendly one. It's more expensive to do things correctly and it's less expensive to do things "quick and dirty."

Because of commodity values, recycling doesn't pay for itself. If you recycle a mobile phone, you're going to spend more getting that mobile phone to the recycler than you'll get out of it, even in Europe. That means you need an additional source of income. The money needs to come from somewhere.

Over the last 20 years or more, the focus on getting money into the recycling industry in Africa has been to take what we did 30 years ago in Europe and try to replicate that in Africa. And, sure, that might work. But in the Netherlands, for example, we're about 60 percent effective. I don't know why we're trying to copy a solution that is 60 percent effective. I often tell people, if a plane is 60 percent safe, I'm not going to get in it.

I think that's one of the reasons why there's been a slow adoption, because the solution we have is good regulation and good enforcement. And that is lacking in a lot of developing countries. If you lack enforcement and regulation, how are you going to solve this problem? Over the last 30 years, they've really focused on regulation. And now lots of African countries have regulations in place that say you have to recycle your electronic waste, but they have no resources for enforcement. And they have a whole industry that has been created in the meantime that they then have to suddenly do something about. So there's a mismatch.

There's a lot of power behind these European schemes trying to do it the same way in Africa. This hasn't worked for 30 years, why do we continue doing that? The money that has come in has mostly been donor money, because private money does not go to increasing regulation and enforcement. Private money goes into business. And so if regulation and enforcement are the way to go, then obviously the money is coming from nonprofits. If it comes from a nonprofit, then there's not a business model behind it. And that's basically the reason why recycling is not effective.

By bringing in money with a commercial business model, Closing the Loop can pay more. The fact that we're able to pay more means we can process e-waste correctly. We can force people to wear gloves, or we can force people to have a contract with us or to not work with children because we're paying them more. And so they're incentivized to do it differently.

That's an interesting wording. You force the workers in Africa to do these things?
I use the word "force," but it's in their financial benefit to do so. Because we have a consistent business model, it means I can pay them today, I can pay them tomorrow, I can pay them six months from now. And they know I can, so I have a good relationship with them. If you look at the others collecting electronics, they come every now and then. They might say, okay, everybody has to wear gloves now. And then they take a photo of everyone with the gloves, and then six months later, no one hears from them. So that doesn't help the local collectors. They think, great, so I got some gloves and a nice photo again. And now what? So I guess nudging is a better word than forcing. There's basically no alternative if we come with a better deal.

Do you have any ideas for how we can improve the collection of e-waste in Europe or in North America? Collection rates are low everywhere.
Thinking out of the box or not trying to do everything the traditional way of doing it is the key. One challenge is that there are a couple of really big players in the recycling industry. For formal recycling, there are six smelters in the whole world. Giant waste companies run the business. They kind of dictate how things go. And they also in a way, I think, dictate what people hear.

Another thing is people keep trying to use traditional incentives to get people to do things. For example, hand in your mobile phone and well pay you five euros for it. I'm not going to go and look, dig for my drawers, find a phone, make sure it's empty for five euros. Sorry, but it's not worth five euros to me, and therefore I have a pile of phones at home, even working for Closing the Loop. So you really need to think, how do I incentivize people to turn in their phones? What does the consumer already do? How can I make it easy for them?

You need to fit into people's normal patterns of doing things. So one way is to make it more logical for people to bring back their electronics. You can charge money when people buy a phone and then give them 50 or 100 euros back when they return it. For that amount, or even 25 euros, people will do it. It is all related to money and to habit.

In the Netherlands, there's a big box at the supermarket, and you can drop most small electronics in there when you go shopping. So people will usually do it. It's a simple way to solve it. The process costs a lot of money. Transport is the most expensive part. The EPR system pays for it. But that is a way to do it, because they're making it convenient and financially worthwhile for people.

Why can't all the manufacturers go to a more modular kind of system for electronics, especially for phones? That can extend the product lifetime.
Because we don't want it as consumers. I mean, I can buy a Fairphone, but I don't.

Interesting. You can buy a Fairphone because you live in Europe, but you don't. Tell me why.
Because it's thicker, it's heavier. Fairphone has its own software. Unlike larger brands, they don't have thousands of people working on the software to make sure it's perfect. So there's bugs and stuff in the system, that for a basic user of a phone, you know, wouldn't be a problem, but I use mine very intensely. I'm not saying the Fairphone has lots of bugs, I'm saying that a user like me will reach its limitations. And I like that my phone is thin and light.

I'm not saying there's anything wrong with the Fairphone. I just think it will take a very long time for us to find sustainability so important that we will sacrifice things like size and weight and speed.

I hope we get there. It's great that Fairphone is pushing the limit in that sense. But that's going to take a while. You need to realize what the consumer wants. You need to match those wishes if you do something new, because otherwise you're not going to get the masses to agree with you. You need to think commercially.

One of the great things that Fairphone has accomplished is getting its suppliers to do things for everybody in the industry. They're now using more sustainable gold. In that sense, they are changing the industry. Maybe I don't mind where the gold comes from. It doesn't change my experience. So the modular part, maybe I don't want that. But the more sustainable resources, sure. That I appreciate.

Is there anything else you want to share that readers would find valuable?
The most important thing is people need to look out of the box to try and solve these problems. We're not going to solve the problems with the same solutions we had 30 years ago. When you're looking at material value, looking at the actual value of materials, these are all commodities. We need to realize that someone is never going to pay $3,000 an ounce of gold if gold actually costs $1,800 an ounce. So you really need to ensure that if people pay 5 percent extra, you give them 5 percent more value, and then get people to pay 7 percent extra, so you can do 7 percent more and then grow from there.

I think there are way too many people only looking at the extremes. If you tell people, you are not allowed to eat meat, it won't work. If you say, what about one meatless day per week? I'll think, sure, I can do that. And then two, and then three meatless days a week as an example. When people are talking about sustainability, too often everybody wants perfection rather than small steps.

Improve e-waste, streamline manufacturing

Consumer electronics are here to stay, but it is possible to reduce the environmental hazards associated with their production. Improved e-waste recycling is one approach. Changing the way products are manufactured represents another avenue. Keep reading to see how printing is revolutionizing the manufacturing of everything from electronics to bridges.

Note

1 Statista, "Number of Smartphones Sold to End Users Worldwide from 2007 to 2021," October 18, 2022, https://www.statista.com/statistics/263437/global-smartphone-sales-to-end-users-since-2007/.

11   It Adds Up
3D Printing and Sustainability

In some ways, additive is like where cell phones were in the early 2000s.
— Sherri Monroe, Additive Manufacturing Green Trade Association

Choosing manufacturing methods

Parts I and II of this book talked about manufacturing in the context of producing both products—steel, cell phones, airplanes—and the chemicals and materials needed to make these products. We emphasized the importance of reducing the use of toxic substances in all the steps of manufacturing, starting with extracting resources from the earth through building end products with engineered materials.

This chapter focuses on the latter stage—starting with a concept for a product and having chosen the design and the materials from which to build it, what options are available for constructing the final product? Do certain options suggest changes in the design or materials?

We recommend considering manufacturing options in light of the four system conditions, introduced in Chapter 3. These conditions lay out the responsibility of product manufacturers to consider ways to minimize the quantity of material extracted from the earth, the production of toxic substances, the destruction of natural resources, and the exposure of workers to unsafe working conditions.

With the four system conditions in mind, ask specific questions when looking at various manufacturing methods. How do the different options compare when considering worker exposure to toxicants during manufacturing? Do any toxicants from the manufacturing process remain in the end product, creating a risk for customers or those handling product disposal at the end of its life cycle?

What about the waste created during manufacturing? How can our society move toward a more circular economy? As we've seen already, choices in design and materials affect the volume of waste created, and there are opportunities for reuse and recycling at various points along the way. Manufacturing methods also play a role.

Additive versus subtractive manufacturing

Manufacturing processes can be either additive or subtractive. In additive processes, such as 3D printing, a product is built up layer by layer. In subtractive

DOI: 10.4324/9781003409267-14

processes, a product is formed by starting with a block or layer of material and removing excess material to create the desired shape. Wood carving, for example, is subtractive.

Traditional manufacturing relies on subtractive processes. The excess material that doesn't end up in the final part becomes waste. This waste can often be recycled. Companies that machine parts out of metal will ideally collect scraps and shavings and send them for refining into recycled metal. As we've seen in the previous chapters, this concept works much better for metals than for plastics.

Manufacturing of plastic parts often requires methods other than machining. Options include injection molding and extruding.

Injection molding involves injecting liquid thermoplastics into cold metal molds so that the plastic quickly solidifies into the desired shape. The process is inexpensive and efficient when producing large quantities of the same part, but it doesn't work well for complex shapes. Injection-molded parts need additional grinding to remove burrs, and sometimes machining to add more intricate design features.

Extruding forces thermoplastics through holes in a die, somewhat like making homemade pasta or using a play-dough press. It's a low-cost way to make rods or sheets, which are then machined into final parts as needed.

Additive manufacturing, where three-dimensional (3D) parts are deposited layer by layer in a precise pattern, comes with several benefits when compared to traditional subtractive methods:

- Designers can change the physical shape of an object by editing a software file.
- Material waste is minimal.
- There is no need to melt large quantities of material at once, saving the energy needed to run high-temperature ovens.

Additive manufacturing should theoretically result in less waste and less use of toxic chemicals, but that isn't always true in every case. Companies can't necessarily say truthfully that their product is more environmentally friendly than a competitor's product just because they build it with additive manufacturing. Multiple factors affect the overall picture including materials, product volume, and manufacturing strategy.

- *The materials used and their source.* Printing a 3D shape from virgin materials is more wasteful and energy-intensive than machining one out of recycled materials.
- *The number and variety of products produced.* Additive manufacturing is best suited to creating unique designs or a small quantity of each design, rather than building many copies of the same product. That said, advances are making additive faster and more attractive for low- to mid-volume production.
- *How additive manufacturing is integrated into product design and build.* If the ability to quickly make many versions results in an excess number of

prototypes being manufactured and discarded, computer modeling is likely to be a more efficient development strategy. If, on the other hand, additive manufacturing allows a company to create custom products on demand rather than keeping a large inventory of standard products, the strategy reduces waste.

What is 3D printing?

Most people instinctively understand the concept of 3D printing. 3D printers are far more than just a toy for hobbyists, however, and the concept encompasses a variety of techniques suitable for creating products made from a broad array of materials. When implemented correctly, 3D printing has the potential to revolutionize manufacturing.

The leading commercial applications for 3D printing include building prototypes and producing custom tooling that is used in manufacturing a variety of products. The ability to print multiple different prototypes allows engineers to inexpensively test out new designs, saving product development costs and encouraging creativity. It's easier to try out new ideas without wasting a lot of time and materials. Printed tooling is a way to create custom parts that cost no more than mass-produced versions.

3D printing also allows designers to create products that couldn't be manufactured using conventional subtractive methods. When designers think creatively, they can do better than duplicate an existing product. They might be able to reduce weight while maintaining strength or introduce new features without adding processing steps.

Additive manufacturing relies on one of several methods to create parts. The choice depends on the material to be printed, performance requirements, and the customer's budget for equipment.

The machines that most people associate with 3D printing use fused deposition modeling (FDM), in which a filament of material is melted and deposited on a surface in layers (see Figure 11.1(a)). The printers are relatively inexpensive, ranging from tabletop machines for hobbyists to more substantial equipment for industrial use.

FDM printers primarily print various plastics, although the filaments can be infused with metals or other materials. Many use PLA, a bio-based plastic mentioned in Chapter 8. Filaments can also be made from recycled plastics, which seems like an especially good idea when making prototypes or sample products that don't need to meet stringent performance specifications.

It may be possible to print 3D structures using discarded polyethylene. That sounds like a way to encourage recycling of plastic bags. If someone can make money by creating plastic filaments from recycled polyethylene, that increases the value of the material and serves as an incentive to convince more recycling facilities to accept polyethylene bags.

Selective laser sintering uses powders as the raw material. As the name implies, a laser sinters (melts) the powders to fuse them in precise locations, avoiding the

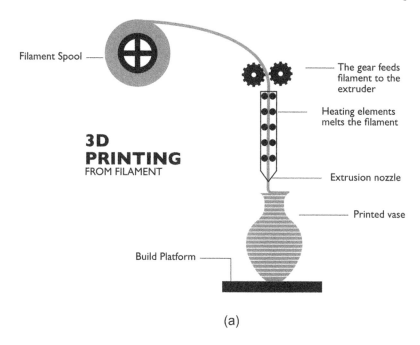

Filament Spool

The gear feeds
filament to the
extruder

Heating elements
melts the filament

**3D
PRINTING**
FROM FILAMENT

Extrusion nozzle

Printed vase

Build Platform

(a)

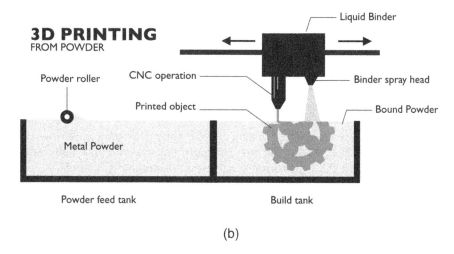

Liquid Binder

3D PRINTING
FROM POWDER

Powder roller

CNC operation

Binder spray head

Printed object

Bound Powder

Metal Powder

Powder feed tank

Build tank

(b)

Figure 11.1 Diagrams of the industrial 3D printing process starting with either (a) filaments or (b) powders.

need to heat the entire part to produce the desired mechanical strength. The process, illustrated in Figure 11.1(b), is versatile and can work with plastics, metals, ceramics, and even exotic materials such as food-based powders, but the machines are expensive and best suited to high-end applications.

Some high-end 3D printers use stereolithography, in which an ultraviolet laser solidifies liquid resins made from photosensitive polymers. The process can print high-quality objects with high resolution and has historically come with a high cost to match. The newest generation of stereolithography-based printers is much less expensive, with models that are even accessible to hobbyists.

As 3D printing advances, the potential applications go beyond what people currently associate with 3D printing. As one example, it is possible to control the amount of air incorporated into a material being printed, creating structures with any desired density.

They are printing what?

A vast array of materials can be 3D-printed. Plastic and metal are the obvious choices, but printers have built 3D structures out of concrete and pulp, produced food, and even created living tissue. The possibilities are endless, but the most outrageous applications are not practical for commercial use. In the early twentieth century, Thomas Edison came up with the idea of cast-in-place concrete houses. It's an understatement to say that this was not one of his best inventions. Creating a concrete house with existing technology required expensive metal molds, and the resulting structures were hardly the durable, low-maintenance buildings that Edison was promoting.

But 3D printing may enable a twenty-first-century version of Edison's concrete homes. After two years of effort, in 2014 Andrey Rudenko completed building a 3D-printed castle made from extruded concrete. In 2015, he printed a hotel suite, which still stands in the Philippines.

Further, 3D printed hempcrete (hemp mixed with concrete) is being trialed in Ukraine, as schools need to be rapidly replaced after shelling. In 2023, Europe's first 3D-printed school is taking shape in a neighborhood of Lviv, in western Ukraine, one layer at a time.

Electronics represent another frontier for 3D printing. When I (Julia) covered the printed electronics market and wrote a regular column for a trade publication from 2011 to 2013, the hype surrounding printed electronics was strong. Proponents envisioned thousands of computer chips being churned out like newspapers, using printing methods similar to those in use since the dawn of the twentieth century.

The reality wasn't as promising. Printing thin metal lines to create circuits is straightforward, and by printing them on paper or thin plastic backings, it is indeed possible to print rapidly in high volumes. But creating the wiring is the easy part. Printing the brains of a circuit—the transistors that today are deposited on silicon wafers under extremely stringent conditions to control temperature, moisture, and contamination—remains elusive. Today's 3D printing methods cannot produce the nanometer-scale features required to make advanced computer chips.

Speeding up the printing process

One concern with 3D printing is that it is a slow process, best suited for creating custom parts rather than mass-producing many identical pieces. Printing a single product can take many hours.

Since the 2010s, we have seen that 3D printing is starting to change. Manufacturers want to move toward higher volume production. To do this successfully, they will need to increase throughput significantly. Printing thicker layers or moving the print heads faster, though, is not the answer, as the result will be low-quality parts that do not meet customer requirements.

The answer for higher-volume 3D printing lies in parallelization—printing many parts in parallel. Professor Jennifer Lewis's research group at the University of Illinois, and later at Harvard, came up with a method to print from 64 print heads at once. The design needed to meet several challenging criteria. The multi-nozzle structure needed to:

- Withstand the high pressures required to print thick fluids,
- Print from a continuous filament,
- Achieve uniform flow rates across the nozzle array,
- Allow simultaneous patterning of more than one material,
- Be scalable for large-area, rapid manufacturing.

The researchers produced what is called a bifurcated structure. Fluid from a single parent channel flows into two, then four, all the way to 64 individual branches. The structure is machined from low-cost acrylic plastic. Connecting two such structures side by side allows the machine to print two different materials. Lewis's machine can print a 3D part in less than half an hour. The same design might take an entire day to print using a printer with a single nozzle.

High-volume 3D printing has not remained confined to university research groups. HP has entered the 3D printing market with an eye on speeding up the process. Its Multi Jet Fusion printers can print an array of parts simultaneously. The company claims that its proprietary architecture can dispense 30 million drops of fluid per second. The process is similar to selective laser sintering, but it is much faster. We spoke with HP's Francois Minec about 3D printing and sustainability.

Interview

Francois Minec, HP

What led you to your current role in 3D printing at HP?
The additive manufacturing industry has always been of interest to me, with my background in chemical engineering and previous roles in plastics, from R&D to

manufacturing and business. Plastic is useful in a multitude of sectors—from medical to packaging and automotive—it's a great material. If used well and dealt with well it has huge potential to revolutionize industries.

I joined the 3D printing industry in 2014 when I created my own company, which was making powders for 3D printing. I sold it to BASF in 2018, and subsequently became CEO of BASF 3D printing in 2019. I joined HP in mid-2022.

At HP's Personalization & 3D Printing business, we work with both polymers and metal 3D printers, though I am personally focused on the polymer side. Today my role is Global Head of 3D Polymers at HP Inc.

How did you get interested in 3D printing?
It's a booming industry, filled with so many possibilities. I wanted to be involved in a growing, dynamic industry, and through my immersion in the industry, realized that it had the potential to benefit society, and the environment as whole.

What got you to especially think about sustainability regarding materials?
I have always been a person who enjoys spending time in nature and being outdoors, and in doing so the importance of sustainability and preserving our natural environment is clear to me.

Greenwashing is also very important to acknowledge. Unfortunately, it is all around us. Everyone uses the word "sustainability" without taking real action. As an example, I recently went to a leading plastics manufacturing tradeshow in Germany. I saw thousands of exhibitors, and there was not a single booth that didn't include the word "sustainability" in its messaging. Unfortunately, very few booths had anything to back up their statements.

I am proud that HP is so committed to sustainability with an objective to reach net zero emissions by 2040.

How does that play into your work?
3D printing offers several advantages in terms of sustainability. The first is lightweight design. Some designs, especially for the transportation industry, which are impossible without 3D printing, can be manufactured with this technology.

Another example is on-demand manufacturing, which is starting to develop. The concept of this is to replace real stock with a digital warehouse of 3D designs, printed only if there is a need for it to avoid overproduction across many sectors.

The 3D industry is talking a lot about localized production, which is a good practice and arguably has geopolitical benefits, but it does not have such a significant environmental impact.

Design is the most important stage of manufacturing from an environmental perspective. Goods must be designed with the carbon footprint of the product top of mind from the start. 3D printing is still small at an industrial level and competes with the injection molding industry, which has 150 years of history of improving its processes. For this reason, if you're going to produce a run of hundreds of thousands of parts, injection molding will always be better.

Now if you're manufacturing 10,000 parts, you start to take into account that you have to make a mold. It takes a huge amount of energy to make a mold out of a block of aluminum. Here is where 3D printing shines: with a small or medium-sized series, it is more sustainable to use 3D printing technology. As the 3D printing industry improves, the size of series you can make in a more sustainable way than injection molding will grow to hundreds of thousands and even millions of parts.

As an industry, 3D printing still has a lot of things to improve. For example, powder bed printers. To make quality parts, the powder needs to be refreshed every so often, and therefore part of the powder needs to be disposed of. To combat this wasteful practice, we now have a program in place with some partners who will take this powder back and recycle it, not for 3D printing, but for injection molding.

Why is it being reused in injection molding instead of in 3D printing?
Because it has lost some of its properties. The 3D printing process is so specific, so sensitive, that you cannot reuse the material. Injection molding is a less sensitive process, so this initial waste material can still be put to good use.

We also think about where we need to progress as an industry, and part of this is to be very transparent and give the customer a calculation of the full carbon footprint of a part. It's not an easy task because you need to consider the material production, the printer process, which type of electricity is used, etc.

That is an interesting aspect regarding companies that are making equipment and looking at Scope 3 emissions. You have to make assumptions about how the customer is using it. What do you consider?
We're working on some simulations where the customer would enter some parameters: Is it green electricity from solar or wind? Is it conventional electricity? What is the carbon footprint of the plant? We're working on this. We're also working on bio-sourced materials. For instance, we have a material called Polyamide 11 (PA 11) which is produced using castor oil.

How did that material choice come about?
We don't develop the materials ourselves. We work with partners. Our printing process has a very specific processing window—not just any material can work in the printer. There's a lot of trial and error, and there are some material families that work better than others. The first powder printer was invented in the late 1980s and it was developed to work with a PA12 powder. Over the years, the whole technology developed around PA 12. New powders need to have properties very similar to PA 12 if you want them to work.

What are the key properties?
It's complicated, but it boils down to having a difference between melting temperature and crystallization temperature that is wide enough to allow the product to work. For example, polypropylene has almost no difference—two degrees of

difference between melting temperature and crystallization temperature. So it's very difficult to make polypropylene work.

You want at least 25–30 °C difference between the melting temperature and the crystallization temperature. And that's what PA 12 has. PA 11 also has this. But PA 11 is bio-based, which is why we promoting it. As a bio-based solution, it has also a lower carbon footprint because you basically absorb carbon in the castor beans. Moreover, the supplier of PA 11, Arkema, recently switched to renewable energy for the manufacturing of PA 11.

But of course, there's a higher price. People always say they want green solutions. The question is, how much are they ready to pay for that? PA 11 actually performs slightly better, but the cost is higher. The consumer is ready to pay between 5 and 15 percent more for the lower-impact product. And very often, the bio-based solutions are 30 percent higher or even double the cost.

We use powder technology, but there are other technologies like UV technology and filament technology. UV technology is lower temperature so it's less energy intensive. The carbon footprint may be a bit lower, but the chemicals used have an impact other than carbon, and the end of life is an issue. Powder technologies, in general, are recyclable because they use thermoplastics. UV resin is not recyclable today. It can just be burned. Burning it for energy recuperation is actually not such a bad idea for plastic, as it avoids using more oil, but that's a debate in itself.

In Europe, since people started to separate plastic streams from normal waste, waste incinerators are forced to use fuel to burn the waste. If you use plastic for a positive impact like packaging goods or automotive lightweighting, or lightweighting a plane, then at the end of its life, if you burn it, actually you avoid burning the oil directly. It ends up burned anyway, but you at least you use it for something in between.

What trends are you seeing in applications? Where is the best opportunity for 3D printing to be a better solution than the conventional way, whether that's injection molding or something else?
The beauty of 3D printing is that it's still a young industry, and it's improving a lot every year, not only in cost but in sustainability. Going forward, the cost aspect of producing anything will be linked completely with the sustainability aspect. As I mentioned earlier, 3D printing is a better solution for when you want to print 10,000 parts or less, but for more than 10,000, it's better to injection mold. That's today. In a few years, it's going to be ten times more. As the technology progresses, we're going to address a bigger and bigger market. That's one mega-trend in 3D printing.

Another area in which we see a lot of application development is electric vehicles. Electric cars need long range. In order to get long range, 3D printing is a good way to lightweight. There are a lot of startups in the EV sector that are forward-thinking and are adopting 3D printing.

What types of vehicle components are being 3D printed today?
It's mostly inside the vehicle, replacing injection molded parts. Inside the doors, in the things that you don't see very often.

Supply chain disruptions have also led to an increase in companies using 3D printing to bridge production when they need to get a product to the market. Out of the hundreds of molds for different parts, if one is lost or stuck in a congested supply chain, then it disrupts the whole production line. Companies can bridge the production gap with 3D printing.

HP received a prize thanks to bridge production for a Detroit carmaker. Thanks to 3D printing, they were able to launch the car on time. That would have been impossible without it.

We are seeing growth in areas where products require mass personalization. Mostly medical—orthotics, prosthetics. We have our own prosthetic insoles brand called Arize, which produces personalized insoles for patients. We also have customers doing the same thing using our printers.

When you were talking about the volumes of 3D printing, part of it has to do with needing massive parallelisation in the production, right? Because if it's going to take eight hours to make a part, that's not going to work if I want 10,000 of them, unless you can make 10,000 at once.
People always say, "3D printing is slow." But you can put more printers in parallel. Our printer, for example, makes one batch in around 12 hours, sometimes shorter. But in one batch, you make hundreds of parts. For injection molding, you need six weeks, because you need to make the mold. That's the beauty of 3D printing. When you do injection molding, you can make up to hundreds of parts every few seconds. But in order to make the first one, you need two or two three months because the mold is very complex and very precise. With 3D printing you get instantaneous production, within 24 hours from design to the finished part.

I remember that HP had a vision of tailoring each tiny cube in a 3D printed product, each voxel, to be different. Is that happening?
Technically many things are possible. We can even print electronics inside. You can do anything at the voxel level, yes. But then, from the technology, you need to develop a product. We have a roadmap to use all that is enabled by technology, but we also are very much focused on developing products that the market will adopt.

What do you think are the biggest challenges going forward in the 3D printing industry?
One is educating the designers around the world on what 3D printing can do. If you come to a 3D printing specialist as a designer, and you say, "I've designed this part, can you 3D print it?" the answer will be yes. But it makes no sense. You designed it for injection molding because people still learn at school to design for injection molding. By then, it's too late. With 3D printing, you can avoid assemblies,

you can have lightweight designs, but you need to design for 3D printing. If you design for injection molding, then you're not taking advantage of the benefits of 3D printing, which, in turn, negates the sustainability and economic advantages of the technology.

Number two is to continue progressing the technology to improve cost per part with portability and reliability. Part of reducing the cost per part is reducing the energy that we need to make the part. Improving sustainability, cost per part, and reliability are all related challenges that the 3D printing industry is tackling.

Replacement parts on demand

3D printing presents an opportunity related to 2D laser or inkjet printers. Sometimes a printer stops working because some small plastic part breaks. Frequently, the solution is to either buy an expensive replacement part and wait weeks for it to arrive, or abandon the printer entirely by discarding it (ideally sending it to a certified e-waste recycler) and buying a new printer. What if a customer could instead print a replacement part using a 3D printer at their home or workplace or somewhere nearby? There is no technical barrier for doing so.

This concept of building replacement parts is, of course, valid for products other than printers. In the future, the immediate response to a broken part could be to download a CAD file from the product manufacturer's website and bring it to a nearby 3D printer to create a replacement in minutes. The product manufacturer would also specify appropriate materials for printing the part. It could be made from the same material as the original part, or from a different material that had the right combination of properties such as strength, weight, and heat resistance.

The ability to print replacement parts is a productivity advantage for factories. If a piece of equipment stops working because of a faulty part, there is no need to take it out of service for days, or perhaps months, waiting for a replacement part to arrive. The design for every spare part that can be printed is stored in your database, and you can have the equipment up and running again in a day.

Other ways to do additive manufacturing

Additive manufacturing extends beyond 3D printing. Some companies create parts using additive manufacturing processes that don't resemble printing in the slightest.

Fabrisonic is a company that creates 3D metal parts using ultrasonic welding. Ultrasonic vibration scrubs the oxides off the surface of metals, allowing foils of the same or different metals to bond automatically without added heat. The process does operate at a slightly elevated temperature, but far below the normal melting point of any of the metals involved. The ability to weld dissimilar metals, such as copper and steel, enables structures that couldn't be made using conventional machining.

Fabrisonic takes advantage of a huge computer-controlled milling machine that the company modified to add ultrasonic welding capability. Users upload designs to the machine, and the internal computer controls the motion of the cutting tools to create the desired shape.

The Fabrisonic process combines additive and subtractive manufacturing. Layers of metal foil are welded together and built up additively, and grooves are machined out before welding additional layers. This approach enables structures with internal cavities. Sample products distributed at trade shows contain an embedded curved groove and a hidden cavity containing tiny metal pellets that rattle when the piece is shaken. That's just for fun, but the process can be used to embed useful things like wires or electronic components.

MX3D in the Netherlands has developed an impressive method of creating 3D metal structures. Its website features a video of one of its industrial robots drawing metal ropes in the air. It looks like the metal strands appear from nowhere. The process relies on welding, with welding tips at the ends of the robotic arms that bond one drop of metal at a time. The robots build structures with remarkable speed.

When MX3D says it is thinking outside the box, the company means this in a literal sense. Every other 3D printing technique creates objects within a box-shaped machine. Whether the box fits on a table or is more than ten feet high, like Fabrisonic's machine, objects still need to be built in a confined space. Six-axis industrial robots, however, can travel to a job site.

MX3D's most ambitious project was a 3D bridge, originally scheduled to be built on-site over a canal in Amsterdam in 2017. The designers envisioned the robots starting the build on one side of the canal and walking across the bridge segments they had just built to create more of the bridge. The reality was a bit different. On-site printing was not feasible, and everything took much longer than expected. The bridge was finally installed in 2021.

A new vision for additive manufacturing

Additive manufacturing has progressed rapidly in recent years, and so has emphasis on how the technology can enable more sustainable manufacturing. The Additive Manufacturing Green Trade Association, founded in late 2019, promotes the environmental benefits of 3D printing. We spoke to the organization's executive director to learn more.

Interview

Sherri Monroe, AMGTA

What drew you to this role with AMGTA?
I have experience in innovation and emerging technology. The current state of additive technology advancement is very much in that space. I've also worked for a couple of very large nonprofits, so I understand bringing together a wide range

of stakeholders around a common cause. Personally, both my dad and my brother were lifelong tool and die makers. So, I have a general understanding of the subtractive manufacturing world.

The sustainability aspect of the AMGTA really spoke to me. I worked for the Red Cross for several years and responded to numerous disasters. I've also lived in Florida most of my adult life and experienced numerous natural disasters personally with my family. While preparing for and responding to natural disasters was immensely rewarding, I thought often of the quote from Bishop Desmond Tutu: "There comes a point where we need to stop just pulling people out of the river. We need to go upstream and find out why they are falling in." I felt that my experience and skills would be put to better use "upstream" working to impact the environmental changes that are leading to the significant uptick in natural disasters. The Red Cross is a great organization that's responding to disasters, but how about let's do something and figure out why these natural disasters seem to be getting worse and worse. I was looking for an opportunity to do something in the positive direction of addressing some of that.

Excellent. How do you anticipate additive manufacturing making the world a better place?

There are many ways for additive to really impact not only manufacturing but distribution, inventory management and all aspects of the supply chain. Additive really has the potential to help address some significant problems. It's a fit for a lot more situations than many realize.

When we consider longevity of equipment, supply chain, shipping components around the world, and paying to have large inventories sitting in warehouses until we finally throw them in a dumpster, additive manufacturing holds incredible potential. But it's a tool like any other. It has to be applied in the right ways.

Part of the role of our organization is to help understand where additive is better, understand the potential, and talk about sustainability within the additive manufacturing community. But we're also talking about additive manufacturing to the broader manufacturing and sustainability community, to those companies that are trying to figure out how to achieve aggressive sustainability goals. We want to help that group of people understand the potential for additive manufacturing and what this can do for their manufacturing, for their supply chain. Let's address the shareholder concerns, employee concerns, customer concerns. Our mission is to be out there talking about additive and un-muddy the waters to help people understand the possibilities.

We have some research projects that are a part for part comparison, because organizations need that information. The answer isn't just a thumbs up or thumbs down. We look at what does it take from an energy consumption and a waste consumption or waste production view? What does it look like when you're able to lightweight a part? Now we have less material. If it's going in something like an airplane, and it's been lightweighted, that's less jet fuel that's required. Those things are all really important. Additive design also enables geometries that simply aren't possible through traditional manufacturing methods.

We have members that are doing things in aerospace, building parts that go on rockets, and some of these parts, there's no other way to make them. So you can't do a part for part comparison, because there's no traditional way to make it. For example, this incredible heat exchanger that's about a meter tall, there's no other way to make it than with additive manufacturing. Also, it is not just the production of that part, it's what it enables. This light-weighted part might enable electric flight.

By looking at things in a bigger way, businesses often will see the real benefit. If you have a very efficient piece of equipment that you've had to take down for maintenance, and you need to run older equipment meanwhile, that's not very efficient. In the meantime, getting that spare part and getting that efficient piece of equipment back up and running quickly, that's the story.

In a presentation, I showed a picture of a Model T Ford with a horse attached to the front of it. That's not making very good use of that technology. The similar thing is when we use subtractive manufacturing as the measuring stick with which to measure additive manufacturing. It's not about one winning over the other. It's about really understanding the potential of this technology and being able to apply it to really move forward. Traditional manufacturing is always going to be there. There's always going to be a need for that. This is just one more really powerful tool.

What are some other examples of additive manufacturing applications?
We have a lifecycle analysis [LCA] underway right now, where we're looking at polymer jetting on fabric for the fashion industry. Anybody that's coming at this from a sustainability perspective knows that the fashion industry has serious environmental challenges. Anybody who's ever had to order T-shirts for their kid's team or for a work function knows it's a nightmare, right? What sizes do you order? For the fashion industry, it's 1,000 times worse when you look at the clothing that's produced and the scrap that's produced from making it and how much over-production goes in landfills. Additive makes it possible to customize and produce things closer to demand. You have a lot less waste of materials to begin with, you have a lot less obsolescence, which applies to really every area of manufacturing. You don't have to guess what quantities you need and produce based on that.

I am really excited for that LCA to come out. The additive manufacturing crowd is going to understand it even though fashion is not the top of the list when they're thinking about additive manufacturing. But for a sustainability audience, they understand how this could be a real game changer. Instead of ordering large quantities ahead of time, we can do this much closer to the user, find out what they want, and adjust. You're not going to run out of the red ones when they turn out to be the hot item instead of the blue ones.

It's not only about environmental sustainability, it's about sustainability from a business perspective. Companies have to sustain their businesses. How do you continue to be profitable? How do you continue to serve your customers and your employees? This is a way for companies to be able to be much more nimble, and also be much more resilient and not at such risk based on supply chain issues and disruptions and the whims of the consumer.

Instead of needing large quantities of parts on a shelf, we fill in on the back end. If it takes a week to make something, we only have to produce a week's worth. We don't need six months' worth in production. There's potential for that sort of thing for spare parts for all kinds of equipment. At some point, the equipment gets tossed out because getting a spare part is difficult and expensive. They don't make them any longer, or they're going to send it to you from across the country or around the world.

We see big manufacturers using additive not only in the things that they produce, but within their operations. One member is a big retailer. It was fascinating to hear what they were doing with additive. They have a huge operation with big equipment. Some of that equipment, they can't buy parts it for anymore, but they can manufacture them and be able to keep their equipment up and running. They don't have to scrap or replace this equipment, they can keep it running a lot longer.

Fantastic. Where do you see the industry going in the next few years, say by 2030?
I think in this kind of innovative space when you talk about 2030, you might as well be saying 2100. With subtractive manufacturing, we have 100 years of past history, so we can kind of see where that might go. With disruptions in supply chains, all the geopolitical issues going on, there are things changing in our world that we would have never thought would happen so quickly. I think as we see greater adoption, we will see more collaboration throughout the entire ecosystem.

One of the things that we are focused on is involving not just the companies that produce source materials or printers. We need end users—people who are manufacturing things and people reusing these parts, the people who need this part printed right now because they need to use it tomorrow. That kind of information is so important because it informs the entire chain. It affects what kind of printers are needed, what kind of source materials are needed. For us, having our membership represent that whole breadth of the of the supply chain is really important because better info from end users produces better products for end users.

The more that we can create, the more we can move everything forward faster. We'll have new printing capabilities, we'll have many, many new source materials. I can see ways of using other kinds of waste, like wood waste, or fishing nets, being able to recycle materials. One of the challenges right now with wood is the need to mix the wood with a binder and produce something. That's one more cycle around the circular economy. That's great, you took wood shavings and produced one more thing with it. But now do you have a way of removing that binder so that these materials can continue to be used? That's the big challenge.

I think that pressure from governments and corporations will drive much more innovation. But you need people that are going to use that innovation. Let's bring those two things together, so we're not just building cool things that nobody's ever going to use.

You mentioned LCAs. Is your organization doing those or are your members doing them? How are you supporting their transition?
We have an ongoing pipeline of projects that answer the questions manufacturers need answered. We work with our member organizations to find use cases to address the challenges to increased adoption of additive. We contract with research institutions. For the first two LCAs, one is with the Yale School of the Environment and the other is with the Rochester Institute of Technology. Our members provide the data. The researchers conduct the testing to compare traditional manufacturing and additive and put all of that together.

The project we did with Yale is a part-for-part comparison. We're not doing any lightweighting or redesigning. Then we're doing some projections beyond that, saying, what if you could lightweight this by 10 or 20 percent? What if you manufactured somewhere where the energy source was different, someplace with very high levels of renewable energy? What does that do? The manufacturer that's working on that one, this is not academic for them, they are planning on making strategic decisions based on the results. So we're really excited about that.

For us, it's very important that this be credible, transparent research. Whether it's a thumbs up or thumbs down, it's not the important part; it's the findings along the way. For any of these projects, if our hypothesis doesn't prove out, it doesn't matter. It's all valuable data. Companies that are already involved in additive, they need to know this information. And it's helpful for companies that are looking to get into additive, or maybe go from just rapid prototyping to production. Before they make that leap of faith, they need some real data that they can use.

The AMGTA is fairly new. What more are you looking to do?
We are increasing the number of research projects and use-case studies. We want companies to understand that sustainability does not need to feel like taking your medicine. Our position is that sustainability for a company is the same as the strategic drivers they're looking at anyway. Lower energy consumption, less raw materials, less waste, less obsolescence, more efficient supply chains, that's what sustainability should look like.

We want to support a community of collaboration where companies, even competitors, realize there's more to be gained than lost by working together. If we work together, and focus on the right things, we're increasing the adoption of additive manufacturing. And if we do that, together, we just expand this pie. There's more than enough business for everyone.

Printed eyeglass frames

As our interviewees noted, additive manufacturing can revolutionize multiple industries and reduce waste. The eyewear industry is an excellent example. Stores change their collections frequently and end up with huge amounts of inventory to scraps. Shops can have a few sample frames to try and then 3D print on demand. They already make lenses to order. With 3D printing, they can do the same with frames.

Part IV

Practical Considerations to Motivate Change

12 Enforce or Encourage? The Role of Regulations and Certifications

A lot of people think the health and safety standard is more important than the environmental one. But if you're judging it based on their effects on human beings, they're equally important.

—Theodora Rondozai, Besa Zimbabwe

The role of regulations

For better or worse, regulations and laws affect behavior. Regulations that either restrict the use of toxic substances or provide a monetary incentive to switch to more environmentally friendly options are often effective when "do the right thing" messages fail. Laws and regulations often force companies to take action, which some in the business community consider stifling. They feel that such laws restrict innovation or increase costs unnecessarily.

Because proving evidence of cause and effect is difficult, approaches that embrace the "precautionary principle," which emphasizes acting when there is a suspected hazard, serve an important role. In the years that it takes researchers to prove a conclusive link between a specific chemical substance and adverse health effects, a lot of damage may occur.

In an ideal world, manufacturing companies would always consider the health and safety of their employees and customers when deciding what safeguards to install or which materials to use. In reality, profit still often takes priority. The story of industries ignoring public health concerns has happened over and over again since early in the twentieth century, such as with radium, tetraethyl lead, tobacco, and oil and gas extraction. Battles over climate change are ongoing even with floods, droughts, hurricanes, and fires breaking all standing records.

There are sound business reasons for embracing healthier business practices. Beyond creating a safer environment for your employees, being proactive enhances reputation and reduces risk.

Companies that take the initiative to invest time and resources in obtaining certifications are in a better position to fairly defend themselves if something goes wrong. If they have been making strides in making their manufacturing processes safer and less wasteful, and they can document their efforts, their customers, shareholders, and the public will be more likely to forgive any missteps.

DOI: 10.4324/9781003409267-16

Sometimes experiencing negative publicity can be a catalyst for change. The court of public opinion provides another impetus for companies to switch their tactics. The US Occupational Safety and Health Administration (OSHA) was founded in large part because the story of the early twentieth-century radium dial painters became national news.

Public outcry against the dangers of plasticizers containing phthalates convinced chemical companies to develop alternatives. For example, BASF doubled its production capacity of phthalate-free plasticizers in 2014 due to customer demand.

Industrial waste production has improved in many ways since 1960, despite continuing examples of companies trying to escape responsibility for their sins in order to make a profit. Many businesses embrace safer manufacturing processes that create less waste. They know it helps both their reputation and their bottom line and want to do more than meet the minimum standards that regulations require.

Do certifications matter?

Certifications indicate a certain level of quality and show that a company is trying to take steps to be a preferred supplier or to stand out. Although certifications can be helpful, they are no guarantee that a company is doing right by its customers. It isn't wise to trust certifications alone, even though doing so is simpler. Due diligence throughout the supply chain takes more work than checking certification status, but it can help avoid unpleasant surprises later on.

The International Standards Organization (ISO) maintains a series of standards that address various aspects of business practices. In the mid-1990s, I (Julia) worked for a company that was going through the process of obtaining ISO 9000 certification, the quality management standard that is now called ISO 9001. We had to document all our procedures and make sure that what we were doing matched what we said we were doing.

Although it's far from perfect, documenting processes is a good first step toward fully understanding how a company conducts its operations. Without knowing the details, it is nearly impossible to know where to look to find areas that need improvement. Going through an ISO certification forces a company to thoroughly examine its practices.

Still, becoming ISO certified requires an investment of time and money. The value of certification depends on your industry. Around 2012, Smokey Peck, the president of Pro Recycling Group whose interview appears in Chapter 9, looked into ISO certification for his business. He found that other businesses in his industry weren't certified, which didn't bother customers. No customer had ever asked Smokey if his company was ISO certified. The company was already doing most of the steps that would have been required to become certified, but Smokey decided that the stamp of approval associated with certification wasn't worth the cost. In other industries such as mining, ISO certification can be essential.

Interview

Theodora Rondozai, Besa Zimbabwe

What got you into working on ISO certifications?
My first encounter with ISO standards was working for a company that recycled paint thinners and mineral spirits back in the 1990s in the UK. And they were certified to ISO 9001. Back then it was called BS 5750.

When I came back to Zimbabwe a few years later, I wanted a job that had to do with standards. I took a few courses in ISO standards. Then I got a job with a consulting company. I wanted to experience auditing, so I joined the local certification body. But I still wanted to go back to consulting so I started my own consultancy. I ended up training companies that were implementing standards and helping them get ready for certification. I'm originally a chemist, so the orderliness of standards appeals to me. Chemistry is in essence predictable, and it's about systems and processes.

Tell me more about your consultancy company. You've had that business for quite some time, right?
Since 2004. It's called Besa Zimbabwe, and BESA stands for Business Excellence Southern Africa. It was actually in partnership with a South African company. In my final months of working for the certification body, after I'd given my notice, they brought in David Crawford from South Africa to teach a lead auditor course. I ended up going into partnership with David, who became a great friend and mentor. Sadly, he passed on in 2023, so now it's just me.

Originally, I just did ISO 9001, which is Quality Management. But as time went on, we found that a lot of companies wanted an integrated system. They wanted the package of 9001 and 14001 (Environmental Management), as well as the Health and Safety standard, which was called OSHAS 18001 at the time. Many companies wanted all three, so I was "persuaded" to go into the other two.

Why did they want all three? Did they think they needed that to be competitive?
To be competitive, yes, because the scope of ISO 9001 is purely product quality. And that's by far the most widely used standard. Of all the certifications globally, about 65–70 percent are ISO 9001. That's obviously the biggest one because most companies are selling a product or service, so they're managing the processes that produce that product.

But if in the course of creating that product, your processes have an environmental impact, or are associated with hazards that cause injury and ill health, then you also want to manage those risks. That's another two standards. ISO 14001 has to do with managing environmental aspects. ISO 45001, which is the health and safety standard, is about management of occupational hazards and risks. Those three typically make up a package that companies want, to manage a broader spectrum of risks.

It also depends on the nature of the company. I deal mostly with mining companies. Obviously, they've got huge occupational health and safety issues, so they almost always need to have a health and safety management system. They also have huge environmental risks. Of course, there's a lot of legislation around both of those, so having systems helps them to manage and to do better as far as compliance is concerned.

Are they mainly concerned with compliance? Or do some of them really want to go further than that?

That's an interesting question. I remember reading about a survey that said there wasn't a big difference in terms of levels of compliance between certified companies and those that were not certified. Because of course, the standards are optional. Compliance isn't. Whether you're certified or you're not certified, you're expected to comply.

While there might be a perception that the standards help with compliance, I think companies do it for all sorts of other reasons. It makes them look good from a brand or marketability point of view. But I think the biggest issue is actually risk management.

Is the health and safety standard primarily for that of the employees? Or does it extend to the local communities?

It's purely about the health and safety of the employees and anyone else who comes into the workplace, meaning visitors and contractors. When it comes to local communities, that is covered by environmental management, because those are environmental impacts. Even if you injure people in the communities. Say there was an explosion and toxic smoke, that would be an environmental impact, because it's affecting the area outside the organization.

A lot of people think the health and safety standard is more important than the environmental one. Because in their minds, it's about people, while environmental standards are about frogs and stuff. But if you're judging it based on their effects on human beings, they're equally important. You could even argue that the environmental standards are more important, because communities don't ask to be affected. At least the employees are paid to take those risks and are trained to handle them.

Certification doesn't mean a company will be a good steward of the environment by default. What's your perspective on that?

Certification doesn't mean perfection by any stretch of the imagination. What it does mean—or what it should mean—is that the organization has gone to considerable lengths to identify its risks and has controls in place to manage and monitor them.

The whole system is there to prevent stuff going wrong. Companies that are certified should have a lot fewer incidents than companies that are not certified.

It doesn't guarantee that things won't go wrong—certified companies have incidents, too. It also depends on what the motivation is for the certification in the first place. Because some do it as a marketing strategy, and others do it because they have a genuine desire for improvement.

If things do go wrong, the certified company is going to have a process to investigate and get down to the root cause, adjust their risk assessments, and put in place better controls, and so on. So there should be a big difference in performance.

Do you have any data to demonstrate that?
Not specific data, but anecdotally, I would say absolutely. Whenever I'm doing workshops, I ask for stories about when things went wrong and what they did about it. There is definitely a considerable difference in the approach of certified versus uncertified.

Data might come from regulatory authorities, because when companies have major incidents, they are required to report them. They should have statistics, but I don't know if they would record whether these companies are certified or not.

What are some of the concerns about the process that might stop companies from becoming certified?
The biggest one is cost. It's not cheap. There is the process of preparing for certification itself. They need training, they may need consultants. And of course, certification is not a one-off. You need surveillance audits for as long as you're certified. But those that approach me have usually already decided that they're going to do it. Those that don't do it typically don't because they think it's too expensive, and there isn't enough pressure to make them do it. Sometimes there is shareholder pressure, because now many investors won't deal with companies that don't have certification as a means of risk management.

Is that because the certification tells them there's a minimum standard of care?
They're not going to be in the headlines on the news, and they're less likely to lose money. Occasionally, an incident is so bad that the company gets shut down. Recently, there was a story about a mining company that had a fatality, and they had to shut down because their investor withdrew. The fatality investigation had revealed that there was negligence on their part. And they were definitely not certified.

The certification can weed out those bad actors.
For sure. There is a perception among a lot of people that an ISO standard, first and foremost, is about procedures and documentation. I always say to them that while there is a considerable amount of documentation, that's really not where all the work is. The documentation is not the system, the system is what you're actually doing. Your biggest job is changing the culture in the organization.

There are different kinds of risk—there's the risk of what could go wrong, and the risk of not acting. How much does that come into play?

The standards are really all about identifying what could go wrong. The idea is that you look at your processes and identify all of the hazards associated with each activity. You assess the risks, then decide if you need to take action. If you need to put controls in place, you do so, and monitor them on an ongoing basis.

There is a risk of not acting, which is as much a problem as acting in the wrong way. With health and safety, a lot of things go wrong because people underestimate the risk that they are facing. For example, someone not shutting down a conveyor belt to do a quick repair, and then ending up being pulled into the conveyor belt and getting horrible injuries because they underestimated what could go wrong. Nobody wants to get injured, but they think they can take shortcuts.

How have you seen organizations integrate the environmental aspect?
I always make it very clear that the scopes are different, that Environmental Management and Health and Safety Management are two very different things. If they want to be certified to both, they have to pay equal attention to both.

Even if they integrate the system, there is no such thing as an integrated standard; they are two separate standards. Even though they can have combined audits, technically, it's two separate audits. They can do well in the health and safety one, and not get the environmental certification because they haven't paid attention to the environmental impacts.

The integration comes when you are looking at a particular process, for example water treatment. The aim of having a water treatment plant is so that you can release the wastewater to the municipal sewer. It's got to meet certain environmental requirements, like pH, for example. Those are environmental requirements. But from a health and safety point of view, the process of water treatment includes the use of hydrochloric acid, which is a hazardous substance. The handling and storage is going to have health and safety risks associated with it. The people that are carrying out the process have to take into account whatever they have to do to avoid injury from the hydrochloric acid. Preventing leakages and spillages would be an integral part of what the workers do on a day-to-day basis.

In the mining industry in particular, a lot of dust is produced from the blasting and crushing processes. Those are the sorts of things that can generate complaints from the local community and that they have to manage. Those are also environmental issues, but when the dust is affecting the employees, then it's a health and safety issue.

Some companies talk about responsible gold mining. Is it really possible?
The best we can hope for is somewhat responsible gold mining. To produce one ounce of gold requires a stupid number of tons of ore. They're literally digging up mountains. But if they are being responsible, the claim is that during the life of the mine, or when they close down the mine, they will have restored everything. As far as the communities are concerned, they will say that they benefit from the mine being there because there's the whole economy around the mine, the jobs, schools, and so on. They also sometimes help communities get access to water, which they may not have had before.

What are some examples of safer and more environmentally aware practices that companies have put into place because they've become certified?
One example had to do with a tailings dam that failed because they had heavy rain, which they hadn't anticipated. The planning and the risk assessment had been inadequate. After the incident, they went back to the drawing board and created a very different design to try and manage that, so that, should it happen again, they would have other catchment areas to catch the overflow, and a series of dams before it ever had a chance to get to the river, then get to the community.

It's all about lessons being learned, maybe from the experience of other organizations, because they will have very similar processes. One company that I'm dealing with went on a benchmarking visit to several other mines because they were implementing systems for the first time. They went to see how other places handle waste management, their tailings, their water management, and so on. Some mines have been certified for decades, and they manage their systems very well.

Are those ones that have been certified for a long time open and willing to share?
For the most part, they are fairly open. It's always about how they are approached. If another mine says, "Can we come and have a look," it's kind of flattery, actually. In my experience, they generally wouldn't say no.

Joining forces

The American Sustainable Business Network (ASBN) serves as an example of the clout that businesses can have if they band together to say that safe, efficient manufacturing and reasonable profits go hand in hand. The ASBN is devoted to promoting triple-bottom-line business practices, emphasizing the need to consider not only profit but also people and planet when making business decisions.

The ASBN's advocacy arm advocates for policy change at both the federal and state levels. ASBN asks its members to contact their senators and representatives to express support for certain bills or encourage voting against others.

The Accurate Labels Act was one of ASBN's 2018 targets. This federal bill was sponsored by a group called the Coalition for Accurate Product Labels, which made it sound like an organization promoting product safety. Don't consumers want clear labels so they can understand what's in the products they buy? That's the messaging that the bill's sponsors were highlighting.

But ASBN pointed out that clear labels were not the entire goal. Instead, the act was designed to limit the ability of states to enact labeling requirements that went beyond national standards. Coalition members included a long list of associations representing wide-ranging industries: coatings and sealants, various food products, construction materials, and more. The coalition members had a vested interest in limiting or streamlining the labeling requirements for their products. They didn't want to deal with an array of varying requirements from different states and preferred to avoid excessive labeling.

Some of the points the proponents made sound reasonable. They said that extensive warnings on products about both serious and minor health risks confuse consumers and don't necessarily help people choose the healthiest, safest, or least dangerous option.

The bill mentioned using the "best available science" to determine the appropriate level of warning on a product. That sounds good on the surface. Relying on peer-reviewed studies improves the chance that the research is impartial. But the bill provided a loophole in the case that such studies weren't available. The "best available" research could be funded by the very companies that stand to make a profit selling products that would require warnings if states were empowered to create and enforce labeling laws.

Companies making environmentally friendly products opposed the Accurate Labels Act. Their actions are not wrong, but they are not necessarily as altruistic as they seem. Companies in the natural products sector benefit from legislation—whether at the federal or state level—that would require their competitors to post warnings on products or list all the ingredients they use.

State by state

Under the specter of looser regulations from the U.S. federal government between 2016 and 2020, states stepped up to create legislation, with the hope that their regulations can spread throughout the country. A state-by-state approach makes sense in some situations. Emissions controls on vehicles in California, for example, have been adopted by other states. When I (Julia) moved to Washington in 2014, I could only bring my car with me if it met California emission standards. Fortunately, I came from California, so the requirement wasn't a problem.

California has long been an early adopter of regulations designed to improve safety. Proposition 65, the Safe Drinking Water and Toxic Enforcement Act of 1986, requires labels warning consumers that places or products "contain substances known to the state of California to cause cancer." The warnings probably don't do as much good as the authors of Prop 65 intended. When warnings appear everywhere, people become immune to their effect. If cancer-causing substances surround us, how are we supposed to avoid them? It seems inevitable that if we live long enough, something in our environment will give us cancer.

Regardless of the real service to citizens, California continues to lead the way with legislation aimed at restricting certain substances of concern. One example is Senate Bill 258, the "Cleaning Product Right to Know Act of 2017," which passed in California in September 2017. The law requires all manufacturers of consumer cleaning products to disclose full ingredient lists on their websites and on product labels if they want to sell their products in California.

Such regulations affect businesses nationwide. Manufacturers can't afford to ignore California—it's too large a market—so they will be driven to create compliant products. It doesn't make sense to create different products or labels just for one state.

The role of local government

Local governments have an important role to play in encouraging (or discouraging) sustainable business practices. In some cities, companies wanting to gain government contracts are graded on their adherence to environmental initiatives. One such city is Portland, Oregon.

Suppliers submitting bids to do work for the city of Portland earn points for sustainable practices such as providing products with a certain percent recycled content or making a less toxic or more energy-efficient product than their competitors. But suppliers need to back up claims with data and follow the guidelines of the ISO 20400 sustainable procurement standard, first introduced in 2017.

The ISO website states that sustainable procurement "involves ensuring that a company's suppliers behave ethically, that the products and services purchased are sustainable and that such purchasing decisions help to address social, economic and environmental issues." The concept can apply equally to corporate and government suppliers.

Portland is far from the only city with policies that encourage environmentally friendly business practices. Cities up and down the West Coast and beyond operate similarly, and the national trend is heading toward rewarding businesses for removing toxicants and reducing waste.

Possible new laws: a wish list

When we interviewed people for this book, we asked most of them this question: What new regulation or law would you like to see by 2030? Here are some of their answers.

Karen Brown, Brewer Science: I would love to see more climate action. I was thrilled that the U.S. Inflation Reduction Act included as much as it did. And I would love to see the government continue funding alternative energy, and continue energy credits for businesses and consumers who use those things.

Paul Randle, marketing consultant: Ban all advertising communications companies from serving the petrochemical industry.

Alexis Eyre, marketing consultant: Make it so that everyone has to report on the triple bottom line. I think we're never going to get anywhere until every single company in the world has to report on it. Then it will be all about reputation management, because you can't hide behind the figures.

Jen Keane, Modern Synthesis: I would like to see taxes on fossil fuel-based or non-circular products.

Ramón Arratia, Ball Corporation: Legislation around transparency of carbon in companies is necessary. Like what the World Economic Forum and First Mover Coalition are doing with the hard to abate sector, looking at where the interventions are most needed in order to have a big disruption and uptake of new technologies for those hardware sectors.

Jan Dell, The Last Beach Cleanup: We need better laws for fast food packaging. There's not enough attention to this, especially in America, because we are a Fast Food Nation. And that is the stuff you always find in the top ten items from the beach cleanups.

Jonatan Kleimark, ChemSec: We would like to see a law banning the use of harmful chemicals in consumer and professional products. That would require a lot of work, but will also ensure that we have a safer environment and better health for people.

Sherri Monroe, Additive Manufacturing Green Trade Association: The AM Forward Initiative in the US is incredibly important. And even though it sort of pertains to the US, it really pertains to the world.

Neva Murtha, Canopy Planet: Conserving forests is the fastest and cheapest way to mitigate the climate and biodiversity crises. We'd love for nations to take conservation of vital forests seriously by protecting more carbon and biodiversity-rich forest area. This will be good for the planet, as well as local and indigenous communities living near and in forests.

Oliver Harry, Encirc: What we really need is an increase in the circular economy through recycled glass coming back to us and contained in new bottles to get as high a recycled content as possible, up to 90–95 percent.

Andrew Winston, author and consultant: The easy answer for me has always been some form of price on carbon. Also something that helps manage misinformation. It's not any one law, but I think it's killing us. There's a percentage of the population that believes really very wrong things based on anti-science, and it's dangerous.

Many of these answers reflect our interviewees' specialized work. When you have a hammer, everything is a nail. But we have a feeling that if we asked specifically, nearly everyone we talked to would support a tax on carbon emissions.

The triple bottom line

Companies that are forward-thinking about materials sourcing and use often embrace the concept of the triple bottom line or the three Ps: people, planet, profit. Companies need to create profit, of course, or at least have a goal of doing so. Otherwise, they would be nonprofits or NGOs. Focusing on people means doing right by employees, customers, and the communities in which they operate rather than only prioritizing returns of shareholders. Focusing on the planet means keeping environmental concerns in mind: limiting pollution, emission of greenhouse gases, and waste.

As David Biello eloquently points out in *The Unnatural World*, people and planet are linked. The survival of the human species should be the ultimate goal of pro-environment efforts. If some combination of pollution, rising ocean levels, natural disasters, and disease were to wipe out the entire human population on the earth, the planet would continue spinning on its axis and orbiting the sun. Some life forms would survive—probably things like insects, bacteria, and various aquatic species—and the world would continue without us.

More and more companies are getting on board with the concept of triple bottom line, but it can be tricky to avoid this becoming yet another example of greenwashing. Companies want to claim that they are responsible corporate citizens. But saying that they care about the triple bottom line is not enough.

All three aspects of the three Ps need to be balanced, which will often look like profit needs to take a back seat. Depending on where a company starts when it embarks on a three-pronged approach to measuring success, quarterly profits may indeed take a dive as money is invested in improving business practices. Paying workers fairly or redesigning a manufacturing line costs more money than continuing business as usual. Done correctly, however, committing to the three Ps will likely have only a short-term negative impact on profits.

B Corp certification

B Corp certification through the nonprofit organization B Labs demonstrates that a company has met strict standards addressing corporate structure, employment practices, environmental impact, and community involvement. Certified B Corps are making a public statement that they support a triple bottom line. When sustainability-minded customers who are familiar with B Corps see the B Corp logo on a product, that gives them a positive impression of the brand.

The B Corp certification process is quite involved, with many detailed questions, and it isn't easy. The answers to those questions do matter. It's not just a matter of completing a simple application and filling in the boxes. Companies must recertify regularly and pay an annual membership fee to be part of the B Corp community.

A company must receive a minimum score of 80 points out of 200 to qualify for certification. Even the top-performing companies will likely have scores well below 200, as the maximum is designed to be a high bar to encourage continual improvement. If it were easy to score 100 percent, the incentive to improve would disappear.

Companies that start the certification process often realize that they will need to make many changes in the way they do business to become a certified B Corp. That realization forces them to either embark on a major effort—which will cost money and compete with the daily demand of running the business—or abandon the goal of B Corp certification.

The B Corp community grew significantly in 2023, and over 6,400 Certified B Corps now operate in 88 countries and 159 industries. This represents an increase of over 20 percent from the previous year. The European B Corp community grew by 63 percent and is now represented in 27 countries across the continent.

Several factors have contributed to the growth of the B Corp movement. One factor is the increasing awareness of the importance of social and environmental impact among consumers and investors. Another factor is the growing availability of resources and support for businesses that want to become B Corps.

We interviewed Karen Brown at Brewer Science, the first company in the semiconductor manufacturing sector to earn B Corp certification.

Interview

Karen Brown, Brewer Science

How did you become interested in social and environmental issues, especially living in the St. Louis area, which is not necessarily the hotspot of those kinds of ideas?
I've always been on the progressive side of things. And so I think that is part of what drew me to Brewer Science as an employer all those years ago. Here in our red state, I wouldn't say that Brewer Science is a bleeding heart liberal. We're not a Ben and Jerry's or a Patagonia. But we have a CEO who has made it part of the fabric of our company that we're here to do good. We're here to have a positive impact and to leave the world a better place than it was.

A lot of companies will say that their people are their most important resource. But Brewer Science walks that talk. We may not be out there leading the activist charge with other B Corps. But we're making a difference. We're doing things in the sustainability space that not everyone in our industry is doing. We have phenomenal employee programs and benefits. We have great relationships with our local communities and your community involvement. We've made great strides in our supplier development and relationships.

How did you get involved with the B Corp certification at Brewer Science?
In 2018, two executives learned about the B Corp certification. They talked to [founder] Terry Brewer, and the three of them and the senior leadership agreed that Brewer Science values and vision really was a great fit with B Corp certification.

Alan Gerson, our chief legal officer, and Doyle Edwards, director of government relations, approached me. They said, we know that you are great at managing projects, we know you have a passion for the types of things that B Corps do, we are going to pursue this certification, and we would like you to lead the effort. We talked with my manager, and she agreed. And then the adventure began.

We had our first kickoff meeting with the internal team on St. Patrick's Day of 2020. And then, of course, everything went south quickly after that.

When I had agreed to do this, and my manager had agreed that I could devote the time to it, B Lab was estimating that it would be about a six to nine month window from start to finish. Well, apparently, when everyone went into lockdown and moved to remote work, people decided that that was a great time to get B Corp certification. B Lab was just slammed with applications. And so it actually took us 13 months.

I've been involved all that time. After we got our certification, we started to do all of the follow up. The B Lab folks want you to have a point person. And they use all of this B-related terminology. The online community, they call it the B Hive. And the contact person at each company is called the B Keeper. I've been functioning as the B Keeper.

Who else in your company is involved?
We have two internal teams going at this point. We had the initial team that we call the B Certified team. That was the group of functional area folks who helped me answer the impact assessment and round up all of the evidence that we needed to to substantiate our answers.

I think we started with about six people and ended up with ten or twelve. The areas of the assessment match what the B Corp folks call the Five Pillars of impact. Governance is one of those. So I depended very heavily on our finance folks, on senior leadership, because governance has to do with your written policies, procedures, your transparency, and your ethics. Employees is another one of the areas. So of course, I relied heavily on several people from HR. Recruiting, benefits, finance from a payroll perspective, training and development, performance reviews, and all of those things.

There's an environmental piece, which for us was the largest piece because in addition to the five impact areas, every company that gets certified has to choose a business impact model. And we ended up choosing environmentally innovative manufacturing, so that area became a double whammy. I relied on the EHS folks.

Then we have the community pillar, which is sort of part of employees, it's all about people. We added some new folks that head up our community volunteering. There's a big push on suppliers. So we have people on the team from purchasing and our supplier management.

And then there's a pillar that's called customer, but it's not what you would typically think of. It's not really customer service, or customer relations, it's really about doing business in a way that your customers can have faith in you and trust in you. That you do what you say and you say what you do. How open are you? Do you allow customers to come in and audit? Do you have certifications like ISO?

After we got certified, our focus shifted more towards informing and engaging our employees with the certification. So then we have that other team called B the Change. They've led some activities, volunteer efforts, educational efforts, to help everybody understand what it means that we're a certified B Corp. What does that mean for me as an employee, if I'm at a trade show, or if I'm at a family dinner, and somebody asks me? How do I answer that?

Yes, it's quite the endeavor to achieve certification. I looked at the requirements on the B Lab website, and there are a lot of questions to answer. Where do things stand now, in early 2023?
What currently is complicating things for us right now is that you have to recertify every three years. Our official certification date is April 21, 2021. The B Lab folks recommend that between 6 and 12 months in advance of your expiration date, you start getting ready and working on recertification. So we've started having those conversations and are preparing to do that. But last fall [2022], B Lab released an updated version of those standards and those questions for conversation.

It's still not clear for us and for all the companies that are going to be recertifying this year and next year. Which set of questions will we answer on the impact assessment? I've distributed the proposed new standards internally, and we're looking at those and going ahead and trying to align with those where we think we may have some work to do. Because we know that if not in 2024, then definitely in 2027, those are going to apply to us.

That is an issue when any kind of certification or standards body does an update. Where do you fall in terms of do you go by the old rules or the new rules?
And they can't tell us that. They hold monthly "prepare for recertification" webinars. I attended one and asked that question, and they said, we don't know yet.

As I understand it, and you may know a lot more about this than I do, the changes are geared toward making sure that companies are doing something in all those five categories versus just being really strong in one. There were companies that were earning most of their points from one category and in the other areas, they really weren't doing a very good job. What advice would you give to other companies in your industry that are considering B Corp certification?
One of the lessons that we learned and one of the things that I would share with other companies who would decide to pursue this certification is documentation. There were areas where we were doing things and gave ourselves full points when we did the self-assessment, but ended up not getting points because we didn't have a written policy. Or we didn't have the proper data to back it up.

I'll give you an example. One of the things that we have always been strong in is community involvement. I mean, Dr. Brewer himself personally has been recognized by the state of Missouri for outstanding philanthropic activity. Our employees are always volunteering, we have multiple volunteer opportunities, food drives, etc. We even have community service leave and have had for probably at least 10 or 12 years a policy where every employee gets 32 paid hours a year to volunteer.

But we didn't do a very good job of tracking when people use that leave. And so we didn't get credit for any of that. That was really disheartening. Since our certification, we've looked at where we didn't score well and what we could do to change that. The two women who head up the employee volunteer area have just really stepped up. They wrote a very detailed policy. They've led informational meetings with employees. They have got a new tracking system. They have got a little carrot in there to help people make sure that they are submitting the hours that they volunteer. They recognize an outstanding volunteer every quarter.

I feel very confident that when we do our recertification, we will score very well in that area. We were doing all of the work, we just didn't have the documentation. A big piece of advice that I would give any company is that you prepare for this type of certification. It's not just, are you doing the work, but do you have a documented process? And can you easily pull the data that shows that you are following that process?

It sounds like those employees were managing the volunteer tracking in a way that people didn't feel like it's this additional burden.
Absolutely. Our team made it very easy to do.

Another area where companies can get a lot of points is being very engaged in your local community. I mean, that's huge. They want you to be sourcing and using suppliers locally, and they want you volunteering in your local community.

One of the areas is locally impactful banking. We have a great relationship with a local bank in Rolla. They are very engaged in the community. So we very confidently thought, hey, we'll get full points for that. That was another area where we got no points, because the bank that we use is a branch of Bank of America. We discussed it with our auditor, and said, they are very engaged in the community, and we partner with them. And she said, "That's all wonderful, but they are a corporate entity. They are not a locally owned bank. And so it does not fit our definition of local banking." So we didn't get any points for that.

That's interesting. So are there local banks that you would want to switch to?
That brings up a point that we have discussed internally. We've gone back, and looked at how we scored and where we did not score particularly well and have discussed, what it would take to to do better? And whether doing that makes sense for us. And the decision has been no, in this particular instance. We like the relationship we have with that bank. It's important to us and so we're not going to make a change in our banking relationship.

Another area that we struggle with in our industry is getting local suppliers.

I was thinking about that because it's not as though there's a huge pool of semiconductor industry companies near you.
We've just had to accept it for what it is and we've tried to focus on that nonproduction supply area. For things like groundskeeping, cleaning services, cleaning supplies, food supplies, maybe coffee for the break room, each of our local offices will and should give preference to local suppliers. We know we're not going to get full points. But we've done the best we can because we know that, like you said, there are no chemical suppliers in our area.

Same thing with diversity and inclusion. Because we are limited in some of the chemicals we purchase for our manufacturing. There's one two suppliers in the entire world. Where we can, we give preference to diverse suppliers. And we include that in the sourcing. When we evaluate new suppliers, they get more points if they're diverse. But that can't be the only criteria.

In the semiconductor industry or in chemicals manufacturing, there are going to be limits to what you can do. It is different than if you're making consumer goods where you have a lot of choices. If you're sourcing cocoa beans, for example, you have choices. Some are better than others from the viewpoint of finding local suppliers or supporting diversity. How do you think about that?
We're not ever going to be the perfect B Corp. But as Dr. Brewer always likes to say, and has said since he founded the company, that we're not in business to make a profit, we're in business to leave the world a better place than it was. And so I think for us, that is the way we look at being a B Corp. We've now achieved B Corp certification, which validates that we have made and continue to make a positive

impact on our community, on our employees, on our customers, and through our suppliers on the manufacturing process.

I often focus on the question, what is your company's purpose? And how does that inform some of the decisions about which types of customers to serve, or what types of products to develop, or how to deal with toxicity and similar issues?

I'm sure we could get better at that. But we do make decisions in light of those values. When we built our newest manufacturing facility, that was something that Dr. Brewer wanted to do. He wanted to look at alternate energy sources. We use some geothermal energy for that facility. Know that probably would have been cheaper to just use straight electricity. But he was very adamant about that so that we do make those strategic choices.

We made that strategic choice to be zero waste to landfill. Even 20 years ago, when I started working there, and to this day, not a single employee on site has a trash can at their desk. They just have a small recycling container.

My colleague Edna is taking on a new project, getting rid of the plastic water bottles that we still have in vending machines, and that we still use when we have events where guests or customers come on site. And nobody really thinks about that. But really, if we're a B Corp, and we're thinking about sustainability, we should have a written process that we aren't going to offer disposable plastic bottles, we're going to use filtered water. For customers and visitors who may not have their own drinking container, we will provide a reusable cup. And employees will just know that if you want to drink water at work, you better bring your own container from home.

If you look in the whole scheme of things, it is probably a small piece of your whole footprint, but it's visible. Something simple as installing a dispenser with filtered water and buying some reusable containers with your logo on it to give out to visitors sends a message.

European Union pioneering role in certification

The EU has been a pioneer in environmental certification, developing a number of schemes to help businesses and organizations reduce their environmental impact. These schemes include:

- The EU Ecolabel: This is a voluntary scheme that sets high environmental standards for a wide range of products, from cleaning products to textiles.
- The EMAS (Eco-Management and Audit Scheme): This is a voluntary scheme that helps organizations improve their environmental performance by setting up an environmental management system.
- The EU Green Public Procurement (GPP) Directive: This directive requires public bodies in the EU to consider environmental criteria when purchasing goods and services.

Two other certifications deserve a more in-depth examination: the EU Ecodesign Directive and the EU Corporate Sustainability Due Diligence Directive.

European Union Ecodesign Directive

The EU Ecodesign Directive has evolved since its first set of Ecodesign measures in 2009. Amendments have extended the directive to cover product groups and strengthened requirements.

The EU Ecodesign Directive was updated in 2023 to include new requirements for energy efficiency and sustainability. The updated directive covers a wide range of products, including appliances, electronic devices, and lighting.

The updated Directive:

- Sets new minimum energy efficiency requirements for a wide range of products to reduce energy consumption. For example, new washing machines must be at least 21 percent more energy efficient than current models.
- Requires manufacturers to make their products more durable and repairable. They must make it easier to replace batteries and other components.
- Requires manufacturers to provide information about the environmental impact of their products. This information must be made available to consumers before they purchase a product.

EU corporate sustainability due diligence directive

EU Corporate Sustainability Due Diligence Directive ("CS3D") became law on December 1, 2023. The companies within its scope will be required to:

- Integrate due diligence into policies.
- Identify actual or potential adverse human rights and environmental impacts.
- Prevent or mitigate potential impacts.
- Bring to an end or minimize actual impacts.
- Establish and maintain a complaints procedure.
- Monitor the effectiveness of the due diligence policy and measures.
- Publicly communicate on due diligence.

The new EU rules will apply to:

Group 1: All companies with 500 employees or more and at least net €150 million turnover worldwide in every industry.

Group 2: Companies with 250 employees or more and at least net € 40 million turnover worldwide that operate in defined high impact sectors, e.g. textiles, agriculture, extraction of minerals.

Circular economy legislation

Legislators across the globe are passing new laws relating to the circular economy. Often they take their cues from European Commission legislation, as this has been on the statute books for many years, and businesses in the EU are already implementing new materials strategies to comply.

What does EU legislation say about the circular economy? This question is highly important because ultimately what will drive the circular economy for materials is legislation. The majority of businesses are focused on being compliant, rather than delivering better environmental impacts.

As of late 2023, few businesses are truly focused on genuine circularity or protecting biodiversity. Many of our interviewees are exceptional in their grasp of circularity and the execution of their materials strategies. Most businesses are concentrating on recycling, reducing emissions, and studying impacts.

The 2022 EU Circular Economy Action Plan (CEAP) contains some key clauses related to materials. The new action plan announces initiatives along the entire life cycle of products. It targets how products are designed, promotes circular economy processes, encourages sustainable consumption, and aims to ensure that waste is prevented and the resources used are kept in the EU economy for as long as possible. It introduces legislative and non-legislative measures targeting areas where action at the EU level could bring genuine environmental improvements.

The CEAP's focus mirrors many of the ideas we discussed in earlier chapters, including:

- Reducing the use of hazardous chemicals,
- Improving product durability and repairability,
- Countering planned obsolescence,
- Increasing recycled content,
- Maintaining product performance,
- Addressing both finished products (electronics, furniture, etc.) and the materials needed to make them,
- Reducing packaging waste,
- Making packaging simpler by reducing the number of different materials,
- Supporting extended producer responsibility.

Clause 3.4 in the CEAP warrants in-depth reading, as it contains a huge amount of detail around plastics and bioplastics. The EU Strategy for Plastics in the Circular Economy recognizes the problem of explosive growth in plastics consumption. It announces the need to tackle global plastics pollution.

Since the first publication of this action plan on March 30, 2022, the EU has regularly published more detailed guidance, which each EU state is to bring to the statute book in its own country. There is some margin for interpretation, but each state must implement a version of the plan. France has already begun.

Not surprisingly, this legislation has been criticized by single-use packaging suppliers. The associations for single-use paper and carton in particular have begun an extensive lobbying campaign to discredit rewash and reuse ecosystems.

Looking to the future

We can unequivocally predict that legislation that is already in place is affecting materials decisions in a major way, from low carbon cement to advanced biopolymers. There are changes happening in every material, in every sector, in every application.

Considering the existing legislation and commitments made by governments and companies, the following trends are expected to shape the materials sector of the future:

- Decarbonization to meet carbon neutrality goals,
- Reuse of materials and scrap that would otherwise become waste,
- Use of durable, nontoxic and recyclable materials in a circular economy,
- Use of renewable bio-based and biodegradable materials in a bioeconomy.

In addition to the circular economy, another policy area that is expected to influence materials sector is bioeconomy. The bioeconomy within the EU is promoted by the EU Bioeconomy Strategy from 2018. The main objectives of the EU Bioeconomy strategy related to materials is the support of research and innovation in the development of biobased, recyclable and marine-degradable materials to substitute for fossil-based and conventional materials.

The main sectors targeted by the strategy are packaging (use of bio-based and biodegradable polymers instead fossil-based ones) and construction (use of wood instead of concrete and steel). As shown by the EU Bioeconomy Strategy progress report published in 2022,[1] Europe has been successful in mobilizing investments and innovation in biobased materials and has a strong position in the global market. As the support for bioeconomy continues, the future of sustainable bio-based materials looks promising.

In broader terms, the bioeconomy is part of the key to transitioning away from our current fossil fuel-based economy. The EU Commission lists a biological-based approach amongst the EU's core tasks. There will be trade-offs, and solutions will likely vary from region to region depending on the local available resources. We (the authors) support these efforts to discover how to best make use of biological resources in a way that protects biodiversity and emphasizes circularity.

Note

1 European Commission, Directorate-General for Research and Innovation. 2022. European Bioeconomy Policy: Stocktaking and Future Developments: Report from the Commission to the European Parliament, the Council, the European Economic and Social Committee and the Committee of the Regions. Publications Office of the European Union. https://data.europa.eu/doi/10.2777/997651.

13   The Message You Send

The Value of Transparency and Disclosure

A lot of companies are promoting sustainability and also conflicting with it massively at the same time. They aren't realizing they're doing it.
—Alexis Eyre, The Sustainable Marketing Compass

The sheen of transparency

Capitalism is not inherently good or inherently evil. At its best, it encourages innovation and creativity. At its worst, it prioritizes the wealth of the few over the rights of many. Business fulfills an important role in society. Companies large and small produce goods and services that people either need for survival or want to own to improve their quality of life. At the same time, many industries exploit the natural resources of the planet with seemingly little concern for the negative consequences of their practices.

The path forward can take a positive direction, but that requires transparency. Greenwashing, in which companies tout advances in sustainability while continuing damaging practices—producing vast streams of toxic waste or burning excessive quantities of fossil fuels, for example—is a real concern.

This chapter looks at the stories that companies tell and shares some specific examples. These stories emphasize the importance of not only doing the right thing but communicating actions in a way that is honest and resonates with those affected.

Transparency is an important concept as people try to distinguish what is really going on behind the scenes. In a world that seems in so many ways like George Orwell's *1984*, how do we know the truth? Transparency is a valid goal. People appreciate stories where companies talk honestly about what went wrong and how they are fixing it. We hope that the next generation of products will have nothing to hide. In fact we'd like them to be not just transparent, but *actively* transparent. We want to see businesses publicize their failures as much as their successes on their road to embedding more responsible business practices.

But what *is* hiding behind the sheen of transparency? The magician says, "There's nothing up my sleeve" and reveals a bare arm, hoping that the audience will focus its attention on the sleeve and not notice as she sneaks something into her pocket with expert sleight-of-hand. A company spokesperson says, "Look, here are the windows, we cleaned them, you can see everything that's inside. Tour our

DOI: 10.4324/9781003409267-17

facilities, look at our shiny new certifications." Yes, everything you can see looks good. But what if all the clear windows are meant to distract the viewer from the one window in the corner where the shades are drawn? What nefarious problems or toxicants are hiding behind that window?

Companies, like performing magicians, need not share everything. That destroys competitive advantage. Companies can't let their customers in to see all that happens behind the scenes. They justifiably need to keep proprietary trade secrets away from the prying eyes of their competitors. If they divulge everything that's in a proprietary formula, including how to process all the ingredients, a competitor could make the same product at a lower price.

The trick involves achieving the right balance. How can a company honestly share its story, and convince customers its products are pure, safe, or wholesome, without giving away too much? For companies that have no skeletons in their closet, this shouldn't be too difficult. They can share a story explaining how they evaluated the products on the market, considered how to make theirs more effective, and always chose a path that avoided toxic ingredients or wasteful manufacturing processes.

Some companies have championed such efforts from the beginning. These companies are always under pressure to keep to their principles, though. They can't let the lure of extra profit tempt them to consider a material or process that doesn't mesh with the values their brand promotes.

Companies long associated with responsible business practices are also under heightened public scrutiny. People try to poke holes and search for signs of hypocrisy. They doubt the company's motives and criticize minor missteps. The most responsible companies take note of negative comments and either refute them (with science and facts) or work to improve those aspects where they may not perform so well.

Tactics for messaging depend on whether a company is operating in a business-to-business or business-to-consumer model. Companies selling materials or products to other businesses need to provide a level of detail that will give engineers or chemists the information they need to make an informed buying decision. Selling directly to consumers requires a less technical message.

The confusion around labels

Consumers need information presented in a way that they can understand. Most people aren't stupid, but they may be ignorant. An ingredient list means little if the audience doesn't know the difference between one ingredient and another. Just because an ingredient has a long name, that doesn't mean it is toxic. Nor does labeling something "natural" mean it must be safe. Oleander is natural, but all parts of the plant are highly poisonous. Ingesting the leaves, flowers, or stems or breathing smoke from burning the branches can be fatal.

The drive toward removing chemicals from products has led to more products being labeled as "natural" and "simple." They tend to have fewer ingredients than the products they are replacing, but that doesn't necessarily make them safer or healthier. So-called natural products are often safer than conventional ones made with synthetic industrial chemicals, but that is not always the case.

Many consumers do not understand the limitations of the "natural" label. Calling something natural requires no certification or audit. It is one of those greenwashing buzzwords with no teeth behind it. The word can mean whatever a company wants it to mean.

This may change in the future as legislators all over the world are planning to pass laws requiring brands to have claims backed up by an independent authority or disclose evidence of valid scientific test results. New laws were introduced in the EU in 2023 that oblige brands to prove their environmental claims and labels through independent verification will make it harder for brands to label their products "natural" or "nature friendly" without firm scientific evidence.

Companies should automatically explain what they have done to make a "greener" product, why they have taken the steps they have, and which steps aren't possible right now. And they should do so in plain language. That way, the customer will be in a better position to make an informed decision. Positioning one product as "sustainable" or "safe" and competing products as "unsustainable" or "unsafe" is oversimplifying the situation. But it's clear that legislation is required, as many sectors are awash with greenwash and exaggerated claims.

Some customers want to know more details and need to understand the challenges that manufacturers face. What limits their efforts? Manufacturers face constraints on materials, technology, or costs. More environmentally friendly materials may not be commercially available. Technology may not be able to produce certain products reliably or in high enough volume. The costs of making a change may be too high for the market to bear.

Regardless of the audience, messaging should be clear rather than confusing or contradictory. That sounds obvious. In reality, figuring out what to say when and how to say it is tricky. Your audience may not read your message the way you intended. Consultants Alexis Eyre and Paul Randle have been tackling the challenge of appropriate messaging for several years. We spoke to them to learn the story behind their work developing the Sustainable Marketing Compass.

Interview

Alexis Eyre, founder of Green Eyre, and Paul Randle, founder of Pickle Consulting

What sparked your interest in working in the intersection between marketing and sustainability?

Alexis: I ended up in hospital for the third time for severe stress. And I said to myself, "I can't do this anymore. I just need to get away." So I quit my job that fall.

I've always wanted to sail across the Atlantic. There's a sailboat race every year in October that is called the ARC. It's a massive race that goes across the Atlantic from Gran Canaria to Saint Lucia. Hundreds of boats take part. I had missed it.

Then someone contacted me and said, "Do you want to come back with us? We're going to be sailing the other way, from the Caribbean back to the UK." I told them that I would love to join.

We set off into this wonderful world in one of the most remote places on this planet. At some point, we no longer saw any boats and started not to even see any wildlife, apart from birds. I realized how much more diverse the world is closer to the shores where it is shallower, and there are more plants and therefore more fish life.

And yet we were surrounded by plastic bottles. We were literally 1,000 miles from land, almost one of the furthest points you can be from land and we kept on seeing plastic bottles. Then a plastic chair passed me, and I just couldn't get my head around it. How are we in the middle of this wilderness and yet, we see almost more human stuff than wildlife?

That upset me hugely. When I came back, I started this new job more for recovery than anything. I was looking for education about sustainability, something I could do. I wanted to earn a master's degree but couldn't afford it. So I enrolled in the Cambridge Institute Sustainability Leadership course in early 2020, and it changed my life. That's where I met Paul.

Paul: I have been a marketer for my entire career, ever since university, and worked a lot in the corporate global space. I have been consulting for about almost a decade now.

At one point, I was consulting with an automotive client. I just finished a call about promoting one of their cars. And my 13-year-old daughter wandered up to me and simply said, "Daddy, is your job good for the environment?"

I've no happy answer, to be perfectly honest.

Way back at the start of my career, I'd been in the marketing team at the British Standards Institution. And I had worked on the launch of ISO 14001, the environmental best practice standard. I worked with people like Jonathon Porritt from Friends of the Earth. So I knew that world, and it had been a personal passion. But somehow I got kind of diverted into the world of big tech and things of that nature. My daughter's question was the kick I needed to go and change things.

As part of my retraining, I took the Cambridge University Institute for Sustainability Leadership course. Alexis and I sat on that course as one of the very few marketers, increasingly feeling like the devil incarnate. You know, it's kind of like we were viewed as the problem. And complicit in making things far, far worse.

My initial knee-jerk reaction was, I'm gonna retrain and I'm getting myself out of marketing. I'm going to do some good with the rest of my career.

Alexis: We both said, we're quitting our jobs. One of the professors from the course told us, "Please do not quit your jobs. You now have the knowledge, you now understand the systemic change that's required. Now go back into marketing, because you've got all the expertise, and make sure it becomes a force for good."

Paul: This professor sat us down and said, "Look, marketing has a lot to offer. Marketing can change hearts and minds, marketing can change behavior. And if one of the things you need most at the moment on the planet is behavioral change, it is just that marketing is pointed in the wrong direction."

And that, I suppose, became our mission, Alexis' and mine, to change the direction of marketing.

The two of you developed the Sustainable Marketing Compass to do just that. What are the first things that people need to know about this compass?
Paul: It's the intent behind it. When we had that kind of aha moment with our professor, we asked ourselves what's causing marketing to be pointed in the wrong direction. We looked at all the foundations of marketing, the strategic toolkits that we use, things like the four Ps [product, price, positioning, promotion] going back to the origins of marketing. Without exception, they all have a commercial performance intent behind them. There's no toolkit for marketing that looks at environmental performance. There's no toolkit for marketing that looks for societal impact, and nothing that ties them all together.

So the idea behind the compass was to re-equip marketing with a toolkit to drive that thinking. What we've found more than anything, it drives a mindset shift. It gets people to think about the United Nations Sustainable Development Goals first, rather than just thinking, money, revenue, and things of that sort of nature.

What kind of response have you gotten from people in marketing about that?
Alexis: They absolutely loved it. Because predominantly, the companies we've worked with have been companies that want to push the boundaries in everything anyway, on the sustainability front. We've gone into contracts with them explaining that this is an evolving framework.

When we went to launch it to the world, it was extraordinary. Our post was viewed by almost three quarters of a million people in the first 24 hours it went live. The main thing that really came out was, "Finally there is something we can do."

We've got people who are passionate about sustainability, but don't know anything about it. They want to do something, but just have no idea even where to start. We had sustainability professionals who understand marketing respond with delight. Finally, they think, we can give something to the marketing teams and actually know that they can make a difference. Because we've always focused on every other function, but never really considered marketing apart from how we use marketing to communicate the sustainability plans of a company. We never thought that marketing itself can actually positively contribute.

Other people responded, "Brilliant, what is sustainable marketing?" Literally, as in what is this new marketing thing? So, it was amazing to see. It's picked up a lot of interest. And I think hopefully, it's started to help fill a gap. We made a planning framework that can be easily navigated that pulled all this thinking and all these wonderful pockets of amazingness that we're seeing out there together into one place. It's taken us a year and a half to plot out all these things. And everyone doesn't have a year and a half to map it out. So I think that's where it's also hopefully made people's lives a lot easier.

That's fantastic. Alexis, you talk in social media posts about deceptive advertisements. Tell me about situations where companies are not purposely trying to hide everything, but that's what they're doing accidentally.

Alexis: I think you've got a lot of companies who are kind of promoting sustainability and also conflicting with it massively as well at the same time. To your point, they aren't realizing they're doing it. They're talking about their company's sustainability objectives, and then using disposable plastic glasses at their event. Now, that's a really minor example. But they don't see the connection the whole way through. They just say, we've communicated that [our sustainability plan] over here. But we're going to carry on with our marketing without thinking that we need to connect the dots. That's what we're seeing the most, it's that lack of understanding that marketing needs an entire sustainability lens for every single decision, not just communicating the company's sustainability objectives.

Paul: There's a lot of talk about greenwashing. And it's a huge problem. To your point earlier, though, most people aren't doing that maliciously. We can all think of a couple of industries that might be, but most industries and most marketing teams are absolutely not trying to do that. They just don't know the best way to talk about it. Talking about sustainability as a job done, for example, is always going to fail because we're never finished with the transition. The pace of change in sustainability itself means that what you're communicating today can suddenly become wrong tomorrow, but not for any fault of your own. What we realized through the development of the compass was that we ask companies at the start to redefine success. We will define success across commercial, environmental, and societal. When you're trying to think what are you doing in those three areas, you suddenly come to the realization that you can't stretch the balloon across all of them equally. Sometimes you might be overcooking on your commercial performance to the detriment of your environmental performance. So you need to rein in your commercial performance. And that really pivots the role of marketing.

Rather than just being about a growth engine, which is the whole way that people think about marketing at the moment, it's more of a kind of regulator valve that says, we need to de-perform here to increase performance there. So you actually kind of shape the success footprint of the organization. And that leads to some phenomenal briefs. You know, lots of people have talked about the Patagonia campaign, "don't buy this jacket." That was saying keep brand loyalty, but don't sell anything. There's some brilliant new challenges for marketers in there, we've just got to realize that the world is changing.

How can consumer-facing brands help their customers understand the difference between this certification and that one and figure out which eco-friendly claims actually have anything behind them? People don't want to spend ten hours researching to figure out what type of shampoo or shoe to buy.

Paul: That is a massive challenge. I think it's going to be about that kind of shift where brands start to really stand for something and deliver against societal things and deliver against their environmental objectives. It becomes fundamental and part and parcel of what they do and what their products and services are. At the moment, industry standards are just a hygiene level, really, getting to the bare minimum. Ideally, you're going a lot further. Certification marks are great, but they all just highlight the lowest common denominator. What you want are companies that are going way beyond that, and being transformative. And you only get to that place when it becomes truly part of your ethos and your culture of what you're doing.

Do you have an example of a manufacturing company that is doing a good job of telling stories about the sustainability benefits of its products, about what they've done and about what they haven't done?
Alexis: VEJA is probably one of the best examples I've seen. I love when you get a pair of trainers [athletic shoes], and it goes through everything. What happens if you get a hole? It tells you how you repair it. It tells you exactly where every single material in your shoe has come from, why they've chosen that material, the benefits, the downside. It's all encompassing, it tells you everything you need to know about your shoe, how you prolong its life, what you do with the end of life. It's a full double-page spread of information. But in a really interesting, wonderful way that you're actually quite interested in because they set out like a page from *The New York Times*. I think they're absolutely brilliant.

Radium, a supposed wonder material

The Radium Girls by Kate Moore, published in 2017, tells the story of the women and girls who worked for the United States Radium Corporation (USRC) in Orange, New Jersey, and the Radium Dial Company in Ottawa, Illinois. Business began booming for the USRC during World War I, with glow-in-the-dark watches headed to soldiers overseas. Even after the war, demand continued, and more companies sprung up as the radium industry grew. The Radium Dial Company was one of these.

News in those days didn't travel instantly, like it does today. When the USRC dial painters in New Jersey began falling ill and dying while still in their twenties, as a result of daily exposure to radium, the workers at the Radium Dial Company in Ottawa knew nothing about it. Girls and young women flocked to dial painting jobs at the new company for the money and the camaraderie, just as they had halfway across the country a decade earlier.

Day after day, young women painted dials onto clocks and watches with glow-in-the-dark paint. The source of the glow? Radium, a naturally radioactive element. It seems shocking today, but 100 years ago the company instructed the workers, many of whom were still in their teens, to lick the ends of their paint brushes to achieve the fine point necessary to paint details on miniature watch faces. The company told them it was perfectly safe. Safe? The girls were slowly poisoning themselves by ingesting small quantities of radium every day for years.

The disfigurement of these girls from radium poisoning and their painful, drawn-out deaths is horrifying and sickening. Perhaps just as sickening is the attitude of the companies that employed the dial painters. Predictably, they denied responsibility for their employees' ailments despite mounting evidence to the contrary. They hired their own doctors and hid any evidence that suggested that the radium in the paint was linked to sickness or death.

USRC and Radium Dial Company may be considered as artifacts of the early twentieth century, a time supposedly before people understood the dangers of toxic materials. Although it seems hard to believe, radium was promoted as being healthy. People actually drank tonics containing tiny amounts of radium. But there were hints about the dangers as early as 1901.[1] Marie Curie, who earned a Nobel Prize for her discovery of radium, died from radium poisoning in 1934.

In *The Radium Girls*, the companies that were benefiting from selling radium products come across as being completely heartless, pursuing profits with no concern for the health of their employees. Kate Moore's book points out that the companies knew of the dangers of radium but hid it from workers, perhaps not unlike the attitude of the tobacco industry toward its customers decades later. Certainly, a corporation wouldn't dare lie to their workers, customers, or communities like this today, right? As we have seen in stories from earlier chapters, some companies are still acting in ways that can only be described as reprehensible.

We are struck by some parallels in the stories of the Radium Dial Corporation and DuPont (see Chapter 2). The Radium Dial Corporation hired its own scientists to publish research claiming that radium was safe, even healthy. DuPont hired its own veterinarians to examine Tennant's farm and determine whether DuPont's chemicals or Tennant's negligence were to blame in the cattle's demise.

It is more important than ever to approach companies who are guilty of polluting with a message that will encourage them to change their ways. As hard as it is to keep an open mind and learn all the facts before reacting, that's probably the best way to effect change.

Fortunately, change is happening. Workplaces in the US are safer today than they were generations ago, in part because of the radium girls' story. Their lawsuits played a role in developing the Occupational Safety and Health Administration (OSHA), which protects workers in the US. Labs, factories, and even products on store shelves are filled with warnings, and workers wear protective apparel when handling dangerous materials. Safety Data Sheets are mandatory. When radioactive materials or X-ray radiation are present, workers wear dosimeters to continually monitor their exposure levels.

Unfortunately, even organizations like OSHA and the European Agency for Safety and Health at Work (EU-OSHA) do not guarantee the health and safety of workers. And they offer no protection to customers or communities.

Clean diesel? Sorry, but no

Volkswagen (VW) boasted a position on the Dow Jones Sustainability World Index in 2015, the year its emissions cheating scandal became international news.

That year it had also been recognized as one of the most environmentally sustainable automobile manufacturers. Its cars, including some with diesel engines, won awards for being environmentally friendly. Unfortunately, a company can outwardly advertise its positive environmental impacts while hiding worse sins behind closed doors. We'll get to those sins in a moment.

The VW diesel scandal affected me (Julia) personally. When I was deciding which car to buy in 2011, I created a list of desired features and compared my top five cars. I chose the TDI diesel version of the VW Jetta Sportwagen. I reread my list in late 2016, shortly before selling my Jetta back to VW when the company offered a generous buyback program. The Jetta wasn't the obvious winner. What sold me, ironically, was the high fuel economy, along with the cargo space. I wasn't concerned about high fuel prices as much as buying a car that was relatively environmentally friendly.

In retrospect, the VW was a poor choice. VW's so-called clean diesel engine was anything but clean. It seems hard to believe that engineers purposely installed software to cheat the system, but that's exactly what happened. During emissions tests, the cars appeared to pass with flying colors. They could even meet the tough California emission standards.

On the road, it was another story. My car, along with millions of others, emitted toxic nitrous oxides (NOx) at levels far above those deemed acceptable anywhere in the US. As Steven Howard says in his book *Leadership Lessons from the Volkswagen Saga*, VW engaged not in accidental negligence but "deliberate corporate malfeasance." VW could have spent a few hundred dollars per car to install a catalytic converter that would have reduced emissions to an acceptable level. Instead, they deliberately misled their customers, creating a health hazard and polluting the environment.

The CEO didn't allow the cost increase and instead tasked the engineers with coming up with a different solution. In a corporate culture where whistle-blowing wasn't an option, the engineers didn't have much of a choice. They had to "park their morals at the door." They developed software that made it look as though NOx emissions met the standards.

In a strange twist, VW issued a recall of some of its TDI vehicles that were underperforming, some months after the emissions scandal had become public. It turns out that the cheat device software was responsible. Did VW admit what was happening? Absolutely not. It simply told customers to bring in their recalled vehicles for a free software upgrade. Without divulging the nature of the upgrade, they installed a new version of the cheat software that didn't interfere with vehicle performance. After the upgrade, the vehicles continued to emit just as much toxic NOx as before, only now with improved fuel mileage.

A snapshot of the VW website in 2023 highlights one of the company's new electric vehicles. The text reads, "We upgraded the traditional sedan. And turned it into a premium EV." A link to a page called "TDI Emissions" appears much further down the page. That link explains the now-closed settlement that offered customers a buyback or modification of their vehicle.

Progress isn't always consistent

In Chapter 3, we mentioned The Natural Step and its four principles for controlling the amount of resources we extract from the earth to produce goods. The Natural Step advocates for changes such as substituting less energy-intensive or less toxic materials. The organization works with both local governments and businesses large and small, including such giants as Nike, which adopted its approach back in 1998.

Nike worked with The Natural Step from 1998 to 2001 and then again in 2008. By 2008, Nike had already addressed problems related to treatment of workers who were manufacturing its products overseas. It was no longer being accused of labor violations, and it had already made strides in reducing toxicants. Nike began phasing out PVC from its products in 1999. The company was buying organic cotton to avoid the high levels of pesticides used to grow conventional cotton and had replaced petroleum-based adhesives and cleaners with water-based products. These steps created safer working conditions and reduced negative environmental impact.

Nike wanted to expand its environmentally sound production practices and make sustainability central to its core mission. Reducing a toxic by 90 percent is admirable, but removing it entirely is much better. In partnership with The Natural Step, Nike began to develop a long-term vision called the North Star that set concrete, challenging goals such as designing all products to consider closed-loop materials usage. It looked like Nike was on its way to embracing the circular economy.

Unfortunately, Nike's mission never progressed. In 2023, Nike stood accused of crossing a line on green product manufacturing policies. Nike was facing a lawsuit in Missouri alleging the company of "false and misleading marketing" by claiming its products meet government sustainability standards and are environmentally friendly.

"Of the 2,452 Nike 'Sustainability' Collection Products, only 239 products are actually made with any recycled materials," the lawsuit stated.[2] That's a 90 percent non-compliance rate, the lawsuit noted, adding that while Nike claims it makes its "Sustainability Collection" products with recycled fibers, the goods are manufactured using environmentally unfriendly synthetic materials.

Digging deep and telling the whole story

A thorough evaluation of the four system conditions requires digging beneath the surface. This involves investigating what is happening upstream and downstream beyond a company's own manufacturing facilities.

For example, companies should look at not only what materials they extract from the earth, and in what quantities, but where the materials come from. For example, does the company avoid using conflict minerals, those mined from war-torn regions of the world where workers are subjected to horrifying conditions?

Toxic substances of concern pose a difficult challenge. Getting rid of environmental toxicants is much harder than simply reducing exposure. A level of zero is impossible to measure, even with today's advanced sensors. Getting below detectable limits is the best to hope for.

If a company is absolutely dedicated to removing toxicants, and top executives are behind the effort, it can happen. Companies still need to invest time and money to determine which toxicants various products contain. They must trace everything back to suppliers and suppliers' suppliers. If products contain recycled materials, those materials sometimes include unintended toxic contaminants, as we noted in earlier chapters. Recycling isn't without risks.

Sourcing wood or palm oil from sustainably managed forests, where more trees are planted than harvested and clear cutting is usually avoided, reduces the destruction of natural resources. Not all mining operations are equally destructive. It is also possible to reduce the quantity of mined metals a company is using to begin with, through substituting recycled metals or making design changes.

Increasingly, environmental sustainability is being linked with social justice. It is more just to produce environmentally friendly products that average citizens can afford, and also to consider the conditions under which those products are being made. Worker safety cannot be ignored. Today's environmental conferences include a much greater emphasis on social justice, sometimes devoting entire sessions to the topic.

Pressure from customers is often what motivates companies to change. If executives fear that customers will flee unless they change their ways, they are more likely to make the necessary investments.

NGOs also have a role if they approach companies in a way that the executives will listen. That might involve a cooperative stance, while putting pressure where it is deserved. When a company that uses large quantities of water partners with an NGO working on water security, that can be a win-win. Sometimes a more aggressive stance is warranted. For example, boycotting fur has put many fur producers and tanneries out of business. PETA's "blood on the catwalk" ad was highly effective.

All of the examples above—removing toxic compounds, sourcing from more sustainable sources, and improving worker conditions—are better for people and the planet. They are also good business practices. For those practices to spread throughout industries, companies need to share their success stories. They also need to share their struggles. An honest message explains what the company has achieved, how that compares to its short-term and long-term goals, and what obstacles stand in the way. That type of message can inspire other companies and may lead to systemic change in the right direction.

Notes

1 Clark, C., C. E. Rosenberg, and C. Press. 1997. *Radium Girls, Women and Industrial Health Reform: 1910–1935*. Chapel Hill: University of North Carolina Press.

2 "United States District Court Eastern District of Missouri Eastern Division." 2023. https://s3.documentcloud.org/documents/23813170/10may23-missouri-nike-greenwashing-complaint.pdf.

14 Real-World Implementation for Businesses, Governments, and Individuals

I don't believe beach cleanups should be glamorized. If we have to still keep picking this stuff up, it means we're failing.

—Jan Dell, The Last Beach Cleanup

The change has to be systemic—the companies have to change, the policies have to change.

—Andrew Winston, author of Net Positive

Our many roles

Through reading this book, we hope you have learned at least a few new things. Perhaps you didn't know where metals and plastics come from, or if you did, you didn't know how they could be made in less wasteful ways. Perhaps you learned about companies you didn't know existed and how they are innovating to make practical use of materials that would otherwise go to waste. Perhaps you gained a new perspective on the role of laws and regulations or appreciation for the challenges facing companies whose reputation has been less than stellar.

Knowledge is good, but without action, it fades into the background, and we move along doing things the way we always have. We all play many roles in our lives: citizen, consumer, employer, employee, volunteer, and family member. Some of these roles afford us a particular advantage or disadvantage when deciding to remove pollutants or reduce waste. This chapter looks at each in turn and offers suggestions for ways to make a positive difference.

We are all citizens

Most adults are citizens of the country in which they were born or the country in which they reside, or in some cases, both. For those who are old enough and not otherwise barred, the status of citizenship conveys the right to vote and the right to run for office.

In the US and Europe, we can choose how to react to the prospect of national and local government removing restrictions on industries that pollute and contribute to

DOI: 10.4324/9781003409267-18

wasteful practices and increased burning of fossil fuels. We can decide that the situation is hopeless and do nothing. We can pretend that if we wait, the situation will take care of itself. We can take the view that it's someone else's problem or that it won't affect us personally. This is not an uncommon viewpoint, but it's not the best approach.

Instead, consider reacting to the loosening of federal restrictions by supporting state and local legislation aimed at improving public health and safety. We can vote for candidates who support responsible business practices.

Be an informed citizen. Whether the issue is a proposed ban on single-use plastic bags in your city or changes in the tax structure for businesses with manufacturing facilities in your region, learn about upcoming legislation. The more you know, the better you can decide how to vote or whether to do more than merely cast your ballot.

If you have a strong opinion on an issue, volunteer your time by:

- Gathering signatures to get a measure on the ballot,
- Signing online petitions supporting or opposing a measure,
- Calling your neighbors to encourage them to vote,
- Calling your congressional representatives at the state or federal level, MEPs, and local councilors and asking them to support or reject legislation which makes a difference,
- Joining a campaign to elect a candidate whose positions align with yours.

For those inclined to get more deeply involved, there are many opportunities, from volunteering for a committee or planning commission in your city to running for office. Plus, if you own stock in a corporation, you have a say in that company's actions. Jan Dell, who founded The Last Beach Cleanup in 2019, is doing just that.

INTERVIEW

Jan Dell, The Last Beach Cleanup

How did you come to found The Last Beach Cleanup?
I'm a chemical engineer, and I had a 35-year career working in 45 countries making stuff. I helped companies make everything from oil and gas in the Arctic and Libya to beverages, toys, and footwear. I helped Nike set up its first sustainability program starting in 1997.

In my last professional job in 2018, I was leading clean energy developments for a global engineering company. I led a whole division, with hundreds of people reporting to me. I was the vice chair of the US Federal Climate Committee in the Obama administration. I was an early proponent of adaptation to climate change.

People aren't going to quickly stop using energy or eating beef. In 2018, the world changed for me because Trump was elected, and he canceled the Climate Committee. And then, the company that I worked for bought another company that was building all the new plastics plants, for all the big oil and petrochemical companies. And my job was going to have to change from clean energy to helping them spew more plastic pollution into the world. And I said, no, I can't do this.

At that point, I was furious. I had been watching all the news about plastic production, expansion, and pollution. I had worked all over Asia and seen how bad plastic pollution was. I knew that what companies were saying about recycling was fraudulent. In those days, I understood it on an economic basis. But now I understand the toxicity issues around recycled plastic. This is actually the real deal killer, along with microplastics generated from recycling, but the toxicity issues have been completely overlooked by proponents of the circular economy of plastics. You can't take plastic and recycle it back safely into new food grade plastic, you cannot do it. It is not inert, like metal or glass.

I decided to write a book. I was going to call it "The Last Beach Cleanup," and my book was going to be set in 2036. I started to interview people and spent probably six months trying to map out this book. But the people I talked to kept saying, Jan, don't write the book. No one else is working on the issues the way that you can. What I heard from people, over and over again was that my chemical engineering background and my corporate experience was something that no NGO had. They didn't understand the solutions I was bringing forward. Everybody urged me to get working on it, not to write about it. And so I did. Finally, about a year later, I started my own NGO and figured out how to create a website to share my research.

Tell me more about how you started.
One of the first things that I had a major influence in impacting was ending plastic waste exports. I had worked in all these countries in Asia that are receiving our plastic waste. And it's just horrific the idea that we export our plastic waste to them, and California was the worst. So I started publishing the waste trade metrics, talking about the numbers. And then I started going to the waste companies and saying you need to commit to not doing this. They agreed, and then I got all these NGOs to sign on. We got the world's third-largest shipping company to say we won't even load it anymore. Plastic waste exports, especially from the US, have really declined.

In terms of the timing of China's ban on imports of trash and recyclables, was it just fortuitous that that happened around the same time that you were doing this work, or were you in some way involved?
I didn't have anything to do with it. This was just coincidental in my life, like the universe spoke to me.

Back in 2007, my husband and I took a walk on the beach in Bali at the COP13 Climate Conference where I was giving a speech on the need for proactive adaptation and building resilience to climate change. The beach was covered with plastic pollution. I told my husband, I want to quit my day job. Forget adaptation. I want to fight plastic pollution. It had bothered me for a long time. But if that random thing hadn't happened with my job change in 2018, I would probably still be over there working on clean energy.

There are many organizations claiming to deal with the plastic pollution problem. Some of them have very similar names. How can people without extensive scientific knowledge know which ones are really doing good and which ones want to continue to promote business as usual?
Look at who's funding them, period. Who is sponsoring them? If they have product companies or plastics companies as sponsors, there is a clear conflict of interest. Follow the money. Some of them hide it really well. What you have to do is read publicly available tax statements.

You show me someone promoting plastics or plastic recycling, and I'll show you someone getting a paycheck or other financial benefit from doing it. Plenty of activists like me take huge pay cuts to fight for progress on environmental, social, and health issues. I give up money to fight this. Every single person who's promoting any kind of plastic recycling solution is in it for the money.

I understand you do advocacy work. What is a recent win?
I work to propose effective laws backed by strong research and publicize the benefits. We got SB 343, the "Truth in Labeling" law, passed in California in 2021. It is going to get the chasing arrows off almost all plastic packaging and allow only bottles and jugs without bad shrink sleeves to get labeled. I take photos of products in stores with false recyclable labels. I'm starting to see progress. Even Target took "recyclable" off of polypropylene hummus tubs and Coca-Cola took "please recycle" off of Fairlife milk, which is an unrecyclable opaque plastic bottle with a bad shrink sleeve.

Our California label law is going to become the law of the land in the US because product companies label their products for nationwide sales.

Why don't the big waste companies—Waste Management and Republic Services—fight harder about plastic bag contamination in curbside bins when it hurts their operations? I think the big waste companies are sold out to the big retailers and product companies and don't want to criticize them.

I just filed a shareholder resolution with Kraft Heinz. I have stock in the company. A friend of mine has stock in some other companies, and I'm going to file more shareholder resolutions. I'm dying to find somebody with $2,000 of stock in Target or Walmart or Wendy's.

What about people who own stock in those companies through mutual funds?
No, it has to be in direct ownership, and you have to own the stock for at least three years. The issue I'm taking on right now is false labeling, and I'm filing shareholder resolutions that require companies to do a full report on whether their labels are legal or not, per California's law.

Back to beach cleanups. I sometimes mention beach clean-ups as a feel-good measure that corporate green teams do that temporarily raises morale. What is your take?
I don't believe beach cleanups should be glamorized. I'm not happy about Ocean Conservancy, who's funded by Dow and Coca-Cola, publishing these reports showing people celebrating big bags of plastic that they picked up from their beach. This is what we want to end, not to celebrate. If we have to still keep picking this stuff up, it means we're failing. That's why the goal is to get to the last beach cleanup, which means we've solved the problem.

When you're the CEO

The journey of World Centric demonstrates how to impact more people as a for-profit business than as a nonprofit organization. World Centric started as a non-profit but quickly realized that the demand for their compostable food containers was considerable. The organization began at a time when customers were aware of the problems with extruded polystyrene foam and willing to shell out money for an alternative. By transforming itself into a for-profit Benefit Corporation, World Centric can make money by selling products. It then invests some of those profits in projects benefiting communities around the world.

Closing the Loop (see Chapter 10) experienced a similar journey in the EU, transforming itself from an NGO to a social enterprise corporation. A market for used phones provided a business opportunity that aligned with the company's mission.

If you own a small business, you get to call the shots and determine how you want to implement sustainability. Small and privately owned businesses have an advantage over public companies in that they don't have to answer to shareholders. You can prioritize sustainability goals by choosing suppliers based on quality or ingredient lists without worrying about how that will affect the stock price. You can choose which certifications will be worth the investment of time and money required to obtain them.

On the flip side, small businesses don't benefit from economies of scale that keep costs down and enable larger margins. Suppliers who produce relatively small quantities of products have to pass an increased cost per item to their customers to stay in business. Large companies are in a position to lobby suppliers for discounts on environmentally friendly materials or products in exchange for publicity or a promise of regular orders. If your company is large enough, your decisions can sway an entire industry. Small businesses do not hold the same level of influence. They can, however, band together to effect industry-wide change.

Publicly held companies face different concerns than privately held ones. If you own a public company and are responsible to a board of directors and shareholders, they expect to see a return on their investment. Profit is always important. The tide is turning somewhat, though. Investors are also looking at social and environmental performance and long-term climate risk when deciding which companies to support.

Approaches to sustainability will necessarily differ by company, depending on what the top executives believe to be the most important values, those that their stakeholders will care about. Culture starts at the top, meaning that executives need to take ownership of the company culture, brand, and image and how they communicate that culture to employees and customers.

The importance of corporate culture is true for small businesses and large public companies alike. If you are in the executive suite, what message are you sending with your business practices?

If you want to lower your company's carbon footprint and reduce waste by addressing plastics usage, for example, consider the following:

- How does your company use plastic, and does it make sense to replace disposable or durable plastic products with those made from other materials?
- What does your waste stream look like? How much is discarded into the trash, recycling, or compost bins each week or year?
- Are employees and customers aware of recycling and composting processes? Do they know what to toss where? If not, clearer signage and employee training will help.
- Can you find opportunities to buy lower quantities of disposable plastic, or switch to compostable products if there are appropriate composting facilities in your city?
- Analyze your supply chain. Can you buy products that use less material, or buy products that last longer, whether they are made from plastic or other materials?
- If you ship products, examine how you are packaging them and whether you can reduce packaging, use more recycled content, or shift to reusable packaging, while still ensuring that your products arrive undamaged.

It will take some digging to figure out the best answers to the above questions. You need to carefully examine possible tradeoffs when swapping out materials or suppliers.

For companies in industries that generate toxic emissions or hazardous waste, the issues are much more complicated. Still, it is possible to limit the hazards by implementing more stringent safety procedures or swapping out chemicals for less toxic ones that can still achieve the desired goals for product performance.

In the second instance, nontoxic chemicals may cost more up front, but a thorough analysis could still show a cost savings. Hazardous waste disposal costs money. Even if the analysis doesn't directly demonstrate lower cost, it is possible to make a case for changing materials. Cost pressures are real, but businesses that create products sold directly to consumers can appeal to those who prefer an environmentally friendly product and are willing and able to pay a bit more.

Influencing your employer

If you work at a company, your ability to influence corporate practices is related to your job responsibilities and the size of the business. In many companies, the higher your relative rank, the better positioned you are to convince your company or department to change suppliers or package products more efficiently.

In a small company, it can be easier for any employee to have an influence. Company executives are more accessible, as opposed to some larger companies that have a hierarchical structure in which the chances of a message reaching the CEO seem remote. Without the top executives on board, company policy isn't going to budge.

Employees who care about environmental issues should understand how their company is positioning itself. Does the company prioritize addressing environmental problems because it is the right thing to do for the future of society regardless of short-term cost? Or is the focus more on doing the minimum required to give the impression of being a good corporate citizen? Are there specific incentives or penalties driving change toward new policies or procedures? Legal restrictions or the prospect of reduced taxes both exert pressure to adapt.

If you work for a company where the executives support a triple-bottom-line approach and value all aspects—people, planet, and profit—you can expect that your supervisor will listen and consider suggestions that will improve any of these aspects. Hopefully, your work environment is such that you feel empowered to propose suggestions based on your knowledge of current practices at your workplace.

The more you know, the more effective you can be in instigating change. Be aware of common industry-wide practices and those of the most forward-looking companies in your industry. Learn whether city, state, or national laws support or restrict the ideas you wish to implement. Armed with this knowledge, you have a greater chance at success.

If, on the other hand, you work at a company where profit is king and the executives have little patience for changes that cut into sales margins, your situation looks different. In this case, we see three choices: accept the way things are, look for a job at a different company, or propose radical changes anyway. If you choose the third option, realize that doing so will probably not earn you brownie points and might get you fired.

Positive trends across industries

Does the company where you work embrace less wasteful, more sustainable practices and policies that support a triple bottom line? If it doesn't do so today, chances are increasing that it will soon. We see progress when we browse social media and the newsletters arriving in our email inboxes. More companies are going public with commitments to corporate responsibility, environmental stewardship, and the health of their employees and customers. These companies span industries as varied as food and beverage, textiles, construction, electronics, hospitality, and even petrochemicals and mining.

Yes, companies realize that publishing sustainability reports is a way to gain positive publicity. But the reports are public, and anyone can read them. Even if some companies are merely jumping on a trend by writing sustainability reports or adding "sustainability" or "environment" pages to their websites, it's a good trend to be joining. We spoke to Andrew Winston, coauthor of *Net Positive: How Courageous Companies Thrive by Giving More Than They Take*, to get his perspective.

Interview

Andrew Winston, author and consultant

Tell me about how you became involved in sustainability and looking at responsible business practices.
Whenever there's deep changes going on in the economy or society—like during the pandemic, and after the 2008 crash—I think a lot of people change directions. My change came out of the dot com crash in 2000. I worked at big media companies and then I went to a small dot-com, then the crash happened and everybody ran out of money. I knew I wanted to do something different, but didn't really have the language for it. I had already become vegetarian, and was changing light bulbs and doing things like that, but it didn't feel like enough.

I talked to friends, and then heard the word "sustainability." I read a few of the key books at the time, like Ray Anderson's book *Mid-course Correction*, and they changed my view of the world. There's this sense that the way the business world works can't continue—we can't keep going on a finite planet. I felt like this was what I had to do. I'd been in business for ten years and had an MBA, and I thought there's got to be a way to combine these things. I went back to school, to Yale, for an environmental management degree, and then started working with a professor there, Dan Esty. That led to the book *Green to Gold*.

I've always come at this in a practical way. I didn't grow up as this big environmentalist. But it's logical—we can't thrive unless the planet's thriving. I've always wanted to work on the biggest issues and I've thought climate has been the core big issue for humanity for a while. Unfortunately, now I think democracy and freedom is more pressing. Because without it, we can't tackle climate. If we don't have functioning democracies, it's gonna be really hard.

Environmental issues shouldn't be political.
Climate in particular became political, and "became" sounds like a passive verb, but it was much more active than that. It was Exxon and others, convincing people that the science wasn't truly as bad as it might seem, or it's not right, or it's a lie. That let people feel like we shouldn't have to make changes or do anything that costs any money, and led to this political divide. Now it's really tribal. It's part of the GOP [Republican Party] mindset that they don't do climate action. It's going to be very hard to break that.

There's been a lot of discussion about individual responsibility versus corporate responsibility. How do you see that balance?
For so many years, it's been very much about changing your behavior. That's another thing some vested interests pushed as a concept, because then you don't have to make systemic changes, you don't have to change what you do as a fossil fuel company. There's increasingly been a pretty strong set of voices in the

environmental movement, and in general, saying there are choices an individual can't make. The change has to be systemic—the companies have to change, the policies have to change.

I think the role of individuals is not so much, "I'll use less energy, I'll put solar on my roof." That matters. But "I will reward the companies, politicians, communities that go down the right path, I will vote for the people that will tackle climate and I will buy from the companies that do it." That's the real power. It isn't an individual responsibility that there's not enough light rail or public transportation in cities. It's so easy to say "drive less," but that might not be feasible without systemic changes.

As a consultant, what changes are you seeing in terms of who's contacting you and what they're asking you to do?
In the last few years, there have been changes in what businesses think they're supposed to do or the things that are on their agenda in the sustainability or ESG realm. I think there's been more change in the last few years than the 20 that I've been in this, for lots of reasons. Most of which are the mega trends and things I write and talk about all the time, like climate and inequality. Those pressures are very real. Climate is now not some model to debate, but it's happening and affecting supply chains.

The pandemic forced a deep inward look. And then George Floyd, #metoo, there's been a series of things that have forced companies to get involved in society in a much deeper way. What companies are looking for now certainly has broadened. There's a larger sense of the issues on the table. It isn't just, did we write a CSR report, did we cut our emissions this year. It's about climate strategy and how companies handle the pressure for diversity.

One of the things that's dramatically climbed is the interest in having some form of employee education. I do a lot of speaking, but I'm also being asked now to come in and train people. I've seen much more of that desire to understand these issues. The bottom line is companies are at the table, and they're for real. Finally. They still don't know how far they really need to go, and they're not comfortable with it. The mission of my book *Net Positive* is to get them to have a bigger, much broader aim. But the desire to know about this, that alone has just grown dramatically.

What type of information are they really lacking? What can you deliver that's really going to help them move forward?
Even just definitions, like what is sustainability? What does that mean for different parts of the business? What are the goals we should be setting? Should we be net zero, and what does that mean? But what I feel like executives need, or everybody needs, is broader than that. It's really the narrative that we're all living in, the story of business and its purpose. We've had a 50-year run of neoliberalism—where it's just about maximizing profits and pleasing shareholders. There's this knowledge that we have to build into companies, that that's not your only responsibility. It never was. And it's not a very good way to run a business, especially now.

It's really knowledge of what's going on with climate and inequality and biodiversity, just a base knowledge. Executives are supposed to start to understand AI and social media. And also understand what stakeholder pressure looks like, and what investors are looking for. What are all the organizations and acronyms popping up in Europe and the US that are forcing change on companies?

What do young people want from your company, as customers and as employees? It's raising the knowledge of the systemic nature of the problems, what they are, and what people expect you to do about it. Then there's deeper problems of how do we create partnerships? What are the right partnerships to solve big problems? That's the core of Net Positive, the systemic partnerships, and that's much deeper. That's not a class you take for an hour online, that's much more hands-on and involves companies working with NGOs and academics, and learning through doing.

Industry associations can be a positive force. But they can also be obstacles.
The core of Net Positive that I want executives to understand is that the responsibility of business is now broader. It's not scope one and two emissions or even scope three, it's your sector and how it plays in the world. Trade associations and industry associations tend to lobby to stop all regulation. You have companies with these big sustainability goals, and then their trade associations are trying to kill any Build Back Better Bill, anything. It's a total disconnect. Companies need to own their policy engagement at state, national, and global levels. That's new for many companies to actually see that as a strategic and partnership option, rather than fighting anything the government wants to do.

Do you have any examples from manufacturing industries?
The discussions on materials now, especially around plastics, are intense. All the big suppliers to the plastics industry are working on bio-based plastics. I think that's part of the solution. But the more interesting stories are experiments that are building on package-free stores, or reusable packaging. You're substituting a much sturdier metal container for plastic packaging, because you're gonna use it over and over again. That's the experiment Loop is running in New York, and that's been going on for a few years. And Seattle's experimenting with these reusable cups that are going to be at stadiums and universities. Those are the really interesting things.

The heavy industries—steel, aluminum, and cement—are the big question marks on decarbonization. We have the technology to make the grid basically carbon-free, to make transportation carbon-free. But what do you do about the super energy-intensive industries? There's really interesting sector-based movements going on. The World Economic Forum has these partnership meetings of cement and steel and aluminum to work on changing the way they make the materials.

My favorite story is Apple working with Rio Tinto and Alcoa to invest in ELYSIS, the company that makes zero-carbon aluminum, and Apple putting it in their computers. And then Audi bought some of that aluminum for a car. There's this ripple effect. That's the perfect Net Positive example of Apple helping create a market for much lower carbon aluminum, which can then ripple into other aluminum uses. It's going to be how we make this stuff. There'll still be a need to reduce and recycle and all that. And of course, dematerializing in general. It's not just plastics that you can get rid of by reducing packaging, it's also metals.

And paper products.
Well, there's also the paper industry arguing that they have better packaging, they can replace plastic, and you see versions now like liquid containers that are paper based with maybe a little lining inside. They're making the case that they're more sustainable. Probably, because at least they're not as tied to the fossil fuel industry. But the paper industry uses a lot of land and has its own footprint issues.

One of the biggest obstacles that companies talk about when trying to be more environmentally friendly is cost. Have you seen that in companies you've worked with, and how do you help them work through that obstacle?
It's a huge topic in my work. I get asked, what's the business case? Doesn't it cost more? I've gotten some version of that question every day for 20 years. And I'm kind of losing it, because there's a bunch of things under sustainability that save money, like eco efficiency and renewables. Companies tend to say, well of course we're going to do that, it's efficiency. But that counts as sustainable. They only keep things that cost more in the sustainability bucket. When you say it costs more, it's often because you're not actually including all the benefits that you reap from a change. If you use less toxic materials, you may have lower logistics costs, lower safety issues, more attraction to customers, employees like you better, all these other things that are of value that we don't include in a decision.

I do a lot of speaking about rethinking tools like return on investment to start to include these other benefits. In a way, we're under-investing in sustainability, because we don't include these things that are hard to measure. I think if we got better at understanding that, then we could know when it actually does cost more. For example, if you want a different source material, and it's a much smaller business, and the scale isn't there. This is about partnerships. That's the core of Net Positive. People tell me, well, it costs more. I say, well, what costs more? And what's the problem? And how could you solve it? Can you bring your sector together to build the market for this material?

This happened in refrigerants 15 or 20 years ago, with Coke and Pepsi and Unilever getting manufacturers of vending machines to use refrigerants with much lower global warming potential. They built the market for it. When you say it costs more, it's kind of lazy. It's narrow, it doesn't take into account everything, and it doesn't ask what can we do together? There are some things that cost more, like if we're going to pay living wages. But there's plenty of evidence that then there's less turnover. Again, there are all these benefits of paying better.

For me, it's always about whether you're really taking a look at the full spectrum of value. When you do, the conversation should be very different. It's one of my favorite and most hated topics, because I'm so tired of the business case. But there's always one macro point at the end of that argument for me, which is: are we actually being asked to prove the business case for our survival? The discussion needs to be, of course we're going to decarbonize very, very quickly. Let's figure out how to do that most profitably. Not "prove it to me or I'm not going to do it." It's not like business is going to do very well on a planet that's dealing with a third of Pakistan underwater, half of California burning. Business isn't going to be great in those situations.

Is there anything I didn't ask that you would like to add?
There are some people really driving change in particular—the young generations, millennials and Gen Z, and their role. It's really one of the main sources of optimism. They get it, they care about these issues, they demand more from the companies they buy from and work for. I always try to speak to younger groups and tell them that you have power. You're not in charge, you might be just getting your first job, but you have power by who you work with, and who you buy from, and you should use it.

We are all consumers

Regardless of whether you run a company, work for a for-profit business or a non-profit organization, are a student, or have retired from professional life, you are a consumer. In that role, you make dozens of choices every week about what products to buy and where to buy them. You can also choose what not to buy and how to dispose of stuff when you're done using it. Your role as a consumer gives you the power to vote with your pocketbook.

Consumer behavior can shape corporate actions. From bringing reusable bags to the store even in cities that don't ban plastic bags to choosing products that come with less packaging, you send a message. One customer won't convince a company to change the packaging of its products, but thousands of customers will. More and more products boast that they now come with less packaging.

It is, of course, important to look closely. Some products come packaged in plastic for sanitary reasons or to save weight in shipping. As we saw with the example of wooden versus plastic shipping crates in Chapter 9, sometimes plastic is the better choice from a sustainability perspective. As consumers, we can examine packaging to learn about whether it is made from recycled or recyclable plastic or both.

In addition to buying less packaging, we can learn about options for recycling and composting in our communities. Figuring out what is and isn't recyclable can be challenging, but taking the time is worthwhile. We don't want our recycling efforts to contaminate the recycling stream accidentally.

We (the authors) admit that we have not always been as aware of issues surrounding toxic chemicals in the products we buy or the waste inherent in producing, packaging, and shipping them. Our awareness has grown over time, and we have made changes.

Julia:

- I compost at home—a task made easier because my city provides a small compost bin and accepts all types of food waste into the large yard waste container—and make sure I don't include any noncompostable packaging (including those pesky stickers on fresh produce).

- I put leftover food into reusable glass or plastic containers rather than wrapping it in plastic wrap or putting it into a disposable zipper-top bag. I also write dates on the containers to limit food waste. I avoid buying items packaged in disposable plastic when other options exist. When that isn't the case, I reuse the packaging if possible and dispose of it appropriately once I can't reuse it.
- I make bread instead of buying commercial brands. It is healthier and package-free. The sourdough starter I made in 2019 is still going strong four years later.
- I have embraced cast iron, the original nonstick cookware, along with stainless steel pots and pans.
- I never followed fashion trends, ever since I bought a trendy outfit when I was 15 and discovered it was out of fashion the next year. But now when my clothing wears out, I shop at consignment shops for new-to-me items in like-new condition.

Paul:

- I grow as much of our food as possible, and for the past six years, we've had a large compost heap into which goes garden waste, home compostable packaging, pulp trays, paper, etc. It makes excellent compost for growing vegetables the following year.
- We buy the rest of our vegetables and fruit from a community farm which is only a few miles away. Supermarkets don't help when you want to live a zero-waste life.
- We started having our oat milk delivered in returnable glass bottles, and we buy a lot of other food packaging-free from a whole variety of startups.
- We removed toxicants from our kitchen—non-stick frying pans, plastic food containers, food wrap, etc. We now have glass and metal pans, and reusable glass containers for food.
- We switched to "green energy" provider Ecotricity, and to our surprise, we saved money. We also switched our bank accounts and insurance to "green" providers such as Triodos. I have carbon literacy consultant Emma Burlow to thank for pushing us to do this. When we travel to mainland Europe from London, we go by train (the emissions are just one-eighth by train compared to flying).
- I became a big fan of upcycled clothing and products made from "waste" — my glasses are made from coffee grounds from Kyiv coffee shops (Ochis eyewear) and my favorite sneakers are made from old jeans (Vær Upcycled).

Regardless of where you are on the spectrum of caring about the safety and environmental sustainability of the products you buy, there is probably room for improvement. Only you can decide how much time you want to devote to making changes in your lifestyle and habits and how much pressure you want to put on the companies that make the products you enjoy.

The importance of location

When considering steps to reduce waste in your community or remove toxic products from the business where you work, location makes a difference. Are you preaching to the choir or making suggestions that people around you will interpret as too costly or negatively associate with counter-culture hippies? Do you have access to more environmentally friendly products or a local infrastructure that supports effective recycling?

I (Julia) have lived my entire life in the bubble of the West Coast. Sustainability is an easy sell in the Puget Sound region—the greater Seattle area—where I have lived since 2014. Before that, I lived in the San Francisco Bay Area, in a state that led the country in requiring businesses to pollute less and conserve more. Companies in my part of the country recognize that publicizing their sustainability efforts, whether that be using compostable containers or powering and heating their buildings solely with renewable energy sources, will attract customers who value these efforts.

Is the same true for companies based in other parts of the US or other countries around the world? Our research suggests that the message is indeed spreading. The idea of reducing toxicants and hazardous waste is an easier sell in certain markets, but companies everywhere are finding that their customers care. In some cases, the messaging needs to be slightly different, appealing to saving money or keeping their family safe rather than saving the planet, but there is a market for environmentally friendly businesses and products in many places. Some of our interviewees hail from locations not typically associated with progressive policies or responsible business practices.

Despite the evidence that environmentally friendly practices aren't restricted to regions where the message has long benefited from public support, limitations exist. For example, municipal composting programs that collect food waste and compostable packaging are few and far between.

The Seattle area is ahead of the curve with the Cedar Grove facility, which accepts all types of food waste and compostable packaging and turns it into compost. Laws in the city of Seattle prohibiting disposable packaging that isn't compostable encourage businesses to provide single bins for customers to deposit both food waste and serving ware. The goal is to divert as much waste as possible from local landfills.

Oregon has taken a different approach than its neighbors to the north and south, prioritizing the quality of finished compost over landfill diversion. Composting facilities in the state are not set up to handle most compostable service-ware and the composting industry there sees these products as a problem. The city of Portland prohibits packaging or food-service ware in its compost, only allowing uncoated cardboard pizza boxes, coffee filters, tea bags, and paper products in addition to food waste. In the long run, it isn't clear whether Seattle's or Portland's approach should prevail.

In cities without composting programs, simply setting out a container to collect compost won't help. Unless a business has space and resources to set up on-site composting or a homeowner wants to build a backyard compost bin, vegetable scraps are destined for the kitchen sink disposal or the garbage can.

Through the generations

Of the many roles we play in our lives, one of those is family member. Perhaps you are at the stage of life where the word "family" brings to mind your parents and siblings. Maybe you are a parent or grandparent. Regardless of your age and family situation, you should be concerned about the future of this planet, which means the future of the human species. Parents of young children will be especially concerned about toxicants in baby bottles or sippy cups. Even if we aren't parents or if our children are grown, we should still be aware. Poisons are especially dangerous for young children, but adults are not immune.

Ultimately, we need to trust scientists. We should encourage businesses to rely on independent research to ensure that the new products that they introduce will meet customers' needs while reducing the resources required to manufacture them and minimizing health risks. Concern about the health of people and our environment has become mainstream, and choices of materials play an important role in ensuring a safer future for the generations who will follow us. Businesses that understand their responsibility deserve the support of customers who want to promote more sustainable, less wasteful manufacturing. When we use our power as citizens, consumers, and workers to affect what materials go into the products we enjoy and how those products are made and used, everyone benefits.

Conclusion

Looking to the Future

The most ambitious materials pioneers are looking to a future where there is no waste, only resources. They are also looking beyond smelting, extrusion, and molding toward more efficient and completely novel manufacturing techniques.

Biotechnology as a route to circularity

Venture capital and sizable research grants are being invested into biotechnology. Though much of these funds go into health care research, increasingly this capital is being invested into novel materials and manufacturing methods such as biofabrication and microbial manufacturing.

All of this work has been accelerated by governments' insistence and businesses' desire to create a circular economy. A true circular economy is one where products and materials are kept within productive use for as long as possible, then looped (or circled) back into the manufacturing ecosystem. Arriving at *absolute* circularity, rather than *relative* circularity which exists now, would mean for every ton of input there would be a ton of output in new materials. This is judged by some commentators as an impossibility. But academics and businesses are working together to create a wholly new system, based on nature and past economic practices, where waste is designed out entirely. The objective is net positivity, adding valuable resources to the planet instead of extracting resources.

To genuinely take advantage of everything that natural capital—defined as the world's stocks of natural assets including geology, soil, air, water, and all living things—offers, we need to phase out finite materials and focus solely on regenerative biological materials.

Modern Synthesis, featured in Chapter 8, forms nanofibers from microbes that digest waste feedstocks. Microbial manufacturing began in the medical and food ingredient industries. Now multiple materials businesses are looking to harness the potential of microbes and yeasts.

Compared to bacteria, yeast strains are more tolerable to multiple stress conditions, including low pH and high temperature, and also have other advantages such as generally regarded as safe (GRAS), and no phage infection. In addition, synthetic biology and metabolic engineering of yeast have enabled its rapid and

DOI: 10.4324/9781003409267-19

efficient engineering for bioproduction using various renewable feedstocks, especially lignocellulosic biomass.[1]

Just how far could conventional plastic manufacturing be replaced by completely novel manufacturing technologies? A project involving the VTT Technical Research Centre of Finland explored just that when they demonstrated a microbe-grown headset.[2]

A term to describe all of the above that is coming more into usage is "white biotechnology."

White biotechnology is not a new field per se. For example, engineered enzymes for detergents have been produced via white biotechnology since the 1980s. However, it has become increasingly of interest in this decade due to the following reasons:

Development of biotechnology. New biotechnology tools and processes are making it possible to produce a wider range of products through white biotechnology. For example, gene editing techniques can be used to create microorganisms with specific properties, such as the ability to produce a desired chemical or the ability to degrade pollutants.

Growing interest in sustainability. There is a growing awareness of the need to develop more sustainable ways of producing goods and services. White biotechnology offers a potential solution to this challenge, as it can be used to produce products that are less harmful to the environment than traditional petroleum-based products.

The rise of synthetic biology. Synthetic biology is a rapidly developing field that uses engineering principles to design and build new biological systems. This technology has the potential to revolutionize white biotechnology by enabling the creation of new and more efficient bioprocesses.

As a result of these factors, white biotechnology is poised to play an increasingly important role in the global economy. It is a key technology for the bioeconomy, the economic sector that produces goods and services from renewable biological resources. White biotechnology is also a key technology for the circular economy because of its potential to reduce waste and pollution.

Some specific examples of how white biotechnology is being used already are the following.

- The production of biofuels, such as ethanol and biodiesel, from biomass,
- The production of bioplastic from renewable resources, such as corn stalks (stover) or sugarcane stalk waste (bagasse),
- The production of enzymes used in a wide variety of applications, such as detergents, food processing, and pharmaceuticals,
- The treatment of wastewater by using microorganisms to remove pollutants,
- The remediation of contaminated soil and water by using microorganisms to break down contaminants.

Business trends supporting the circular economy

Pressure for greater corporate responsibility is growing. We see more and more stories about companies improving their business practices and reputations. Sustainability reporting is more comprehensive and more uniform. The reports highlight reduced energy and water use for manufacturing and operations, more reliance on renewable energy sources, increased use of recycled materials, and more.

Sometimes we worry that businesses are primarily changing their policies or products to improve their bottom line. We need to remember that progress helps to support changes that lessen negative social and environmental impacts and improve positive ones, even if we take issue with the motive. Profit is one of the three Ps, after all, and we want the most responsible companies to stay in business.

The trick is to read behind the lines and encourage changes that achieve the benefits they promise. When removing a toxic chemical, are manufacturers replacing it with something that is potentially just as dangerous, or are they finding an alternative that is proven to be safer? Do efforts toward zero waste to landfill involve using less material overall? What real changes are behind pledges to achieve net zero carbon emissions? Over-reliance on carbon offsets will not solve the problem.

Looking at how many companies pursue B Corp certification is one way to gauge corporate interest in sustainability. While the certification process measures a wide range of social, environmental, and community engagement practices, many B Corps prioritize minimizing product packaging and cutting out material waste.

As noted in Chapter 12, the B Corp community is blossoming. The certification process is also becoming more stringent. Applicants need to earn points in all the five pillars: Governance, Workers, Community, Environment, and Customers. That means they cannot ignore issues like materials procurement and waste management that are part of the environmental pillar.

The International Standards Organization (ISO) is recognizing the importance of the circular economy. A new standard, ISO/DIS 59004, "Circular Economy—Terminology, Principles and Guidance for Implementation," is under development as of late 2023.

Every month, more companies sign the Climate Pledge, an initiative that Global Optimism and Amazon founded in 2019. The pledge is a commitment to reach net zero carbon emissions by 2040. Signatories agree to report regularly on their greenhouse gas emissions, develop plans to decarbonize their operations, and purchase credible offsets to get the rest of the way to zero. As of October 2023, 436 companies in 38 countries have signed.

Certifications, standards, and pledges are a great step toward more environmentally responsible practices, and they are also not enough. Unless less energy-intensive and carbon-intensive materials are available at scale, these ambitions cannot be met. More efficient and less polluting ways to extract, process, use, and dispose of human-made materials must be part of the path toward net zero.

Celebrate the small steps and encourage bigger ones

We are encouraged by the progress and innovations that we write about in this book. We also recognize that we cannot cover every new development in materials and manufacturing methods without this book ballooning to an unmanageable length. There are many innovative and worthwhile endeavors that we have not included. More will come to light between the time we submit this manuscript and its publication date.

It is possible to celebrate advances while being realistic. We doubt that disposable packaging will disappear in our lifetimes, but progress toward that goal is possible. It is important to proceed with caution. Rather than replacing all conventional plastics with biobased plastics and claiming success, manufacturers need to consider the impact on human health and the environment of increased bioplastics production and choose bioplastics that don't cause more problems than they solve. Or choose a different type of packaging material or even no packaging at all.

We have a great opportunity in front of us to improve circularity by choosing the right materials and processes for each use case and inventing new ones when existing options don't measure up. It is our hope that reading this book inspires you to be part of the solution and encourage others to join you on the journey.

Notes

1 Zhang, Fengli et al. 2023. "Engineering Yeast Cell Factories to Produce Biodegradable Plastics and Their Monomers: Current Status and Prospects," *Biotechnology Advances* 68 (November): 108222. https://doi.org/10.1016/j.biotechadv.2023.108222.

2 Aivan. 2019. "The World's First Microbe-Grown Headset," Aivan. May 15, 2019. https://aivan.fi/case/korvaa-the-worlds-first-microbe-grown-headset/.

Further Reading

Ahmed, Shakeel, Suvardhan Kanchi, and Gopalakrishnan Kumar, eds. 2018. *Handbook of Biopolymers: Advances and Multifaceted Applications*. Singapore: Jenny Stanford Publishing.

Ahrens, Andreas, Angelika Braun, Arnim Gleich, Kerstin Heitmann, and Lothar Lißner. 2006. *Hazardous Chemicals in Products and Processes*. Hamburg, Germany: Springer Science & Business Media.

Allwood, Julian M, and Jonathan M Cullen. 2019. *Sustainable Materials Without the Hot Air*. Cambridge: UIT Cambridge.

Biello, David. 2017. *The Unnatural World: The Race to Remake Civilization in Earth's Newest Age*. New York: Scribner.

Bilott, Robert, and Tom Shroder. 2020. *Exposure: Poisoned Water, Corporate Greed and One Lawyer's Twenty-Year Battle against DuPont*. London: Simon & Schuster.

Braungart, Michael, and William Mcdonough. 2009. *Cradle to Cradle: Remaking the Way We Make Things*. London: Vintage.

Carson, Rachel. 1962. *Silent Spring*. Boston, MA: Houghton Mifflin.

Conway, Ed. 2023. *Material World: The Six Raw Materials That Shape Modern Civilization*. New York: Random House.

Eekhout, Mick. 2022. *Glass Design Innovations in Architecture*. Rotterdam: nai010Publishers.

Ehrenfield, John R. 2008. *Sustainability by Design*. New Haven, CT & London: Yale University Press.

Epstein, Marc J, and Kirk O Hanson. 2021. *Rotten: Why Corporate Misconduct Continues and What to Do about It*. Los Altos, CA: Lanark Press.

Esty, Daniel, and Andrew Winston. 2006. *Green to Gold: How Smart Companies Use Environmental Strategy to Innovate, Create Value, and Build Competitive Advantage*. New Haven, CT: Yale University Press.

Freinkel, Susan. 2011. *Plastic: A Toxic Love Story*. New York: Houghton Mifflin Harcourt.

Geiser, Ken. 2001. *Materials Matter: Toward a Sustainable Materials Policy*. Cambridge, MA: The MIT Press.

Gibson, Ian, David Rosen, Brent Stucker, and Mahyar Khorasani. 2021. *Additive Manufacturing Technologies*. Cham: Springer.

Haffmans, Siem, Marjoleinvan Gelder, Edvan Hinte, and Yvo Zijlstra. 2018. *Products That Flow: Circular Business Models and Design Strategies for Fast-moving Consumer Goods*. Amsterdam: BIS Publishers.

Hawken, Paul. 2010. *The Ecology of Commerce (Revised Edition)*. New York: Harper Collins.

Ikhmayies, Shadia Jamil, ed. 2023. *Advances in Glass Research. Advances in Material Research and Technology*. Cham, Switzerland: Springer.

McDonough, William, and Michael Braungart. 2002. *Cradle to Cradle: Remaking the Way We Make Things*. New York: North Point Press.

———. 2013. *The Upcycle: Beyond Sustainability – Designing for Abundance*. New York: North Point Press.

Miodownik, Mark. 2014. *Stuff Matters: Exploring the Marvelous Materials That Shape Our Manmade World*. Boston, MA: Houghton Mifflin Harcourt.

Moore, Kate. 2017. *Radium Girls: The Dark Story of America's Shining Women*. Naperville, IL: Simon & Schuster Ltd.

Newman, David. 2020. *Everything Is Connected: Understanding a Complicated World*. Cardiff, CA: Waterside Productions.

Penty, Jane. 2020. *Product Design & Sustainability*. London: Routledge.

Randle, Paul, and Alexis Eyre. 2023. *Sustainable Marketing: The Industry's Role in a Sustainable Future*. London: Kogan Page.

Raworth, Kate. 2017. *Doughnut Economics: Seven Ways to Think Like a 21st-Century Economist*. London: Random House Business Books.

Shelby, James E. 2020. *Introduction to Glass Science and Technology*. London: The Royal Society of Chemistry.

Smil, Vaclav. 2014. *Making the Modern World: Materials and Dematerialization*. Chichester, West Sussex: Wiley.

———. 2022. *How the World Really Works: The Science behind How We Got Here and Where We're Going*. New York: Viking.

Thomas, Sabu, Ajitha AR, Cintil Jose Chirayil, and Bejoy Thomas, eds. 2023. *Handbook of Biopolymers*. Cham, Switzerland: Springer Nature.

Turns, Anna. 2022. *Go Toxic Free*. London: Michael O'Mara Books.

Visser, Wayne. 2022. *Thriving: The Breakthrough Movement to Regenerate Nature, Society, and the Economy*. Austin, TX: Fast Company Press.

Index

Note: **Bold** page numbers refer to tables; *italic* page numbers refer to figures.

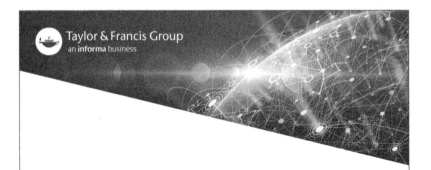